A TEXTBOOK

IN THE

PRINCIPLES OF SCIENCE TEACHING

TEXT–BOOK SERIES
EDITED BY PAUL MONROE, PH.D.

STATE AND COUNTY SCHOOL ADMINISTRATION.
VOL. I. TEXT-BOOK OF PRINCIPLES. *In Preparation.*
VOL. II. SOURCE BOOK.
By ELLWOOD P. CUBBERLEY, PH.D., Professor of Education, Leland Stanford Junior University, and EDWARD C. ELLIOTT, PH.D., Professor of Education, University of Wisconsin.

STATE AND COUNTY EDUCATIONAL REORGANIZATION.
By ELLWOOD P. CUBBERLEY, PH.D.

TEXT–BOOK IN THE PRINCIPLES OF EDUCATION.
By ERNEST N. HENDERSON, PH.D., Professor of Education and Philosophy, Adelphi College.

PRINCIPLES OF SECONDARY EDUCATION.
By PAUL MONROE, PH.D., Professor of History of Education, Teachers College, Columbia University.

TEXT–BOOK IN THE HISTORY OF EDUCATION.
By PAUL MONROE, PH.D.

SOURCE BOOK IN THE HISTORY OF EDUCATION. FOR THE GREEK AND ROMAN PERIOD.
By PAUL MONROE, PH.D.

A HISTORY OF THE FAMILY AS A SOCIAL AND EDUCATIONAL INSTITUTION.
By WILLYSTINE GOODSELL, PH.D., Assistant Professor of Education, Teachers College, Columbia University.

DEMOCRACY AND EDUCATION. AN INTRODUCTION TO THE PHILOSOPHY OF EDUCATION.
By JOHN DEWEY, PH.D., Professor of Philosophy, Columbia University.

THE PRINCIPLES OF SCIENCE TEACHING.
By GEORGE R. TWISS, B. Sc., Professor of the Principles and Practice of Education, Ohio State University.

A HISTORY OF EDUCATION IN THE UNITED STATES.
In Preparation.
By PAUL MONROE, PH.D.

A TEXTBOOK

IN THE

PRINCIPLES OF SCIENCE TEACHING

BY

GEORGE RANSOM TWISS, B.Sc.

STATE HIGH SCHOOL INSPECTOR, AND PROFESSOR OF THE PRINCIPLES
AND PRACTICE OF EDUCATION IN THE OHIO STATE UNIVERSITY
AUTHOR OF "LABORATORY EXERCISES IN PHYSICS," JOINT
AUTHOR OF "PHYSICS," BY MANN AND TWISS
AND CONTRIBUTOR TO "PRINCIPLES OF
SECONDARY EDUCATION"

New York

THE MACMILLAN COMPANY

1919

Norwood Press
J. S. Cushing Co. — Berwick & Smith Co.
Norwood, Mass., U.S.A.

3238

TO

MY TEACHERS

ESPECIALLY THOSE WHO HAVE HELPED ME IN MY THINKING
AND INSPIRED IN ME AN ABIDING ENTHUSIASM FOR
SCIENCE AND THE TEACHING OF SCIENCE, THIS
BOOK IS GRATEFULLY DEDICATED

3238

PREFACE

THIS book is intended primarily to be used in the instruction of young men and women who are preparing themselves in colleges and normal schools for careers as teachers of one or more of the natural sciences; but it is hoped that it will be scarcely less useful to science teachers now in service and to superintendents of school systems and principals of public and private secondary schools whose duties involve the direction and supervision of science instruction. It is thought also that the book contains much that will be of value to professors of the several natural sciences in colleges and normal schools, in helping them to impart to prospective teachers of their sciences the modern social viewpoint and the true scientific spirit that are so necessary for real success in teaching the sciences to boys and girls of high school age.

The volume is a natural outgrowth of a long career as high school teacher of science, high school inspector, and college teacher of education. It embodies the results of constant study of the natural sciences and of psychology, especially in its applications to science teaching and high school administration, carried on during the course of this career. It attempts to show in a concrete and practical way how the findings of modern experimental and educational psychology may be applied in science teaching. The first eleven chapters and the last one develop and formulate principles that are fundamental to all science training; the others are devoted to the explanation of principles and methods of teaching that are especially applicable to the several sciences of the high school curriculum. They contain also practical hints on the selection and organization of subject matter, the planning of laboratories, and the choice of equipment in connection with science instruction.

There are several ways in which the book may be used in the instruction of prospective science teachers.

First, it may be used as a text for a broad general course in the fundamental principles of science teaching, intended for all those who are preparing for the teaching of any of the special sciences. In this case the chapters of general interest should receive the most study and attention; and those devoted to the special sciences, Chapters XII to XXIII, should be touched more lightly, being used for the most part as bases for special reports to the class by those most interested in the particular sciences of which these chapters treat.

Second, the book may be used as a text in a special course on the teaching of any one of the sciences. In this case the greater part of the book would be passed over rapidly to develop the general attitude and point of view; and the chapters on Biology or on Geography, Physics, Chemistry, or General Science would be studied intensively and supplemented by copious readings and reports based on references chosen from the book lists appended to the chapters so studied.

Third, in a university where special courses are given on the teaching of all of the several high school sciences this book may be used as a text in each one of these courses in the manner just described. In this case special joint conferences, attended by all these classes combined, may be arranged for. In these general meetings the leading principles brought out in the first eleven chapters and in the last may be made the subjects of general discussion by both instructors and students each from the viewpoint of the science in which he is most interested. By such a plan the courses of instruction in the teaching of all the sciences would be unified, and a common general viewpoint and a common philosophy of science teaching would gradually develop in the institution. This does not mean that such a unified viewpoint and such a common philosophy of science teaching would necessarily be reached only by adopting the views held by the author of this book, but rather that it would develop out of the discussions that a common study of the book must inevitably provoke.

Besides being employed as a text-book, it is believed that this volume will prove useful as a reference book in connection with more general courses in the principles of teaching or in methods of teaching; for the broader principles developed and formulated in it, and supported by arguments and examples, are those which science shares with all other subjects.

For high school science teachers in service, the book should be useful either for private reading and study or for study in groups such as teachers' meetings, reading circles, and science clubs, or as a text-book in extension or correspondence courses offered by colleges and universities for credit toward a degree.

For the supervisor who is not himself especially well trained in science the book should fill a long-felt want, for he often realizes that something in the science courses or in the way in which they are conducted is unsatisfactory, but does not know just what is wrong or how to go about correcting it. This book may serve to put such a supervisor in possession of principles that will enable him to diagnose the case, prescribe a remedy, and convince the science teacher that he should try the remedy and note the results. On the other hand, if some or all of his science teachers are doing particularly good teaching, a knowledge of the criteria for correctly judging their work will enable the administrator to appreciate its excellence and lead him to use all possible means of providing such equipment and administrative arrangements as are necessary for making it still more effective.

Although in referring to teachers the masculine form of the pronoun is used throughout, it should not be thought that the author wishes to ignore the noble body of science teachers who happen to be women. Let it be understood once for all that the book is addressed no less to women than to men, and that what is said about teachers is meant to apply to teachers of both sexes.

For whatever there may be of truth or merit in these pages I am indebted largely to many persons. To my father, George H. Twiss, sometime teacher, meteorologist, and the founder and first manager of the Columbus telephone exchange, I owe a lasting debt of gratitude for the influences, brought about me during my boyhood, which first aroused and fed my interests in science. To my science teachers, especially the late Principal Albert N. Ozias, of St. Paul, Minnesota, who was my teacher in the sciences while a student in the old Columbus High School, and to Professors Thomas C. Mendenhall, Albert H. Tuttle, Sidney A. Norton, and the late Stillman W. Robinson, Nathan W. Lord, and Edward Orton, Senior, I am indebted for both my undergraduate training in science and much of what I may possess of skill in experimentation and insight into the scientific method. To them also, as well as to William Morris Davis of Harvard University and Charles Riborg Mann of the University of Chicago, I owe much for their inspiring methods of teaching, and the examples that I have observed through personal contact with them of clear-cut and attractive exposition of scientific facts and theories.

That the writings and teaching of Professors John Dewey and Edward L. Thorndike have had much influence in shaping the lines of thought that are developed in the following pages will be sufficiently evident to those who read them, yet it gives the writer special pleasure to acknowledge it here, and include them among those to whom the dedication of this book is addressed.

In putting the manuscript into final form, and in getting it through the press, I have profited by the criticism of a number of persons to whom my thanks are due, and are gratefully tendered; but I alone am responsible for any errors that may have evaded detection. Professor Paul Monroe has read the entire work in manuscript and in proof; and Professor E. L. Thorndike has read the greater part of it in manuscript. Professors M. A. Bigelow, R. E. Dodge, and Alexander Smith, of Columbia University, W. W. Charters of the University of Illinois, and W. C. Curtis of the University of Missouri, have read those parts of the manuscript bearing on the subjects in which they are specialists. I am indebted to Professors John H. Woodhull of Columbia University and Fred D. Barber of Normal, Ill., for references and literature on introductory science. My wife, Blanche Olin Twiss, has helped me in the laborious work of verifying the references and book lists and revising the manuscript for the printers. Her criticisms and suggestions also have enabled me to improve the book at many points, both in clearness and in literary form.

Many authors whose books have been consulted in the preparation of this work have received credit in the footnotes; but there are others whose writings have helped indirectly in various ways to make the book what it is. They are too numerous to mention here, but many of them are mentioned in the text or included in the reference lists that are appended to the various chapters, or in the lists of books for high school libraries to be found in the appendix.

These book lists are not intended to be exhaustive bibliographies, nor are the prices appended guaranteed, but they have been selected with much care and labor; and it is thought that they include a sufficient quantity and variety of supplementary material to be of very considerable value, both for special references and general reading.

In the chapters treating of equipment, where prices are given, and where duty-free importations are mentioned, it is to be understood that reference is made to normal conditions, as they existed before August, 1914.

G. R. T.

July 17, 1917.

CONTENTS

CHAPTER I

THE MEANING OF SCIENCE

CHAPTER II

THE VIEWPOINT FOR THE SCIENCE TEACHER

Contents

CHAPTER III

THE GENESIS OF SCIENCE

CHAPTER IV

SCIENCE AND CHILDREN

CHAPTER V

METHODS OF TEACHING

Contents

CHAPTER VI

EDUCATIONAL FUNCTIONS AND VALUES OF THE SCIENCES

CHAPTER IX

LECTURES, EXCURSIONS, AND REVIEWS

CHAPTER X

EQUIPMENT FOR SCIENCE TEACHING

CHAPTER XI

THE SCIENCES AND THE CURRICULUM

CHAPTER XII

BIOLOGY

Contents

CHAPTER XIII

BIOLOGICAL EQUIPMENT

Contents

CHAPTER XIV

GEOGRAPHY. FUNDAMENTAL PRINCIPLES

CHAPTER XV

METHODS IN GEOGRAPHY

CHAPTER XVI

GEOGRAPHICAL EQUIPMENT

Contents

CHAPTER XVII

PHYSICS. FUNDAMENTAL PRINCIPLES

CHAPTER XVIII

METHODS IN PHYSICS

CHAPTER XIX

EQUIPMENT FOR PHYSICS TEACHING

Contents

CHAPTER XX

CHEMISTRY. PRINCIPLES AND METHODS

Contents

CHAPTER XXIII

"GENERAL SCIENCE" COURSES

CHAPTER XXIV

EXAMINATIONS AND TESTS

APPENDIX A

A Selected List of Books for the High School Library

APPENDIX B

APPENDIX C

Scientific Periodicals

A TEXTBOOK

IN THE

PRINCIPLES OF SCIENCE TEACHING

THE PRINCIPLES OF SCIENCE TEACHING

CHAPTER I

THE MEANING OF SCIENCE

Nineteenth century science. — The nineteenth century has been called the Century of Science, and rightly so, because during that period scientific knowledge and the inventions and arts were perfected more rapidly and distributed many times more widely than they had been in all prior time.

It was in the nineteenth century, also, that the scientific method of study began to be applied to all the fields of knowledge. The ideal first formulated by Francis Bacon, of exploiting the materials and forces of nature for the benefit of mankind, began to exert a dominating influence in the philosophy and conduct of large bodies of men in every civilized nation.

During the same period, through the development of machinery operated by steam and electric power, and the accompanying tendency toward division of labor and specialization in production and transportation, this scientific development brought about great and influential changes in social and economic conditions as well as in thought. Some of these changes, involving the gathering of immense populations into limited areas, are as yet little understood; and they involve great and far-reaching problems that the twentieth century must solve.

Twentieth century problems. — Such are the problems of discovering and applying better and more efficient methods of agriculture; of improving machinery of all sorts; and of devising more speedy and efficient means for the transportation and distribution of fuels, foodstuffs, raw materials, and finished products; of better and safer methods of passenger traffic, and improved devices for the transmission of telegraphic and telephonic messages over land and water. Better methods of producing heat, light, and power are in constant demand, and lead directly to problems connected with the conservation of natural resources.

The ideal of the conservation of human life leads to the problems of personal and public health as related to hygiene, sanitation, and pure water supply; to pure food and drugs; and to congestion in the cities in which great populations tend to concentrate. The same ideal demands the solution of those problems that must deal with the unnecessary slaughter and maiming of thousands of human beings each year by the so-called " accidents " and " casualties " in railroad, marine, manufacturing, and mining operations, as well as with the impairment or death of thousands by diseases that are either now known to be preventable or which through scientific study into their nature and causes may soon become so.

The ideal of efficiency leads to new problems involving scientific organization and direction of the work done by factory operatives and salesmen; and the same ideal, as well as the golden rule, points to the working out of " welfare " plans for improving their condition and brightening their lives.

The ideal of the equalization of opportunity leads to problems that deal with the control of corporations and finance; with the relations of capital and labor; with the high cost of living; with the proper treatment of the defective, incompetent, and criminal classes; and with the grave menace to society involved in the increasing rate at which such classes, when unrestricted, produce defective and degenerate offspring.

Finally the changed conditions confront us with new problems in philosophy and education, physical, intellectual, moral, æsthetic, and religious, through whose agency, if at all, the next generation must be fitted to take up all these great problems and carry them toward their solutions.

Relation of science to civilization. — As the changes that have given rise to these problems have resulted largely from the multiplication of scientific discoveries and inventions, so also science itself has been developed largely because it was needed as a means of solving such problems; and it is by science alone that they can be solved. A few illustrations may serve to make this matter clear.

Science and inventions. — The clock, the barometer, the voltaic battery, the storage battery, the dynamo, the motor, the telegraph and telephone, wired and wireless, the electric light, — all are indispensable, both to modern pure science and to modern industries. The aëroplane and airship are destined to become so. All these were first discovered in principle by men of pure science; and all were perfected by the collective work of scientists, mathematicians, and practical artisans.

The practical usefulness of all the most important instruments used by surveyors and civil engineers depends directly on the telescopes with which they are fitted. The microscope is indispensable alike in the laboratory of the industrial chemist and the physician, and in the research laboratory of the physiologist, the zoölogist, the botanist, and the bacteriologist. These instruments, the necessary tools of both pure science and applied science, were first invented by grinders of spectacle lenses. They were the results of experiments to which these artisans were drawn, probably by purely intellectual interests which grew out of the ideas suggested by their practical industrial interests. The principles of these instruments, once conceived, were seized by workers in pure science; and the instruments have been brought to their present perfection by the joint efforts of scientists, mathematicians, and artisans.

The steam engine and James Watt. — In 1760 James Watt, instrument maker, inventor, and engineer by profession, but scientist at heart, was working to perfect the crude and wasteful " atmospheric steam engine." This machine had been invented a half century before, through the labors of several men, some of whom worked at the problem from scientific interest, and others because such a machine was sorely needed at that stage of civilization, to replace the expensive methods of lifting water from the coal mines by horse power. Beginning by repairing a model of Newcomen's engine for the physics laboratory of the University of Glasgow, Watt after years of thought and labor invented and manufactured practical and fairly economical machines, which embodied nearly all the scientific principles that are now used in the best and most powerful modern stationary steam engines. As an inventor, he worked in a field in which the principles of physics that he most needed to guide him did not exist as established knowledge ready for use. He was therefore driven by practical necessity, as well as by his interest in science, to conduct researches in pure physics. He had to discover the laws and principles that describe how steam behaves under all the conditions in which it must work to drive a practical engine.[1]

The need of research. — The general introduction of the steam engine led to the invention of steam-driven machinery and the consequent " industrial revolution." The factory has driven out the hand shops. The locomotive and the steamship have driven out the wagon train, the sailing craft, and the canal boat. The great cities are sucking our populations into their slums and congested centers. Our social and economic conditions are constantly becoming too complex

---

[1] Cf. Carnegie, Andrew, *Life of James Watt*, N. Y., 1905; Thurston, R. H., *A History of the Growth of the Steam Engine*, N. Y., 1891.

for our methods of control. Philanthropy, government and finance alike, must fall hopelessly behind their tasks, unless they call upon science, the willing servant of society, to give them a larger measure of assistance through new discoveries and new practical applications.

And this movement is well under way. Many of the great manufacturing corporations maintain their laboratories, where research in both pure and applied physics, chemistry, or biology is carried on. The state and national governments maintain their agricultural and engineering experiment stations and their geological surveys, and support such organizations as the United States Bureau of Standards, the Smithsonian Institution, the National Astronomical Observatory, the Geological Survey, the Coast and Geodetic Survey, and the various scientific bureaus of the Department of Agriculture.

The industrial problems that are brought to the laboratories of these institutions, and to those of the great universities, from the farms, the factories, and the cities, demand research not only in connection with the practical application of principles already known, but also for the discovery of principles that are needed, but hitherto unknown.

Science teaching and everyday life. — It is thus apparent that modern science and modern social and industrial life are inseparably linked together, and that each in turn causes the other to advance. They must progress hand in hand; otherwise social conditions will become worse instead of better. So since pure science and applied science, the abstract and the concrete, the theoretical and the practical, are inseparable in real life outside the school, it is important for the teacher to realize that they should not be divorced in the classroom and laboratory. *The science work of the school must be kept in close touch with the doings of everyday life, and especially with the activities that lie nearest to the immediate interests of the boys and girls.*

Science as subject matter and as method. — The foregoing discussion suggests the meaning of science. It consists of both subject matter and method. Its subject matter, viewed in the broadest sense, includes the entire field of human knowledge and experience. Its aim is to become acquainted with facts and phenomena, and to organize them through classification in accordance with appropriate and suggestive ideas by means of which their relations to one another may readily be apprehended. It attempts to describe these relations in the simplest possible manner in the form of laws and principles; so that the knowledge thus acquired and systematized may be used in the process of gaining and organizing additional knowledge. Finally it aims, through the union of ethical ideals with scientific methods, to apply this knowledge in every way that it can be applied for the advancement of humanity.

Hence the method of science implies systematic, orderly study. *It is a method of solving problems.* It includes observation of facts and phenomena as they are, and the process of classifying them into groups and sub-groups, according to their meanings or relations. It includes reasoning, both inductively from particular facts to general relations, laws, and principles, and deductively from laws and principles to other particular facts that may be implied by them.

In the process of arriving at laws and general principles, the scientific method includes the formation of *hypotheses*, or provisional statements describing the manner in which certain phenomena or groups of phenomena possibly or probably are related to one another, and then by deductive reasoning finding out explicitly what particular facts are implied by the hypothesis, and must follow if it be true. If the conclusions implied by the hypothesis are found to fit the facts in every case, the hypothesis is verified; it takes rank as a law, or a theory, or a principle, according to the extent of its application and the completeness with which it has been verified.

In developing the implications of hypotheses that involve quantity and numerical relations, the scientific method makes much use of mathematics; and in testing hypotheses it resorts to experimentation, — that is, to observations, and where they are possible, to careful measurements, under such prearranged and controlled conditions that the significant phenomena related to the hypothesis, and to the solution of the problem, can be picked out and attended to, apart from the insignificant.

Finally the scientific method is constantly bringing the description of phenomena under broader and simpler general statements or forms, such as the laws of motion, of gravitation, of conservation of matter, of conservation of energy, the nebular hypothesis, the wave theories of sound, light and electricity, the electron theory, the theory of evolution, the Mendelian theory of inheritance, and the like. Because of the insight into natural processes afforded by such concise and meaningful forms of description it becomes possible to predict what will happen under given circumstances. It is such *prevision* that leads to new discoveries and inventions and to the intellectual satisfaction that results from finding meaning and order in the world as well as from exerting power and control over nature through knowledge.

The method of science illustrated. Newton. — To illustrate the way in which the great unifying principles of science are used in gaining further knowledge, the case of Newton's laws may be cited. Having made himself familiar with the facts and laws then known about falling bodies, and about the movements of the moon and planets, Newton conceived the idea that these bodies are attracted toward one another and held in their orbits by forces that are of the same nature as the weight or gravity to which we attribute the fall of a stone toward the earth. He applied his mathematics to the problem, and was able to prove that such a force, if it be proportional to the mass of the moon and to the reciprocal of

the square of its distance from the earth, would keep it revolving round the earth in exactly the manner and at the same
speed as astronomical observations show that it does move.
His hypothesis was therefore verified by showing that its
necessary implications are in accord with the facts of the
case. After successfully accounting for the motions of the
moon by means of his laws of motion and his law of universal
gravitation, this great physicist and astronomer undertook
to show, and finally succeeded in proving, that they could be
used to explain the motions of all the planets, as well as to
account for the precession of the equinoxes, for the tides, and
for the oblateness of the earth.

This work was carried on and steadily extended by Newton's successors for nearly a century. As facts and observations accumulated, they were classified, brought under these
laws and accounted for in accordance with them. At last a
" negative instance " was found, that is, a fact that apparently could not be reconciled with these laws. The planet
Uranus was observed to be in a position other than that in
which the calculations showed that it should be at that time.
The effects of all the known planets severally had been taken
into account, so here was a part of the motion which the
theory had failed to predict, or to explain when it was observed. Had the theory broken down in spite of the vast
array of facts that had been found to fit in with it so perfectly?
One thoroughly established fact which contradicts a theory
either overthrows it or necessitates its modification or extension. Did this fact constitute such a contradiction? Were
Newton's laws untrue or inadequate, were the calculations
incorrect, or did there exist some undiscovered fact, which, if
brought under the laws, would reconcile the negative instance
with it?

The rules of logic direct the investigator in such cases not
to abandon the theory, with all the evidences in its favor, but
rather to apply the " method of residues," by searching for

a new " cause " or fact which under the theory is competent to explain that part of the phenomena which cannot be accounted for by any or all of the known causes. To the disciplined thinker, thoroughly versed in the facts up to this point, the proper inference is obvious, although in 1845–6, when Adams and Leverrier made this inference, it required the boldness of a genius to adopt it as a hypothesis and undertake to test it out. " The unexplained disturbance," said these astronomers, " may be caused by another planet somewhere in the heavens, which hitherto has never been seen or thought of ! " Each, working independently of the other, set up for himself the problem, If Newton's laws are true, what must be the mass, the diameter, the form of orbit, and the distance from the sun of a planet which would produce the observed disturbance of Uranus's motion, and where ought it to be in the heavens at some particular time?

Both attacked and successfully solved this problem. Leverrier wrote to Galle at the observatory of Berlin, asking him to search the heavens in a certain longitude for the undiscovered planet. On September 23, 1846, the same day on which he received Leverrier's letter, Galle looked with his telescope for the planet and found it.

This same planet, Neptune, was *seen* August 4 and 12 by Challis at Cambridge, working on the position indicated for him by Adams's calculations: but not yet having compared its positions with those of the known stars, he had not *identified* it. On September 29, before he had heard of Galle's discovery, and following Leverrier's directions to look for it by its *disk shape*, he both saw and recognized the planet.

So these simple forms of description, now called Newton's Laws of Motion, and Newton's Laws of Universal Gravitation, devised by the imaginative genius of Newton, and tested by the indefatigable labors of himself and his successors extending through a century, have passed from the stage of hypothesis to that of theory, and finally to that of fact. They have taken their place among the fundamental laws under which all the apparently complex phenomena and relations belonging to the subject matter of Astronomy, Physics, and Chemistry are organized, and by which they are all " explained."

Davy and the composition of water. — The research of Davy on the composition of water affords us another dramatic illustration from among the multitude that may be cited in explanation of the scientific method of study. In 1781 Cavendish had discovered that pure oxygen and pure hydrogen combine chemically and form water; and in 1800 Carlisle and Nicholson had discovered that when an electric current is passed through water, both these gases are liberated from it. But it had been found soon after that in the process of thus decomposing pure water, an alkali collected at the negative electrode and an acid at the positive electrode. Sir Humphry Davy, reasoning from his store of accumulated chemical knowledge, believed that the acid and alkali came from some sources other than the water, and that, with sufficient care and exactness in carrying out the experiment, it might be proved that, as pure water could be obtained by putting together pure oxygen and pure hydrogen, so conversely if pure water were decomposed, and all adventitious substances were kept out, it would yield only pure oxygen and pure hydrogen. His early experiments were made with two glass tubes containing distilled water, the electrical connection between them being made by means of a strip of animal membrane. Immersing in these tubes the electrodes from an electric battery, he found in the tube with the positive electrode some hydrochloric acid, and in the other some solution of a fixed alkali. Suspecting at once that the acid and alkali came from common salt, which might be contained in the membrane, he rejected the latter and substituted washed cotton fiber to conduct the current across between the two tubes. On continuing the experiment for a very long time he again secured the oxygen gas at the positive electrode and the hydrogen gas at the negative, but no *hydrochloric* acid. Yet in the one tube there was nitrous acid and in the other an alkali. Clearly the membrane was the source of *part* of the acid ; and the sources of the alkali and the remaining acid were still problematical.

Knowing that alkali is a constituent of glass, he inferred that the current might be decomposing the glass, which he therefore rejected in favor of two cups of agate. When, after applying the current as before, he again found both acid and alkali, he supposed that they might come from some impurities either existing in the agate or adhering to it ; so he substituted two cones of gold for the agate cups, and repeated the experiments, but still with similar results. Nevertheless Davy had faith in his hypothesis and knew very well that it had not yet been fully tested. The water now became the object of suspicion. It had been distilled ; but during the distillation of water volatile products pass over with the steam and redissolve in the water that is condensed from it. To test the water he evaporated a quart of it in a silver dish and obtained a very small amount of dry residue. On adding this residue to some of the original distilled water in the gold cones, and repeating the experiment, Davy now found that the amount of alkali and acid yielded was greater than before ; so he had proved that impurities in the distilled water were sources of the acid and the alkali. His logic, however, was as good as his experimental skill ; and he well knew that the impurities he had found in the water were not necessarily the *only* sources of the acid and alkali.

Distilling the water over and over again until it yielded no residue when evaporated, he again made the experiment with the absolutely pure water, in the cups of pure gold ; but still found acid and alkali. On examination, however, the alkali that he now obtained was found to be not fixed alkali, but ammonia. Going back again with the pure water to the agate cups and the glass tubes, he repeated the experiment and got similar results. Therefore he had proved that the impure distilled water was the *only* source of the fixed alkali; but the nitrous acid and the ammonia still remained to be accounted for. Again Davy's chemical knowledge suggested to him that nitrous acid and ammonia contain only the elements nitrogen, oxygen, and hydrogen, which are the elements known to be contained in air and water; so at once the air was under suspicion. Its nitrogen might dissolve and, combining with the oxygen of the water at the positive electrode, form the nitrous acid. Some of it might also combine with the hydrogen of the water at the negative electrode and form the ammonia. To test this last hypothesis he repeated the experiment under a bell glass from which the air had been exhausted by means of an air pump. The result was that though nitrous acid and ammonia were still found, they were found in much smaller quantities than before. Now Davy, of course, knew that the air pump could not remove *all* the air; so he reasoned that if removing part of the air eliminated part of the acid and ammonia, then removing all of it might eliminate all of the acid and ammonia. Accordingly, he followed up this idea by exhausting the air from the receiver, letting pure hydrogen flow into it, and then pumping out the hydrogen. This process was repeated until the last traces of air had thus been removed; then the current was again passed through the pure water in the pure gold cups within the receiver. Davy must have been impatient to know the result, but he left the current passing for twenty-four hours; so that if the smallest quantities of acid and ammonia were liberated, he should get enough of them to recognize. When finally he had opened the apparatus and tested for acid and alkali, he found that there was none. His logic, his experimental skill, and his perseverance were at last rewarded with the complete proof which he sought. The inevitable conclusion was that the acid and alkali had come from impurities in the water and from the air; and that pure water contains nothing but oxygen and hydrogen gases. His hypothesis had now become a fact.

The meaning of science summarized. — Summarizing the meaning of science, we may say that it is " knowledge so classified and organized that it may be used in acquiring other knowledge "; that it implies not only content or subject matter classified and organized, but also a method of investigation or problem solving, including observation and measurement, experimentation, and logical inference, both inductive and deductive, by means of which the subject matter is organized and used in prediction, discovery, and invention; that its subject matter is constantly growing in volume and being brought under simpler and more comprehensive forms of description; that all human experience is legitimate material for its investigation; that it grows out of the problems related to human needs, physical, industrial, social, emotional, and intellectual; and that it is so intimately connected with industrial development that neither can go on without the other.

Division of the field. — The vastness of the domain with which science is concerned has made it necessary for individual workers in the various parts of the field to become specialists, and so to deal mainly with limited groups of phenomena, the members of which are more obviously and simply related one to another than they are to the members of the other groups.

So we have the mathematical sciences, such as arithmetic, algebra, geometry, trigonometry, analytic geometry, and the differential and integral calculus, which deal with the space, mass, and time relations of things apart from the nature or other properties of things themselves. They represent condensed forms and modes of reasoning to conclusions from known data under known conditions, when the data can be measured in terms of definite units and their amounts expressed as numbers of such units. So the mathematicians make it their chief business to deal with the estimation of magnitudes in terms of such units and with the determination of the numerical relations of different magnitudes to one another under various conditions.

A second group called the physical sciences is closely related to the first group, because in the study of them much use is made of the processes of mathematics in reaching conclusions with regard to the materials and phenomena of which they treat. This is possible because these sciences deal not only with such properties of bodies as color, hardness, smoothness, and the like, but much more largely with changes in their sizes, shapes, motions, temperatures, electrical and magnetic conditions, and so on, which can be measured very exactly in terms of such definite and well-known units as the foot or centimeter for length, the cubic foot or cubic centimeter for volume, the pound or gram for mass, the degree centigrade for temperature, the volt for electrical pressure, and others equally definite. The physical sciences treat not only of such properties of bodies as have just been mentioned, as well as of others that are characteristic of them under various conditions, but especially of the phenomena that occur and the relations that exist when such properties are changed in connection with the action of forces or the transferences of energy from one body to another, or with transformations of energy from one kind, such as that of mechanical motion or that of electricity, into another kind, such as heat or light or chemical separation. This group includes physics and astronomy, which deal primarily with such interactions and energy changes as occur without altering the composition of the bodies concerned, and chemistry, which deals with interactions among bodies when the transferences or transformation of energy are accompanied by the formation (through combination or decomposition, or exchanges of constituents) of substances that are different in their characteristic properties from those that were originally under observation before the energy changes took place.

Another group, called the earth sciences, includes geology and geography. Geology comprises a study of the earth as a whole, its present structure, and the history of the changes in rocks, lands, and seas, in physical and climatic conditions, and in animal and vegetable life that have characterized its development from its primitive to its present state. It considers also the agencies that have been causally related to these changes. Geography is a description of the earth's surface as it now is, especially as it is related to man, and of the origin and development of the physical conditions and the distribution of organic life that control his movements or affect his welfare.

A fourth group of sciences, the biological group, includes those that deal with matter and energy as involved in living forms, in the processes of growth, respiration, circulation, nutrition, and reproduction. This group includes botany, the study of plants; zoölogy, the study of animals; general biology, which deals with the structures, life processes, and modes of development that are common to both plants and animals; and human anatomy and physiology, which treat of the structure and life processes of the human body.

Closely related to the biological sciences, and having its foundations in biological facts, is the science of psychology, which deals with the phenomena of mental life, such as sensations, instinctive acts, perceptions, thinking, willing, and emotions, and with the conditions under which these occur.

Finally, there is the group of social sciences, dealing mainly, like psychology, with human behavior, and based very largely, as it is, on biological facts, but devoted especially to the study of the development and behavior of coöperating or interrelated groups of human beings, and of the conditions that determine their welfare and their progress. In this group are included anthropology, the study of man as an animal or an object of natural history; sociology, the study of the composition, phenomena, development, and interrelations of social groups; economics, the study of material wealth, its production, distribution, and consumption, especially with relation to individual and national prosperity and human welfare; and history, the study of past human conditions, relations, and institutions, especially from the standpoint of the development and progress of peoples and nations.

Threefold use of the word "science."—The word "science," then, is used in three senses. It may mean all organized knowledge or some limited portion of such knowledge; it may mean the scientific method; or it may refer to any one of the special sciences. In the popular language of the schools and the street it usually refers to the physical sciences, the biological sciences, and the earth sciences.

QUESTIONS FOR FURTHER STUDY

1. Make a list of the most important inventions and discoveries that have been made within your remembrance, and try to enumerate the important changes in our ways of doing things that have resulted from them.

2. Enumerate the conveniences in your home that are applications of important scientific principles; and try to think how the home activities in which they are used could be carried on without them.

3. Briefly describe the important economic and social changes that have been brought about by the following inventions and discoveries: (1) The steam locomotive, (2) the stationary steam engine, (3) the steamship, (4) the telegraph, (5) the telephone, (6) the Bessemer and open hearth steel processes, (7) the microscope, (8) the telescope, (9) gunpowder and high explosives, (10) the cotton gin, spinning jenny, and power loom, (11) the dynamo and electric motor, (12) the Babcock cream test, (13) research in bacteriology, (14) the United States Weather Bureau, (15) the work of the United States and State Agricultural Experiment Stations, (16) research in economics and sociology, (17) research in psychology, (18) photography, (19) the power printing press.

4. In what ways are the people of the United States at a disadvantage because of their failure to encourage research in chemistry?

5. How did Louis Pasteur help the silk industry in France?

6. What has the geological survey of your state done for its economic development?

7. What are your city chemists, city bacteriologists, or the city or state health departments accomplishing in your home locality?

REFERENCES

BUCKLEY, A. B. (Mrs. Arabella Fisher). A Short History of Science. Appleton, N. Y. 1896. 509 pp. $2.00. Revised 1915.

CAJORI, FLORIAN. A History of Physics. Macmillan, N. Y. 1899. 8 + 322 pp. $1.60.

CARNEGIE, ANDREW. Life of James Watt. Doubleday, Page & Co., N. Y. 1905. 241 pp. $1.40.

CHAMBERLAIN, HOUSTON S. The Foundations of the Nineteenth Century. Tr. by John Lees. Lane, N. Y. 1913. 2 vols. $5.00.

COOKE, JOSIAH P. Scientific Culture and Other Essays. N. Y. 1885. 293 pp. $1.00.

CRAMER, F. The Method of Darwin. McClurg, Chicago. 1896. 232 pp. $1.00.

DEWEY, JOHN. Science as Subject Matter and Method. Science, Vol. 31, pp. 127 ff., January 28, 1910.

MANN, C. R. The History of Science. An Interpretation. Popular Science Monthly, Vol. 72, pp. 313–322, April, 1908.

MIVART, ST. GEORGE. The Groundwork of Science. Putnam, N. Y. 1908. 328 pp. $1.75.

PEARSON, KARL. The Grammar of Science. A. & C. Black, London. 1911. 548 pp. $1.60. Macmillan, N. Y. 1915. 2 vols. $2.00.

THURSTON, R. H. A History of the Growth of the Steam Engine. Appleton, N. Y. 1891. 481 pp. $2.50.

VALLERY-RADOT, RENÉ. The Life of Pasteur. McClure, Phillips & Co., N. Y. 2 vols. 293 and 315 pp.

WHETHAM, W. C. D. Article, Science, Encyclopedia Britannica, XI Ed.

WHETHAM, W. C. D. Science and the Human Mind. Longmans, Green & Co., 1912. 304 pp. $1.60.

c

CHAPTER II

The humanistic attitude. — In order to teach any science effectively, one must obtain a clear and comprehensive idea of the meaning and method of science from the broad humanistic viewpoint that we have indicated in the preceding chapter. He needs this because, for the requirements of modern education, it is not enough to present the organized subject matter of one or two of the sciences, even though it be presented clearly and with numerous experiments and demonstrations.

Aims of instruction in science. — The aims of the science teacher must be:

1. To impart to his pupils some insight into the meaning and value of science.

2. To infect them with the scientific spirit.

3. To train them in a manner appropriate to their particular stage of mental development in the methods of thinking and investigation that are common to all the sciences and, in fact, to all productive intellectual work, rather than to train them in the special technique of any one science.

Such aims are the only ones that can realize in full the true values of science in education for both efficiency and culture. Only a few of the graduates of the high school may by any chance become scientific investigators by profession, but by good scientific training all of them should be enabled,

18

in some degree at least, to approach with the scientific attitude of mind, and to attack by orderly and scientific methods, those problems with which the experiences of their present and future lives must inevitably confront them.

Futility of formal and didactic methods. — For these aims, a recitation so conducted that it serves merely to enlighten the teacher as to whether the pupils have learned the contents of the textbook, or even so that it serves to give him opportunities to explain to them what they could not understand from the text, is not sufficient; and even if experiments and demonstrations are made by the teacher, much that is essential is lacking. Further, if in addition to this the pupils are required to work out the answers to a large number of made-up textbook " problems," and to describe numerous and more or less unfamiliar " practical applications of the principles that have been learned," this didactic method may lack entirely the scientific spirit; and it may fail to afford any real scientific training.

Finally, the deadening effect of such formal and didactic instruction is not wholly counteracted by laboratory work, when the very common practice is followed of requiring the pupils to go through a set list of experiments, such as the so-called " National Physics Course," which are not directly related to the work that is going on in the classroom at the same time. These experiments are designed mostly " to illustrate this principle," " to verify that law," " to demonstrate this fact," " to determine the value of that physical constant," or merely to " measure " something with no other end in view than to acquire technical skill by formal practice. Here again the close contact with things and forces may prove suggestive so as to provoke thinking among some minds that perfunctory didactic methods in the classroom fail to arouse; *but such methods, aimed as they are, either consciously or unconsciously, merely toward imparting information or toward formal discipline, tend to inhibit thought and investigation rather more than to incite it.*   The only reason that they do not fail entirely lies in the fact that many of the phenomena and rela·tions with which the sciences deal are intrinsically so interesting and so bristling with problematic situations that they almost inevitably provoke thought, and in the further fact that no pupils who reach the high school are wholly lacking in suggestibility or wholly without interest in intellectual activity.   Hence there will always be some pupils who develop thinking ability even under the most deadening methods.   The majority, however, acquire no real and permanent interest in science under such teaching; while many are actually given a distaste for it.   Let any one who doubts this ask, not the science teachers, but the *principals* of the next five high schools that he chances to visit.

Four guiding principles. — To one who has a fair grasp of the true meaning of science and has imbibed for himself some of its spirit, the following principles will commend themselves as fundamental in determining the correct attitude toward the work of science teaching.

1. Didactic methods aimed solely at getting the pupils to acquire subject matter presented to them in finished encyclopedic form are alien to both the spirit and the method of science.

2. Laboratory experiments devised merely to aid in the better memorizing of subject matter or to afford formal training in laboratory technique are not very effective in developing the power of independent thinking or the love for investigation.

3. *The true spirit of science grows out of the desire to know truth that may have a useful outcome, and apply it to get results that are felt to be worth while, and hence this spirit can be caught by children only when they investigate, learn, and apply in order to get results that appeal to them personally as worthy of their efforts.*

4. The scientific method is essentially a method of solving problems that present either a utilitarian or an intellectual appeal; *therefore the true way to induct beginners into its use is to confront them with such problems, and guide them in using the scientific method in reaching their solutions.*

Lessons for the teacher from the meaning of science.— The history of scientific discoveries and their relation to the march of civilization contains some most important lessons :

1. Suggestions, ideas, inferences, concepts, grow only out of an abundant first-hand acquaintance with facts.

2. Ability to grapple successfully with problematic situations of whatever degree of complexity depends on fertility of ideas which may be used as hypotheses.

3. Prejudice, hasty generalizing, and premature belief in a suggested law or principle paralyze curiosity and inhibit inquiry, and therefore are fatal to the development of power in thinking.

4. The value of any hypothesis in guiding the mind toward the final solution of a problem depends on the possibilities of testing or trying it out.

5. Hypotheses must be rigorously tested by reasoning out their implications and comparing these with the facts; and the selection of a working theory must be made by considering all likely hypotheses, and choosing that one which best sustains the attacks of such rigorous criticism.

6. Continuous testing of hypotheses leads steadily to the observation and discovery of new facts.

7. As knowledge of the subject matter accumulates, it must be classified and organized with reference to some hypothesis or theory in order to be remembered and recorded in such manner as to be capable of use.

8. The final process in the scientific method is the organizing of the entire subject matter — facts, phenomena, laws, concepts — under some simple fundamental comprehensive laws or principles. Since this process of systematization is the last step in the solution of a problem in the actual work of scientific thought, and is never finished because science is always growing, it should also be the last step taken by the pupil in the process of learning any of the laws and principles of a science in school.

With the assistance of the teacher, the pupils should organize and build their knowledge into a system as they go on, bringing each new part of the subject under its proper head; but not until the end of the course should the attempt be made to have them see each part of the subject in the light of every other part.

The fallacy of abstract presentation. — The method of presentation common to most of the present-day textbooks, and used also by the majority of teachers whose instruction has been observed by the writer, exactly reverses this fundamental psychological principle. Nearly all of them first state the general law or principle, such as the kinetic theory of matter, or the wave theory of sound, then advance a few facts in its favor, and none against it, so as to convince the student of its truth *by making it difficult for him to question or deny it.* They then give him examples and practical applications or problems which he is expected to solve or explain by using it. This exclusively deductive process effectively shuts up the mind, takes the sharp edge off curiosity, and inhibits inductive inquiry at the very beginning.

The fallacy committed by the teachers and the textbook writers who use this method consists in assuming that the words, formulas, or symbols in which a generalization is expressed carry anything more of meaning for an individual than that which he himself has analyzed out of his own first-hand experiences and worked over in his own thought in connection with a considerable number of cases whose relations are described by it.

Superiority of concrete methods. — The correct way is not to have the student memorize the principle first, and then afterwards apply it to the problems, but rather to suggest, challenge, and question in such a way that he will get it out of the process of reflection on problems, and then apply it to more problems.

The point is that a general principle is more eagerly sought for by the student, and the facts out of which it emerges by analysis are accumulated with greater zeal and are more easily remembered when he sees that he *needs* the principle to help him find out something that he really wants to know. Furthermore when he realizes with pleasure that the principle has helped him to find a much-desired answer to one question, he will take pains to remember it in order that he may apply it to other questions which come within its scope, and for which he wishes to find answers. What could Newton have done with his laws if he had not discovered them for himself, but if some dry-as-dust teacher had set them for him as a lesson to " learn " out of a textbook, had duly heard him recite them, and then had sent him out to apply them in making new discoveries? From the little that his biographers tell of Newton's boyhood, we may infer that during the time he attended the Latin Grammar School, at Grantham, he did not work much at memorizing, nor " recite " very glibly; but he put in much of his time making machines, toys, and engineering contrivances of all sorts, — in fact, solving practical problems for himself. His theoretical interests grew out of these practical ones.

QUESTIONS FOR FURTHER STUDY

1. Select any textbook in science that you studied in high school, or with which you are familiar. What provision, if any, do you find

in it for giving the pupils the broad humanistic viewpoint that is out-lined in Chapter I? If commissioned to revise the book would you try to provide for this? If so, submit for class criticism a revision of a few selected pages so as to show how you would provide for it. If not, give a sample outline, providing for it in such manner as you think best.

2. Does the textbook selected provide any definite means for in-fecting the pupils with the scientific spirit? If not, would you provide for it in the book, or would you reserve this to yourself to do through your teaching methods? Indicate very briefly how you would do this in either case.

3. If taught any science by such formal and didactic methods as are criticized in this chapter, can you recollect any feelings or experiences which either confirm or deny the statements made under "Four Guid-ing Principles" or "Lessons for the Teacher from the Meaning of Science"?

4. Have you had any experiences that convince you of the fallacy of abstract presentation? Of the superiority of concrete methods? If so, describe some of them.

5. Pick out a generalization as presented in some science textbook. Does it involve the fallacy of assuming on the part of the pupils experi-ences that they have not had, but which are necessary to the compre-hension of the generalization? How would you revise the presentation to secure this real comprehension? Be specific.

6. Run through a few scientific articles in popular magazines and see if you can find a scientific principle presented through a sufficient number of concrete examples so that it may really be comprehended. Compare this presentation with that on the same topic in a school text-book. Why do so many boys pore over *The Scientific American* in the libraries and at the same time do "poor work" in their physics classes?

REFERENCES

CLIFFORD, W. K. Lectures and Essays. Macmillan, N. Y. 1901. 443 pp. $3.00.

CLIFFORD, W. K. Seeing and Thinking. Macmillan, N. Y. 1890. 156 pp. 15¢.

FORBES, S. A. The Scientific Method in High School and College. School Science and Mathematics, Vol. 3.

KINGSLEY, C. D., Chairman. Preliminary Statement of the Chairmen of the Committees of the Commission on the Reorganization of Secondary Education. U. S. Bureau of Education, Bull. 1913. No. 41.

MANN, C. R.   The History of Science — An Interpretation.   Popular Science Monthly, Vol. 72, p. 313, April, 1908.

NUNN, T. P.   The Aims and Achievements of the Scientific Method. Macmillan, N. Y.   1907.   10 + 144 pp.

PEARSON, KARL.   Grammar of Science.   A. & C. Black, London.   Macmillan, N. Y.   A new edition in two volumes has been published lately.   A philosophical treatise on the grounds of belief in scientific knowledge, which should be studied by every science teacher.   1915. $2.00 each.   Part I.   394 pp.

POINCARÉ, H.   Science and Hypothesis.   The Science Press, N. Y. 1905.   196 pp. $1.50.

POINCARÉ, H.   The Value of Science.   The Science Press, 1907.   147 pp. $1.50.

SPENCER, HERBERT.   Education, Intellectual, Moral, and Physical. Appleton, N. Y.   1894.   301 pp. $1.25.

STRONG, T. B.   Lectures on the Scientific Method.   Clarendon Press, Oxford, Eng.   1906.   7s. 6d.

THORNDIKE, E. L.   Science Teaching Seen from the Outside.   University of State of N. Y., Albany.   Bull. No. 34.   August, 1907.

WOODHULL, JOHN F.   Science for Culture. School Science and Mathematics, 7 : 83–90, February, 1907.   School Review, Chicago, February, 1907.

CHAPTER III

Elementary and concrete thinking. — The methods of learning and thinking characteristic of the young child and the savage are much alike. They resemble scientific thinking in that they have to do with the solving of problems. They differ from it, firstly, in that they are much less exact and systematic, less complex, and less consciously formulated, and, secondly, in that they are employed only with immediate needs, and not with such remote ends as the satisfaction of intellectual or esthetic cravings, or the progress of the race.

Like those of the savage of to-day the needs and desires of our primitive ancestors pertained mainly to food and shelter, to means of attack and defense against fierce beasts and hostile tribesmen, and to such clothing and ornaments as contributed to bodily comfort or the satisfaction of the instincts for personal display and attraction of the opposite sex.

Knowledge in the primitive stage is mainly in the field of sense perception, which begins with the passive recognition of a group of associated sensations, not at first discretely distinguished, but making up a vague whole. For example, a four-legged, sharp-toothed, hairy, growling thing is presented to the savage consciousness through sensations of sight and hearing. This group of sensations calls up memories and images of other sensations which through past experiences have become associated with those actually present. Along with these comes active recognition of the interpretations or meanings that have become associated with this whole group of sensations. Such meanings for example, as a-thing-that-bites, "howls-and-is-answered-by-others-who-come-to-its-aid," "is-dangerous-and-must-be-killed-or-avoided-by-flight" are joined with the sensations of sight and hearing that are actually present, and go to make up a percept. So this percept becomes the object of active attention, which is followed or accompanied by appropriate motor activities, such as fighting, calling for assistance, climbing a tree, or seeking safety in flight.

The particular mode of response to the situation might be the result of involuntary reaction to the instinctive feeling of fear; but in the case of a mature and experienced savage it would be the outcome of a mental act that a logician would describe as the categorical judgment, " This is a wolf," taken along with other judgments leading to the selection of the mode of procedure that was deemed most likely to satisfy immediate needs or more remote aims. If the immediate need were simply to escape, the savage would take to his heels or climb a tree; but if his purpose were to secure a wolf-hide he would fight.

Comparison and classification. — Such judgments grow out of comparison, that is, out of discriminating differences or recognizing likenesses among objects, and they involve classification or grouping in accordance with such likenesses or differences as are related to conscious needs. Through the accumulated experiences of primitive man, some plants were found to be good to eat and some not good to eat; some easy to get, others hard to get; some good for making mats and baskets or thatching roofs, but not good to eat. Some wood was good for making fire, some for making boats, and some for making bows and arrows. Some stones, such as flint, could be chipped and made into heads for arrows and spears, while others could be made smooth, and used for mashing grain or roots. The muscles of some animals were found to be good for food, their skins for clothing, their teeth and claws for ornaments and their sinews for sewing skins together. Thus the various sensory experiences got meanings associated with them. They became facts, and were grouped, however crudely, into a body of classified knowledge, organized with reference to the immediate needs of the savage mode of life.

The function of language. — Along with the acquisition and classification of such knowledge of natural objects there grew up in like manner a knowledge and control of vocal sounds and gestures. Sounds spontaneously uttered, or uttered in imitation of sounds heard, were found to suggest to the minds of others the same thoughts or emotions that were in the mind of the one who uttered them. " Bow-wow," for example, suggested dog, " wak-wak " suggested duck, " ou " suggested pain. Likewise pointing to the open mouth suggested hunger or food, and extending the hands forward with the palms up suggested invitation or welcome. Thus facts as they became known got appropriate sounds or gestures associated with them. These sounds and gestures came gradually to stand for the percepts, the facts, and meanings with which they had become associated. They became, as it were, the signs, the symbols, the labels of percepts present to the senses, or of images or ideas existing in the mind. They served as elements out of which a primitive dramatic language grew up along with the knowledge of facts, and served as an indispensable aid in the evolution of thinking and in communication of ideas.

When by a fortunate suggestion of similarity or difference some savage more gifted than the others thought of and tried a new substance for an old use and found it better for the purpose than other substances, or thought of a new use for an old substance, this newly discovered and useful fact was learned by others from him. So also each generation of children learned by imitation, trial, and success the useful

facts which their elders had learned from the preceding generation or had discovered themselves.

The empirical method of learning. — Such progress in
knowledge and skill occurs only through *variation* and *selection*. Either accidentally or with a definite desire and
conscious aim, different ways of conceiving or classifying particular facts, or new ways of performing certain acts, are hit
upon; and if one of them proves to be better than those
hitherto tried, it is selected and continues to be used until
supplanted in its turn by some still better mode. This
principle of variation and selection applies to the really
marvelous accumulations of useful classified knowledge and
of skill in the arts and crafts that have been possessed by
savage tribes. They learn by consciously or unconsciously
imitating others, or by variation and selection with only the
end and not the process clearly before the mind. This method
of trial and error without any conscious, orderly, or prearranged method to guide and control the variations and
selection is called the empirical method of learning. It is
the only process by which animals learn; and it is the process
mainly employed by young children as well as by savages.
It is also used by most adults when learning in a field in which
they have not had previous specific training. The difference
between the savage and the child or the untrained civilized
adult on the one hand, and the disciplined thinker on the
other, lies just here. The savage learns empirically, thinks
almost wholly in the plane of sense perception, and rarely
rises to the plane of constructive ideas. Hence his methods
of conceiving and doing are regulated by custom, habit, and
tradition. His advances in knowledge are almost incredibly
slow. He adjusts himself with admirable smoothness and
ease, almost automatically, to his simple natural environment; but when an entirely new situation develops, wherein
the customary modes of response do not suffice to meet his need,
he seldom thinks it out, and is at a loss as to how to proceed.

3238

Constructive thinking. — However, it is difficult, if not impossible, to conceive how the more distinct advances made by savages could have occurred without the aid of some *abstract thinking*, — that is, thinking of some quality of a thing apart from its other qualities or even apart from the thing itself. Consider what may have been the mental process which led to the invention of the spear. We know that the art of chipping flint, and shaping it into awls, knives, and daggers was brought to considerable perfection long before the dawn of history. In one of the many fights that took place with flint knives, some unusually bright savage may have found himself at a disadvantage because his weapon was shorter than that of his adversary. He is pressed by the dire need of prevailing over his opponent, but the habitual modes of fighting do not suffice. The *gap between the means at hand and the desired end*, becomes clearly and painfully apparent to his consciousness; and *reflection* on the elements of this *problematic situation* begins. Perhaps he runs away, " lives to fight another day," and sits down to " think it out." One fact after another is turned over in his mind and examined with reference to its bearings on the solution. Out of remembered previous experiences, and through this process of reflection *ideas* emerge, such as the long dagger as the source of danger, the greater length of the dagger as the cause of advantage. A still longer dagger in his own hands would transfer the advantage to his own side. A certain pole remembered or seen is *long*. The pole and his dagger might be fastened together, and thus make a very *long weapon* — so long that he might stab his enemy with it before the latter could come near enough to harm him. He has thus used abstract thinking and constructive imagination in forming a *hypothesis*. He has *analyzed out* the quality of length as significant to the solution, and performed an act of *synthesis* in combining mentally the length of the pole with the sharpness and hardness of the dagger point; and so he has arrived at the new notion or *conception* of a spear, and a hypothesis as to a manner of using it. It is now necessary to *reason deductively* in order to develop the implications of the hypothesis. The dagger must in some way be firmly fixed to the end of the shaft. He thinks of the other things which he knows how to fasten together and concludes that he can split the end of the shaft and bind the dagger in with a thong of hide. Eventually, perhaps after considerable *experimenting*, he succeeds in fastening it firmly, goes out with it to meet his foe, and easily slays him. Having thus *tested his hypothesis* and *verified his conclusion*, he returns in triumph to his fellow tribesmen, and imparts to them this new piece of *positive knowledge*, which is the result of combining sense perceptions and memories with ideas.

A complete act of thought. — This intellectual process performed in a crude manner and without formulation, as it must have been, and probably occupying not merely a few consecutive moments, as it would in the case of a trained thinker, but rather many different moments distributed over considerable time — represents a complete act of thought. There were:

1. The recognition of a discrepancy between the means and the end, giving the occasion and indispensable condition for thought;

2. Reflection, involving analysis, comparison, and discrimination of likeness and difference, and leading to judgment and classification;

3. Inductive inference, leading through the selection of appropriate ideas to a hypothesis;

4. Deductive inference, leading to a probable solution and further reasoning in developing the implications of the hypothesis;

5. Testing of the hypothesis, by comparing its implications with the facts, — a process which leads finally to

6. Verification and conclusion.

We have no historical evidence that the spear was invented in exactly this way. For example, the long stick may have first been sharpened to a point and used as a spear, the weakness of the wooden point noted, and the improvement made by lashing to it a flint arrowhead or knife. Yet be this as it may, we may be sure that thought processes more or less like those described were used in this and every case where distinct advances were made.

Empirical advances. — This review of primitive conditions with regard to thinking suggests that even when thinking is so elementary as to remain in the sense perception or empirical stage, distinct advances can be made rarely, if at all, excepting through processes of abstract thought including analysis and synthesis, induction and deduction, crude and elementary though they be. This is true in spite of the fact that empirical thinking always sticks close to the facts, — at least when it is successful, — that it is intuitive, works without any conscious method, and can produce results only when the road from fact to hypothesis and from hypothesis to verification is very short, direct, and free from complications.

The civilization of the Egyptians, Babylonians, and Chaldeans with their extensive development of skill and organization in the arts and crafts, in commerce, and in political and military institutions was brought about by an immense extension of empirical thinking and classification. Such development of thinking, on the other hand, could have come only in response to the varied and urgent material problems that were thrust upon these peoples by their gradual rise from savage modes of life through the nomadic, pastoral, and agricultural modes into life in organized industrial communities. This development was a process of action and reaction between thinking and practical needs. Empirical variation and selection brought about new conditions and new ideas. These created new wants and new needs. New wants and new needs raised new problems to be solved, and caused thinkers to work at the problems and solve them. Through the solutions thus reached new conditions were brought about — more complex than the old. Hence, again, new needs, new wants, new problems, and so on.

Abstract thought. — *The Greeks.* — To the empirical and material achievements of the older peoples the brilliant and imaginative Greeks added the second vital element of the scientific method, namely, sustained reflection, consciously formulated abstract thought, and methodical rules for reaching and safeguarding conclusions.

The Greeks of the Mediterranean colonies, of Athens, and of Alexandria laid solid foundations for modern logic, elementary mathematics, and anatomy. In astronomy they applied every phase of the scientific method, — collection and organization of observed facts, inductive inference, hypothesis, and testing of hypotheses by comparison of their deduced implications with the results of further observations. It is little to their discredit that they worked on a hypothesis (the geocentric or so-called Ptolemaic) which, in the light of further discoveries, became untenable. " A false theory which can be compared with facts may be more useful at a certain phase of development than a true one beyond the comprehension of the time and incapable of examination by observation and experiment by any means then known." [1]

Facts and hypotheses as related to success in science. — The Greeks succeeded in developing rather fully the scientific method in Astronomy, because the active spirit of intellectual curiosity, which was born among them, was constantly appealed to by the phenomena of the heavens, and because their fondness for disputation drove them back again and again to the facts of observation to check and confirm their own hypotheses or to refute those of their opponents. Thus, in the course of five or six centuries their intellectual leaders gradually grew away from their speculative habit of flying

[1] Whetham, W. C. D., Article, Science, Encyc. Brit., XI Ed.

D

from a few particulars to a simple generalized statement to be accepted as final truth. A few at least of their philosophers learned that solid and substantial progress in the establishment of knowledge can be made only by testing and selecting generalizations through incessant returns to the facts of observation. *It was only because they did form the habit of squaring their hypotheses with the facts that these hypotheses became fruitful and led them to new discoveries.*

In the field of Anatomy, they made considerable advances beyond the stage of empirical classification in which their Zoölogy and Botany remained. Their most gifted physicians were held down to the observation of facts by the practical demands for accurate knowledge of the human body. Accordingly, they were driven to check their theories by the dissection of human corpses and the bodies of monkeys.

On the other hand, they accomplished practically nothing in the field of Chemistry, and very little in Physics, because they looked down with disdain upon the arts, manufactures, and agriculture, out of which there are constantly arising physical and chemical problems that urgently demand solution. They despised industries and trade as pertaining only to menials and slaves. Thus their intellectual hunger did not seek for satisfaction in this field, and their observations therein were superficial and without sustained interest. Furthermore, they were freed by their system of slavery and their simple mode of life from the problems of industry. Finally, it has been shown on economic principles that slavery checks the development of labor-saving inventions. Hence they lacked urgent incentives for gaining that intimate first-hand experience with the facts which, in any field, must be coupled with power in abstract thought in order that phenomena and the ideas through which they are related may be organized into a science.

The contributions of the Greeks culminated at Alexandria during the second century after Christ; and from that time until the end of the fifteenth century few persons are known to have used consistently the scientific method. Although during this long period a few scientific facts and laws were empirically discovered, and many practical inventions developed, there were no great advances in pure science.

The Middle Ages. — This quiescent period in the development of science was due to many causes, three of which underlie all the others: 1. The reaction of the early Christians against the wickedness and cruelty of the Roman world, and the centering of their thoughts on a future state, entailed a lack of interest in industrial life and a disregard of facts and forces, both physical and human. 2. For the defense of the faith, the early Christian fathers worked out systems of dogmatic theology formulated according to the methods of the Greek speculative philosophers; and these dogmatic systems were accepted and enforced during the Middle Ages by the power of Church and State, so that men who were intellectually inclined and who possessed the means of leisure for study ceased to arrive at general principles by inductive methods. Consequently they grew into the habit of neglecting facts and of accepting certain traditional and dogmatic statements of the Greek philosophers and the Church fathers as the premises from which all knowledge was to be deduced by formal reasoning. Thus the higher field of thought was divorced from the humble fields of everyday activity. 3. The Roman social order fell into a state of decay; and Europe was submerged for centuries by the tide of its German conquerors. A thousand years of fighting, turmoil, and industrial struggle were necessary before a measure of peace and stability was gained, industry and trade developed, and an intelligent, enterprising industrial class rose into power and the enjoyment of leisure for intellectual pursuits.

The Renaissance. — Thus at the close of the fifteenth century, the invention of gunpowder and of printing, the rise of centralized, tax-supported governments, and the ascendency of the wealthy industrial class had dealt a mortal blow to feudalism; scholastic philosophy had worked itself out into a state of empty formalism from which no vital problems could arise; and in the reaction from scholasticism to humanism the thoughts of scholars were again directed to the things of this world.

Hence, along with the many scholars of the time who devoted themselves to literature and art, there arose a few men of genius who became interested in the facts and phenomena of nature, and in the objective study of many urgent problems, part of which grew out of those needs that were developed through the now rapid rise of commerce and the industrial arts and inventions, and another part of which was suggested by the writings of the Greeks and the reawakened hunger for intellectual achievement in an active world. Thus through the voyages of Columbus and Magellan, the idea of the rotundity of the earth was transferred from the realm of hypothesis to the realm of fact; and through the constructive thinking of Copernicus, the accurate observations of Tycho Brahe, and the laborious mathematical work of Kepler, the idea that the sun and not the earth is the center of our planetary system was so elaborated and clarified that it had reached the stage where it needed only careful checking with the results of further observations in order to become thoroughly established.

From Galileo to Newton. — This checking was done by Galileo. His discoveries with his telescope, taken along with his theoretical and experimental work and that of Stevinus and Huyghens, in Mechanics, prepared the way for Newton, who united terrestrial and celestial mechanics into a comprehensive system. By means of his mathematical development of the law of gravitation and the laws of motion, Newton completed the foundations upon which both the content and the method of modern Mechanics are laid. His discoveries and those of **Huyghens in Physical Optics** placed that branch of science on a firm experimental foundation. Great advances also were made by the application of similar methods to Botany, Zoölogy, and Physiology.

The work of Galileo was epoch-making, because he revived and applied to Physics as well as to Astronomy the use of the working hypothesis, and first applied the process of sifting and testing hypotheses by the combined use of mathematical deduction, observation, and experimentation. The ideal of explaining laws and phenomena by analyzing out their essential relations and bringing them under simpler and more familiar principles through logical procedure was given its first effective start by him. From the times of Galileo and Newton, and their illustrious contemporaries in many fields of science, the spirit of true scientific investigation has steadily grown, until the ideals of method and system which they set up are now dominant in almost every field of thought.

QUESTIONS FOR FURTHER STUDY

1. From your own experiences during childhood, can you recall any cases of things that you thought out yourself in order to satisfy your needs or desires? If so, describe your thoughts and how you reached conclusions.

2. Do you recollect any of the ways in which things became classified in your mind when a child? If so, describe them.

3. Recall your experiences in learning to write, to ride a bicycle, to skate, to swim, to use tools, to make cake, bread, candy, a willow whistle, or a kite. Describe your experiences in arriving at an efficient method.

4. Among your learning experiences can you recall any cases in which you were helped through having learned the meanings of words? Describe them.

5. Do you remember any cases in which as a child you undertook to communicate a discovery of your own to other children? How did you manage it?

6. From the reference books on the history of science find some cases not mentioned in this book where it can be shown that success depends on checking hypotheses by comparing their implications with the facts.

7. From these accounts pick out and tabulate the cases of inductive and deductive reasoning.

REFERENCES

BUCKLEY, A. B. (Mrs. Fisher).   A Short History of Science.   Appleton, N. Y.   1896.   509 pp. $2.00.   Rev. 1915.

CAJORI, F.   A History of Physics.   Macmillan, N. Y.   1899.   8 + 322 pp. $1.60.

COLVIN, S. S.   The Learning Process.   Macmillan, N. Y.   1911.   25 + 329 pp. $1.25.

DEWEY, JOHN.   How We Think.   Heath, Boston.   1910.   224 pp. $1.00.

DEWEY, JOHN.   School and Society.   University of Chicago Press, Chicago.   1900.   129 pp. $1.00.

DRAPER, JOHN W.   History of the Conflict between Religion and Science.   Appleton, N. Y.   1903. $1.75.   20th cent. series.   75 ¢.

LIEBIG, BARON J. VON.   The Development of Ideas in Physical Science. In Culture Demanded by Modern Life, Ed. by E. L. Youmans. Appleton, N. Y.   1875.   473 pp., pp. 348–369.

SPENCER, HERBERT.   Illustrations of Universal Progress.   Appleton, N. Y.   1868.   451 pp.

WELTON, J.   Logical Bases of Education.   Macmillan, N. Y.   1904. 16 + 288 pp. $1.00.

WHEWELL, WILLIAM.   A History of the Inductive Sciences.   J. W. Parker, London.   1857.   3 vols.   Appleton, N. Y.   1894.   2 vols.

WHITE, A. D.   A History of the Warfare between Science and Theology. Appleton, N. Y.   1914.   2 vols. $5.00.

CHAPTER IV

SCIENCE AND CHILDREN

Race experience and child experience. — The importance
to the science teacher of knowing at least as much as has here
been presented of the origin and growth of science lies in the
fact that children during the period of their advance from
infancy to maturity pass through the various stages of development in thinking power in an order from simple to complex,
somewhat like that in which the race as a whole has passed
through them, but with one very important difference. The
child with whom we have to deal has always about him the
appliances of modern science and the products of modern
thought. Thus his environment is more complex, more artificial, and infinitely richer in means and opportunities for
thinking abstractly than was the environment of any child
in former times. Hence it would be absurd to assume that
the child of to-day must necessarily " recapitulate " the experience of the race in detail. In his learning, unlike the savages
or the ancients, he has behind him the accumulated knowledge
and experience gained by multitudes of men in centuries of
time. Therefore, in so far as he is able to take advantage of
this priceless legacy he may advance by leaps and bounds
where the race was obliged to crawl at a snail's pace. People
all around him are constantly thinking abstractly, expressing
their own thoughts, answering his eager questions, or directing
him to books or papers wherein he can get the information
that he wants. Thus many boys know a good deal of fact
and some theory concerning electric bells and motors, steam

and gas engines, flying machines, wireless telegraphy, photography and the like; and many girls know something about sewing machines, the operations of the kitchen and laundry, the habits and care of domestic animals and plants, and the behavior of people. Most of these things that children know have been learned empirically, but often they have been acquired as the result of considerable thought of a higher type. All such knowledge, because it has been gained through genuine self-activity, tends to arouse interest in any problem of science that is related to it, provided that the problem be so presented to the children as to appeal to their spirit of wonder, and provided that it be made so clear and simple as to fall within the range of their concrete knowledge and their power of abstract thinking. *The new material presented cannot, however, become part of the usable mental possessions of the children unless assimilated with their own concrete and experiential knowledge; and the process of assimilation requires the aid of ideas which, although they may be suggested through the teaching process, must originate in the children's own minds.*

How young children learn. — During infancy, and until they get control of their bodies, children learn as all animals and most savages do, by the trial and error method; and in the acquisition of many kinds of skill, their learning throughout their lives may be of this sort. It begins with a vague and unanalyzed complex of sensations, which gradually acquire meanings through the motor and intellectual reactions that the child makes in response to them — or in other words, through what he does and what he feels in consequence of them, and through what he mentally associates with them in connection with such responses. If a certain reaction, from among the many chance responses that might be made to a complex of sensations, is satisfactory, it is likely to be repeated when the same or a very similar stimulus occurs. Through repetition it becomes **habitual,** and is remembered. On the other hand, if the reaction is unsatisfactory, it fails of repetition and is soon forgotten.

When a group of sensations has been connected in memory with a satisfactory response, it has acquired a *meaning* to the individual. For example, the group of sensations that an adult would identify with a stick of candy gradually acquires to the child the meanings, something to hold, something to throw, something to roll, something sweet to suck, and so on; and according to the system of family government in his home it may acquire either of the added meanings, something to be obtained by crying or something to be obtained by not crying. In this manner, an active and suggestible child acquires through his experiences a multitude of meanings for the things that exist and the events that happen all about him; and he acquires skill in dealing with things by making chance variations in his modes of response and more or less consciously selecting the better modes as time goes on.

Empirical thinking by children. — Children soon begin to do some empirical thinking when the conditions are problematic. Thus, when habitual modes of response do not result in satisfaction, action is suspended, ideas of new modes of response arise, and these chance ideas are tried out, with the result that the most satisfactory response is selected. Thus the child's modes of doing things may be progressively improved as his wants and needs expand. His stock of meanings grows larger, and things become more definitely classified with reference to the ways in which they contribute to his pleasure or satisfy his needs. The more self-active and varied his experiences with the things that he finds all about him, the greater will be the stock of meanings which he accumulates and classifies, the more and the better will be the kinds of motor skill that he acquires, and the more able will he be to have ideas that enable him to cope with new conditions and learn new things. Ideas can spring up only by suggestion and association, out of accumulated first-hand experience of the things whose interrelations they stand for. Hence, the wider and more intimate the child's experiences with his environment, the more abundant and fruitful will be the crop of ideas that sprout from them in response to problematic situations.

Instruction must begin with the child's experience. — That child has the best preparation for science therefore — to say nothing of other kinds of education — who, through the performance of many juvenile tasks in the home or on the farm, through play activities, excursions, manual training and construction, home gardening, sewing, cooking, care of animals, observation and collection of rocks, minerals, fossils, woods, stamps, photographs and the like, has had the largest amount of child experience. It is out of such experiences only that he can accumulate a large store of meanings and many kinds of skill. He can control and use this knowledge and skill, as needed, only when and because the things and the processes have interested him so as repeatedly to engage his childish thought and effort; and he can get ideas out of them because they have thus become concrete, familiar, and easy to recall.

Thus the fundamental process in the learning of science consists in the accumulation of meanings, and the acquisition of motor skill and useful habits of all kinds, through first-hand experience with the phenomena of everyday life, and in connection with the satisfaction of intimate personal interests and needs. Hence the fundamental process of teaching consists in so arranging suitable stimuli in the form of challenges to his curiosity, questions, demonstrations, suggestions, statements of fact, experiments, and any other suitable means, that the children will be assisted in recalling, selecting, ordering, and making explicit the meanings already accumulated by them and having a possible bearing on some problematic situation that the teacher has caused to develop out of the thing to be taught.

These mental processes cannot be performed *for* the children. They must be performed *by* the children. It is the teacher's work to start these processes and keep them going, by questioning, by suggesting such new related facts, and by providing such new related experiences as the learners may be able to read appropriate meanings into. Thus they can be made to assimilate the novel with the familiar. This process on the learner's part is *apperception;* and on the teacher's part is sometimes called preparation, or the first of the so-called " five formal steps " of the recitation.

Rational thinking by children. — With children as with adults, rational thinking starts from a basis of meanings already accumulated and classified through first-hand experience. It arises out of a desire to meet a need in the best possible way, or out of the desire to bring an event or phenomenon into an intelligible system into which it fits, in such a way as to satisfy an instinctive craving for harmony of meaning or completeness of knowledge and understanding. The scientific spirit includes both this spirit of wonder and the desire to use materials and processes for the satisfaction of practical needs ; but the needs with which it deals are more remote than those occasioning the lower modes of thinking. The action or judgment for the sake of which the thinking occurs is suspended until the thinking process is as nearly complete and final as is demanded by the ideal of perfection which guides it, or as is necessary for the best practical results obtainable under the circumstances.

Rational thinking in its early stages is apt to fly from a few particulars to broad and more or less vague generalizations, leaving relations and consequences insufficiently thought out. Most children have this tendency, as many of the Greek philosophers had. As a result of this kind of hasty induction, or jumping at conclusions, the generalizations so arrived at are likely to be erroneous, because their implications have not been fully developed and tested by comparison with the facts. When particular cases are brought under them, such untested generalizations are liable to be unfruitful and to leave knowledge at a standstill; or they may lead to wrong or foolish acts. The obvious remedy is to show the children the errors and absurdities of untested generalizations by leading them to work out the implications of their ideas somewhat as Socrates did in his dealings with the Greek youths. By causing his pupils to follow out every statement that they make far enough so they may " see whither it leads, and upon what it bottoms," [1] the teacher may train them into the habit of doing this for themselves. Thus they may avoid reliance on untested conclusions, the besetting sin of superficial minds. In this connection, however, the young teacher should be on his guard. Socratic questioning when mainly destructive, or when tinged with sarcasm, discourages original thought. It should therefore be offset by much constructive suggestion, and by generously commending those pupils who venture sensible, guarded, and thoughtful ideas and statements.

Scientific thinking. — Rational thinking on the scientific plane includes as a basis all the other forms of thinking; but its chief characteristic is the habit of suspending judgment, until, through careful reflection and guarded, methodical inference, that suggestion, idea, or generalization has been selected which is likely to be most fruitful in the solution of the problem under consideration. This idea or generalization is then used tentatively as a working hypothesis; its implications are developed by methodically safeguarded reasoning, and tested by comparison with " brute facts " through further observations and experiments. The trained thinker keeps his concepts, generalizations, and classifications in a semifluid state. He is always ready to enlarge or extend them, and rearrange the data under them, at any time when such revision may be necessary to meet the demands of newly discovered facts and novel situations.

The teacher of science therefore should aim to train his

---

[1] Cf. Locke, John, *Conduct of the Understanding*, Jno. B. Alden, N. Y. Sect. XLIV, p. 82.

students in the habit of finding hypotheses and adopting them tentatively during the solution of their problems. He should cause them constantly to suspend judgment until all available facts have been examined, and should habitually warn them to keep their minds always open to new suggestions and new points of view. This does not mean that they must never be allowed to be sure of anything. *They should become convinced of something definite during the course of every lesson; but belief, the feeling of certainty, should habitually come to them only as the result of full and convincing evidence carefully considered and weighed.* Neither does it mean that nothing should be accepted on authority, but only that when statements are so accepted by the pupil he must have adequate evidence of the competence and reliability of the authority. The pupils must take many things on the authority of teacher or textbook; but, on the other hand, the teacher who never allows his own statements or those of authorities to be questioned can never train his students to think for themselves.

The processes involved in scientific thinking are, — (1) discrimination, comparison, and abstraction, leading to location or definition of the problem, or toward some general principle; (2) reflection, leading to the selection of some appropriate idea as a hypothesis; (3) reasoning, observation, and experiment, to develop and test the implications of the hypothesis. The process works toward (4) a conclusion involving appropriate action or involving reference of a fact or phenomenon to its appropriate place in a general logical system, or organized group of facts and ideas. In the reflective and reasoning processes that lead to the conclusion, the mind does not move in a uniformly definite order, as it does in following a finished argument or exposition in a textbook, but leaps freely from known facts to hypothesis, and from hypothesis back to other facts. It does not hamper itself by adhering to logical forms excepting when such attention to forms is necessary in guarding against fallacies; but nevertheless either formally or informally every idea or suggestion is tested as thoroughly as is necessary to insure the logical soundness of every essential link in the chain.

Everyday thinking and scientific thinking. — These stages in the thinking process cannot be sharply differentiated. All forms of learning and thinking are used in some measure by every intelligent person. The difference lies in the degree of perfection in the technique or method. The method in accordance with which the scientific investigator thinks differs from that in accordance with which the child, the savage, or the untrained civilized adult thinks, only in that his problems are more difficult and complicated. The ends sought are more remote; the reflective and reasoning processes are farther removed from direct observation, are expressed more in symbols, formulas, and technical terms, and are therefore at the same time more abstract and more logical. The solution of the scientist's problems requires and implies a wider, more intimate, and hence, more accurate knowledge of the facts, ideas, concepts, and principles of the sciences within the domains of which they lie. It involves more careful measurements of quantities, and more extensive use of reasoning in mathematical form for determining the quantitative relations existing among phenomena. It involves more careful sifting and checking of hypotheses through logically safeguarded inductive and deductive inference, and a more rigorous testing of conclusions through extended observations and carefully planned experiments. Hence the conclusions reached by the scientists in the particular fields in which they are trained usually possess a higher degree of certainty, and nearly always possess a higher degree of accuracy and precision, than do those reached by other persons. It is a subject of common remark, however, that outside their special fields, the conclusions of scientists are often neither more certain nor more accurate than those of ordinary people; and this fact has certain very definite pedagogical implications which will be mentioned farther on.

Ability of children to think. — The ability of children to think empirically increases steadily, under normal conditions, between the ages of six and twelve, the grade of ability depending on their native endowment, on the richness of experience afforded by their environment, and on the quality of the training that they have previously received.

Children usually begin to do some rational thinking long before they reach the high school age; and many of them, under skillful stimulation and guidance, are able to think their way out of problematic situations of considerable complexity by the time they have reached the second or third year of the high school. From that time on, in the case of all those who are not considerably below the average in native mental endowment, the inborn tendency to reflect, reason, and investigate responds very readily to good teaching, and improves rapidly. If children of average ability are not successful in school, it is usually because of a lack of proper adjustment between the matters and methods of the schoolroom on the one hand, and the child with his native and experiential equipment on the other. Many children who are not successful in school reflect well, reason cogently, and test keenly outside the schoolroom when dealing with problematic matters in which they are deeply interested, and for which they have had the necessary preparation through concrete experiences.

This fact should constantly be borne in mind by every teacher, and should lead him to adjust his methods to the pupils, as far as the circumstances will allow, rather than to persist in attempting to adjust the pupils to his methods. Ordinarily, he is not able to change the condition of the pupils before they are placed in his hands; and therefore he must accept them as he finds them, and do the best he can for them, wasting no time in useless criticism of what has been done with them before he gets them. However, in so far as they may be able to exert an influence on the school, the community, or the home, high school teachers should do all they can towards bringing about such conditions that the children may come to them with the largest possible amount of concrete experience and empirical knowledge.

The tendency of teachers in the grades below the high school of trying to overdevelop in young children the ability to handle abstract ideas, with the consequent sacrifice of opportunities for sense perception, is very common. It is one of the faults to which most of the current criticisms of the schools are chargeable. Ideas can arise only out of present or remembered concrete experience, — perceiving and doing. They can come only from within. They cannot be grafted on.

Thing thinkers and idea thinkers. — Some children are " thing thinkers." They care to think, and can think successfully, only in terms of what they can see, hear, touch, and manipulate. Words and symbols have meaning to such children only in the presence of the things themselves which the words and symbols represent; and their main interests are in doing, — bringing things to pass, getting practical results. Others are " idea thinkers." These grasp ideas much more easily than do those of the former group; and it is comparatively easy to interest them in abstractions. At the high school age, many of them are attracted by broad principles and comprehensive statements, but are not fond of details. They like talking better than doing.[1] As Professor I. E. Miller has said,[2] many of them have an almost fatal facility in handling abstract formulas and juggling with symbols.

The teacher must constantly be adjusting his methods to provide for both of these so-called types of mind; but fortunately, the greatest need in both types is the same. Both

[1] This is an extreme statement of the kind of individual difference that it describes. There are of course no such actual "types of mind"; but rather all gradations between the two extremes. The terms are very convenient, however, when understood to have the meaning here indicated.

[2] *The Psychology of Thinking*, Macmillan, New York, 1910, p. 170 ff.

require to have constantly kept before them an abundance of concrete facts and materials for observation, — out-of-door objects and processes, pictures, models, maps, specimens, simple apparatus. With such materials before them, the thing thinkers can be assisted in the processes of discrimination, comparison, abstraction, and generalization, *and the coupling in memory of the things with the symbols that stand for them in thought.* With the same means, the idea thinkers can be taught to avoid premature wordy flights *by compelling them to square what they say with what they see.* Thus both types will get practice in the kinds of mental operations in which they are deficient. One of the best things that a teacher can do in this connection is to get the pupils to disputing on the problem among themselves. He can thus incite them on the one hand to stimulate ideas in one another, and on the other hand to hold one another to the brute facts that have been placed before them, to the end that the ideas advanced in the discussion may be either confirmed or rejected, and a rational and definite consensus of opinion reached.

Training in the technique of thinking. — Scientific technique in thinking develops in the individual youth, only as it has in the race, *through practice in dealing with many problematic situations under the spur of real needs.* Perfection and efficiency in this technique can be gained with economy of time and effort only when the training is such that the student is stimulated and guided in controlling and regulating his procedure by correct ideas of the methods that have proved themselves to be most expedient in the field where his problems belong. The technique of thinking is perfected by rationalized practice in dealing repeatedly with problematic situations, no less truly than the technique of any kind of motor activity, such as typewriting or pole vaulting, is perfected by rationalized practice in performing repeatedly the acts that are to become habitual in order to attain to good form in that kind of activity. But while correct habits of

E.

thought are no less truly habits than are correct habits of action, the lower methods of attack and procedure must never become wholly automatic, but must be constantly controlled by a higher habit of mental alertness — of open-minded hospitality to appropriate suggestions that come up in the process of reflection — coupled with an ideal of selecting and using whatever idea, method of procedure, or form of thought may be of most service in the particular problem that is in process of solution. In other words, although the best and most effective modes and forms of thought should come by practice to be used habitually, and to go on almost automatically *when started*, the habit should also be formed of consciously selecting and starting at any point in the solution of the problem that idea, form of thought, or mode of procedure which is the best one to use at that point. Problems even in the most limited field present an immense variety of individual differences, while as between problems belonging to different fields the differences are so wide as to call for somewhat different modes and forms of thought; *hence the importance of rationalizing the practice gained in their solution by constantly guiding the learner so as to help him to judge suggestions for himself and select at all times the best procedure through knowledge of why it is best.* This can sometimes be done most effectively by letting him go on with a faulty method till he finds by failure that it is faulty, and then telling him why. He will then be interested, when the best method is suggested, in thinking out why it is best, and in proving its superiority by the success that it brings to him in getting results. *This kind of lesson in open-mindedness, however, like all other negative methods of teaching, should be used sparingly, and with much caution.*[1]

It may be argued that we cannot make scientists out of children. While we must admit that most of them will never become scientists, yet we can start them all on the

[1] See comment on the Socratic Method, p. 44.

road toward becoming thinking men and women. *We can teach them to think well and truly in so far as they have strength to travel that road.*

Any one who has had large experience in teaching the sciences in high schools will agree that the average boy or girl of high school age can begin with simple problems that appeal to his native or acquired interests and challenge his thought, that he can be stimulated to recall facts that he knows, and observe facts that are new to him yet relevant to his problems, that he can be led to make simple and obvious inferences from these facts, that he can be assisted in forming for himself and testing simple hypotheses, that he can be gradually taught to reason with careful regard to the avoidance of fallacies, and that he can be trained to test conclusions by observation and experiment.

Motivation necessary. — It should be evident that he can grow in power to do these things only by doing them; and he will do them in an effective way only when he is genuinely interested in doing them. He will learn to observe only by observing because he wants to observe for a purpose of his own. He will learn to draw inferences only by inferring because he feels the need of a principle that will help him to bring about a desired result. He will learn to form hypotheses for himself only when he wants to reach a conclusion and hopes to hit on a hypothesis that may assist him in arriving at it. He will learn to reason carefully, not merely by " following through " a fine example of finished argument, but mainly by reasoning for himself, and because he has been made to see by many experiences that through correct reasoning lies his only road to valid conclusions. Finally he will form the habit of testing conclusions only by testing his own ideas because he earnestly desires to know the truth about his problems, and finds by experience that untested conclusions are liable to be misleading and troublesome, if not disastrous.

*It follows, therefore, that the problems through which one
expects to teach the facts, ideas, laws, concepts, and principles
of the various branches of science must be found among those
that lie near the interests and experiences of the students and
can be led up to in such an interesting way that they will appropriate them as their own.* The ability to find and use such
problems is one of the highest phases of the teacher's art.
Some teachers have it born in them; but all may acquire
it in some degree by realizing its importance, and trying
constantly to gain it through experience.

QUESTIONS FOR FURTHER STUDY

1. If you have some child friends, talk with them about some of the
scientific facts that you know, and try in each case to get an inventory
of facts of a scientific nature known by the child. (Avoid theory.) Report several such inventories to the class.

2. Watch a boy who is interested in making things with the "mec-
cano" or "erector" sets now sold by all toy dealers, or one interested
in a toy electric railway, or "wireless," or in collecting stamps or birds'
eggs. Analyze as far as you are able the steps by which he collects and
organizes the knowledge that he wants, and how he solves his problems.
Report your observations to the class.

3. Compare the methods of thinking of the boy of Question 2 with
those described in this chapter. Compare them with those of a young
girl who is learning to cook, or run a sewing machine, or embroider, or
make doll clothes, or furnish a doll's house.

4. What evidences can you cite from your own observation of the
ability of children to do rational thinking?

5. Have you ever in school witnessed a pupil who had started on
a good piece of rational thinking and was going forward with it in his
own way, when he was turned aside or discouraged by a thoughtless
teacher because the pupil's line of thought was not tending toward the
answer that the teacher wished to get? If so, relate the incident and
say what you think should have been done.

6. Is a pupil in geometry who demonstrates in class all the "regular
propositions," but who never works out an "original exercise," acquiring logical habits of mind? Justify your answer.

7. From your observation as a pupil or teacher in Grades Seven to
Twelve, what cases can you recall of good rational thinking by pupils?

REFERENCES

BOOLE, MARY EVEREST. Preparation of the Child for Science. Oxford Press, England. 1904. 50 ¢.

CLODD, EDWARD. Childhood of the World. Humboldt Pub. Co., N. Y. 1884. 33 pp. 15 ¢. Macmillan, New and Enlarged Ed. $1.25.

COLVIN, STEPHEN SHELTON. The Learning Process. Macmillan, N. Y. 1911. 336 pp. $1.25.

DEWEY, JOHN, How We Think. D. C. Heath, Boston. 1910. 224 pp. $1.00.

HALL, G. S. Contents of Child Minds on Entering School. Barnes. 25 ¢.

HALL, G. S. Adolescence. Appleton, N. Y. 1905. 2 vols.

JAMES, WILLIAM. Talks to Teachers on Psychology and Life's Ideals. H. Holt & Co., N. Y. 1915. 301 pp. $2.00.

KENT, E. B. Constructive Interests of Children. Teachers College, Columbia Univ., N. Y. 50 ¢.

McMURRY, F. How to Study, and Teaching How to Study. Houghton Mifflin, Boston. 1909. 324 pp. $1.25.

MILLER, I. E. The Psychology of Thinking. Macmillan, N. Y. 1909. 303 pp. $1.25.

STARR, FREDERICK. Some First Steps in Human Progress. Flood & Vincent. 1895. 305 pp. $1.00.

WELTON, J. The Logical Bases of Education. Macmillan, N. Y. 1904. 16 + 288 pp. $1.00.

CHAPTER V

METHODS OF TEACHING

Lessons on heat. — In order to show in a concrete way how the actual work of teaching a science should be carried on so as to exemplify its spirit and realize its educational values, suggestions are here offered for beginning the subject of heat with a class in physics that has completed the subject of mechanics. The choice is made from this portion of the science of physics because the facts and ideas that constitute this subject matter are likely to be more generally familiar to readers of this book than are those that might be selected from other sciences. The purpose is to suggest the best methods of teaching, and to furnish concrete examples for illustrating the discussions that follow, rather than to impart knowledge of the subject matter to the reader, or give him a syllabus of lessons ready made. The reader who takes the trouble to study the manner in which the spirit and principles of the discussion that precedes it are carried out in this suggested scheme of teaching should have no serious difficulty in planning and carrying out for himself lessons in any science in the same spirit and according to the same principles. A certain amount of training in one or more of the sciences is presupposed. *If the reader has not had such training, no study of pedagogy can help him to become a real teacher of science, until such time as he may have acquired it.*

The lesson plan. — The teacher who wishes really to grow in power and resourcefulness should make a definite plan for each lesson. It is well to keep such plans in a loose-leaf notebook, together with notes and comments on how the plan worked when followed out in the classroom or laboratory. The plans may thus be modified, and the methods improved with each repetition of the work. All teachers —and science teachers especially — ought to apply the scientific method in the study of their teaching problems and in the adjustment of their methods to the natures and needs of their pupils.

GENERAL TOPIC — HEAT

Sub-topic — Distribution of heat by convection.
Lesson unit — Uses and control of heat in the home.
Lesson problem — How to start a fire without getting smoke into the house.

I. *A.* General preparation.
    a. What does heat do for us? (Uses.)
        1. It keeps us warm. Generalization — It is necessary to all life, animal and vegetable. (*Physiological.*)
        2. It cooks our food. Generalization — It is essential to a multitude of industrial processes (blacksmithing, tin-smithing, making glass, bricks, and pottery, metal working, etc.). (*Industrial.*)
        3. It runs our steam engines and automobiles, and gives us our electric lights. Generalization — It is the source of our mechanical power and artificial light. (*Industrial.*)
        4. The sun's heat causes winds and ocean currents which distribute water vapor and heat over the earth. (*Physiographic.*)
    b. From what sources do we get it? (Sources.)
        1. Wood, coal, peat, oil, gasoline, natural and artificial gas. (*Fuels. Combustion.*)
        2. Friction, impact, abrasion. (*Mechanical Work.*)
        3. Sunshine.
        4. Animal and vegetable life processes produce it.
        5. It comes from volcanoes, hot springs, and geysers. (*Vulcanism.*)
        Generalization — Our sources of heat are, — burning fuels, mechanical action, living organisms, the interior of the earth, and the sun.

    c. How does it travel? (TRANSFERENCE.)
        1. Along or through metals. (*Conduction.*)
        2. Through space, from the sun, stoves, radiators, etc. (*Radiation.*)
        3. By means of currents of air or water. (*Convection.*)
        Generalization, — Heat is transferred from place to place by three processes, called respectively, conduction, radiation, and convection.
    d. Why must heat be controlled? (CONTROL — NECESSITY OF.)
        1. To prevent conflagrations.
        2. To prevent smoke and dirt.
        3. For convenience in use.
    e. How do we control it? (CONTROL — MEANS.)
        1. The means of control are fireplaces, stoves, and furnaces, with their chimneys.
        2. The essential factors of these appliances are a grate to support the burning fuel, a fire pot to confine the fire, a chimney to conduct away the smoke and gaseous products of the combustion, an ash pit to receive the solid products of the combustion, and one or more dampers to regulate the "draft."
        3. General principle : In all apparatus for the use of heat there must be means of maintaining free circulation of air through the burning fuel. And if the material to be heated is not to be placed directly in the fire, there must be means of transferring the heat to the places where it is wanted.
I. *B.* Statement of the aim.   The lesson problem.
What is the best way of building a fire in your grate, stove, or furnace, in order to avoid smoke, dirt, and trouble?
II. *A.* Specific preparation.
    a. Materials : matches, shavings or paper, fine kindling, coarse kindling, small lumps of coal.
    b. Method of laying the fire. — First, see that the chimney and all the flues of the apparatus are clean, that the space under the grate is clear of ashes, and that all dampers are arranged for free draft.   Then build up the materials in the order named, beginning with the shavings and ending with the coal, taking care that it be piled loosely, so as to leave a lot of "little chimneys" through which air and flames can come up and get into contact with all parts of the fuel.   Apply the lighted match or paper to the shavings at the bottom.   For the grate, put on the "blower"; for stove or furnace close

all openings into the chimney above the fire and leave the draft-door open below the grate. When the first coal is well started, add more, cautiously.

    c. Principles to be abstracted from concrete experiences with fuels, fires, and heating apparatus. (COMBUSTION — PRINCIPLES.)

        1. Fuels burn only when they have been heated to their kindling temperatures, which are different for different substances, but always the same for the same substance.

        2. The kindling temperature of coal is relatively high, hence very hot flames from the kindling must be made to circulate rapidly through it.

        3. For this purpose the kindling must be burnt rapidly with a rapid circulation of air. (See I. *A. e.* 3.)

II. *B.* Reflection.

In the early fall, when the air is not very cold, it often happens when building a fire that the smoke refuses to go up the chimney, but pours out into the house. Here is a problematic situation the solving of which requires a general principle. To discover the principle in accordance with which we can so keep conditions that the smoke must go up the chimney instead of down, analysis, synthesis, and inductive interference are necessary. The *cause* of the movement must be discovered.

    a. Suggestions likely to be offered as to the cause of the phenomenon.

        1. "Hot air rises."

        2. The chimney "draws," or "pulls."

        3. There is a "circulation."

        4. "Something must push the smoke up."

    b. Examination of these suggestions in the light of the facts.

        1. Experiment with an exhausted flask on a balance, to show that hot air falls. Hence this is useless as a general principle. It is also useless because it tells nothing as to a possible cause.

        2. Since the different portions of a gas have no tendency to cling together these terms are absurd in connection with this case.

        3. This statement affords us a brief description of what occurs. But what causes the circulation?

        4. This is a fruitful suggestion, to be developed by comparison of the air in the chimney with balloons in air, and corks, air bubbles, etc., in water. Recall the principles of

equilibrium in fluids from previous study of mechanics (principles of Archimedes and Pascal).

III. *A*. Hypothesis.

The air inside the chimney may be lighter than an equal column of air outside, which because of its greater pressure would flow under the lighter air and push it up.

III. *B*. Developing and testing the hypothesis.

    a. How may the air inside become lighter?

        1. By expanding and overflowing at the top.

        2. Experiment with an air thermometer to show that air is expanded by heating it.

    b. Experiment with two connected lamp chimneys, kept at different temperatures, to show that cold air descends and displaces the warmer air. Direction of air current marked by smoke from a "joss stick."

    c. Similar experiment with convection tube filled with water. Direction of current marked with scrapings of blotting paper.

IV. Conclusion. Statement of the general principle of convection currents in fluids.

V. *A*. Applications.

    a. Tall chimneys, straight flues, dampers, chimney caps, etc., and their influence on the draft.

    b. Cooking ranges, — their construction and management.

    c. Construction and management of hot air heating apparatus.

    d. Construction and management of hot water heating apparatus.

    e. Ventilation systems (of the homes and the school particularly).

V. *B*. Making an outline of the organized subject matter.

Advantages of having a plan. — It requires time and thought to work out such a lesson plan, to prepare one's self to anticipate the questions, the answers, and the difficulties of the pupils, and to fill one's mind to overflowing with illustrations and suggestive thoughts that will stimulate the pupils to think hard and fast; but it will repay the time and effort spent on it. It requires good judgment and alertness to know how far to develop each thought as it comes up in the discussion. One has to draw the line between discouraging vagueness on the one hand and tiresome reiteration and detail on the other. Many facts and questions will be suggested that have no direct bearing on the main problem in hand, but these should not be allowed to lead attention away from it. If not worth while, such questions must quickly be shown to be so, and must be promptly eliminated. If they are worth while, they should be developed far enough to stimulate interest that will arouse a desire to learn more about them, and will cause the students to wonder and reflect about them, so that they will be eager to undertake further study at the proper time. It is well to have each pupil keep a " Wonder List " in which he is encouraged to record such questions, so that he may bring them up on occasions when they are relevant to the problems that are then under discussion. He will then wish to join with the class in finding answers for them. Such a device will assist in fostering the true spirit of investigation, and in cultivating the joy of discovery. It will also tend to check a discursive habit of mind by showing the advantage in the long run of noting problems for future investigation, but shelving them temporarily, in order to stick to the main question until it has been satisfactorily disposed of.

On this principle, therefore, many topics should be partly developed, and left for further study; while others, which are more direct factors of the main problem, should be thoroughly worked out. The lesson will never go exactly according to plan; but the plan serves to control and guide the discussion, to keep it within proper bounds, and to insure logical and methodical attack and procedure. The superiority of such a method of preparation by the teacher to that of trusting to the inspiration of the moment, or of simply following the order of the text, if it is not already obvious, will be so as soon as it is submitted to the test of comparing results in the classroom.

No real teacher will follow any text in detail; he must cut out here and supplement there according to his own interests and those of the class, and according to the kinds of illustrations and facilities that are available in his school and community. Experienced and well-trained teachers may be so practiced and expert, and may have their information of the subject so well systematized in their minds, that they will not need to set down so many details in the lesson plans, but even the most expert should plan their lessons carefully in general outline; and for the beginner it is essential to form the habit of working out the lesson plan thoroughly, setting it down clearly, and studying it carefully. "By the character of his teaching, the teacher largely determines the character of the thought processes in his pupils. If the former is unmethodical and ill arranged, if it permits invalid inferences or encourages rash and unwarranted conclusions, then the pupils will not be helped to think clearly and accurately, but will rather be hindered from doing so. But if, on the other hand, the teacher's presentation of every subject is well arranged, if his inferences are not only just, but shown to be just, if the importance of weighing evidence is insisted on, and no conclusions are drawn that the evidence at hand does not warrant, then the pupils are being unconsciously trained to habits of accurate thought."[1]

It may be added that nothing will be lost, and much may be gained by occasionally commending cases of systematic arrangement, of inferences that are logically justified, and of evidence that has been carefully weighed, and contrasting them with examples of the opposite. *Thus conscious ideals of logical and valid procedure may be built up in the pupils' minds.* A teacher's enthusiasm for good thinking, manifested by occasional genuine pleasure in finding that his pupils are growing in such power, is easily infectious. It is more effective than any amount of "driving and hammering," necessary at times as the latter may be.

The assignment. — *Teacher.* " We have completed our spe-

[1] Welton, J., *The Logical Bases of Education*, N. Y., 1908, p. 248.

cial and formal study of Mechanics, but we have not finished it. No one will ever finish it. There will always be something new to learn. We shall use again and again the mechanical principles that we have studied, and shall often have to review many of the facts in connection with later problems in heat, electricity, sound, and light. We shall also review Mechanics at the end of the year when you are in a position to see its fundamental relations to the whole subject. To-morrow we shall begin the study of heat — I wonder how many of you have had experience in building fires. Those who have, please raise hands — Good! That is experience that is likely to be valuable to almost everybody at some time or other. How many of the others have watched some one build a fire, and think they could do it if they had to? John, did you ever find that smoke persisted in coming out into the house instead of going up chimney, as well-behaved smoke should do?"

John. "Yes, it usually does that when I first start our furnace in the fall."

T. "Who of you have had similar difficulties? Well, there is a problematic situation, and we shall take that as our next lesson problem. I am sure we all want to know the best method of building a fire, and how to keep it from smoking up the house. In solving that problem, we shall get very quickly into the theory of air currents. Many other interesting questions are sure to come up, such as these, which I wish you to set down and try to find answers for. What does heat do for us? Where do we get it? How does it go from one place to another? Why must it be controlled, and how do we control it? What makes the smoke go up the chimney? Is there ever a draft moving down the chimney instead of up? Examine the heating and cooking apparatus in your home, and find out all you can about it. Get illustrated advertising matter from hardware stores; and look at the stoves and furnaces there. Bring the circulars to class, and put your information into shape to be imparted to the others. Don't study your textbook, nor any other book just now, *and don't try to theorize about what heat is.* I shall give you opportunities to do all that later. What we want first is *knowledge of facts;* theories will come when we need them. Think up what you already know from your past experiences with heat, and use your eyes, hands, tongues, and ears to get new facts for yourselves. Make notes of what you find out; and try to arrange the facts in some systematic way, by grouping them with relation to the questions I have given out. To-morrow we shall discuss all the facts that you bring in, and put them together in logical order, so as to have a basis for solving the lesson problem. Finally, I want each of you to hand me to-morrow, neatly written, according to the usual directions, a paragraph or two describing some definite fact or bit of information about heat that you have found out for yourself between now and then, and not obtained from a book. Hand in also a question in the subject of heat, that you are interested in and want to find out how to answer."

The purpose of these papers is to insure the devotion of thought and attention to the general assignment. By being given something particular and definite to do, each student will know that he cannot trust to the inspiration of the moment on the morrow, for the teacher will know by the character of his papers whether he has *thought and worked* on the assignment.

General preparation. — The efficient teacher will have his class seated in alphabetical order, and will have on his desk a plan of the seats, with the names of the pupils who occupy them. When the class is seated, he will give the signal to pass the papers on the assigned subject that were to be handed in. These are passed from one side to the other, and from back to front in such order that when the complete pile reaches the first pupil of the front row, the papers will be in alphabetical order. Each paper should have the date and the pupil's name at the top, and should not be folded. While the papers are being passed, the teacher marks the absentees in his grade book.

Adjusting windows and shades, reading the thermometer, cleaning blackboards, distributing materials, marked papers, or notebooks, and other mechanical operations of the school-room may be attended to at this time, and should be done by pupils. The teacher should not take his time to do any such mechanical work that he can train the class to take care of in a coöperative way. By efficient organization ten persons can do in one minute what it would take the teacher ten minutes to do, — with a consequent saving of nine minutes of his time for real service to the class.

Teacher. "William, write at the top of the blackboard, near the middle, the general topic which we are about to study."

W. writes HEAT in large letters.

T. "Before we attack the main problem which I assigned you yesterday, let us put together in systematic form the knowledge that we already possess. We shall need to have it fresh and well ordered in our minds as a source of ideas for the successful solution of the problem. Each one be ready to contribute something in answer to the questions.

"What does heat do for us? — John!"

J. (who drives his father's car). "It makes power to run gasoline engines."

T. "Yes, it runs your motor car for you. You know the principle of gas and gasoline engines, I suppose?"

J. "Yes, sir."

T. "Give it to the class, very briefly."

J. "The gas is mixed with air in the carburetor, and is drawn into the cylinder of the engine; when the mixture has filled the cylinder, the piston moves in and compresses it; then it is exploded by an electric spark, and drives the piston out again."

T. " Why is it able to drive the piston out? "

J. " When the gas mixture explodes it is expanded by the heat."

T. " Does the explosion of the gas produce heat? "

J. " Yes, sir."

T. " Is exploding the same as burning? "

J. " I am not sure, but I think it is."

T. (to class). " John is right. Exploding is nothing but very rapid burning. We shall ask John more about automobiles and gasoline engines when we take that as a special topic. Such engines are called internal combustion engines because the fuel is burned inside the engine cylinders instead of under a boiler."

T. nods to *J.*, who seats himself, pleased with the recognition given his knowledge, and resolved to get more for that future occasion.

T. " What else does heat do for us? — Mary! "

M. (interested in home economics). " It cooks our food for us, and keeps us warm."

T. " Very well. Write ' Uses ' on the board. Under that we shall write your two answers. Which should come first? "

M. " Keeping us warm."

T. " Why? "

M. " I think it is more necessary."

T. " Why? "

M. " Because we could get along without cooked food, but we could not live at all if our bodies were not kept warm."

T. " That is logical. Can you develop the last idea, and generalize it? "

M. " I don't know what you mean."

T. " You said that we cannot live without heat. What about other living things? "

M. " Many birds go South in winter to find warmth; and they have feathers to keep out the cold from their bodies."

T. " Yes, but by cold we mean simply absence of heat. Please correct your last statement."

M. " The feathers keep the heat of the body in."

T. " That is correct, but you have mentioned only human beings and birds as needing heat. Are they the only animal forms to whose life it is essential? "

M. " Heat is essential also to horses, dogs, and insects."

T. " How about fish, reptiles, and the lower animal forms? "

M. " I think they need it also, but I have heard fish and reptiles called cold-blooded animals, and am not sure about them."

T. " Could they be frozen to death? "

M. " Yes, I understand. They need some heat; but I have learned that some disease germs, and other bacteria, live for a long time at temperatures below freezing point."

T. " True, but can they grow and multiply at very low temperature? "

M. " No; they need heat for that, but temperatures *above* the boiling point will kill them."

T. " Are bacteria animals? "

M. " No; they are plants."

T. " Now, Mary, I asked you to generalize your statement about the necessity of heat. Try to make one sentence that will include all the particulars you have given, and any others like them."

M. " Heat supports all life, vegetable and animal, including human life."

T. " That is *good*. We may call that a physiological use. Now write ' 1. Physiological,' and after it your generalization." (To class) " Mary mentioned the use of heat in cooking. Are there other chemical and physical processes in which it is used in the industrial life outside our homes? — Volunteers, please." (Hands are raised.)

T. " Frank! "

F

F. " Heat is used in blacksmithing, tinsmithing, and in making metal castings."

T. " Josephine ! "

J. (interested in china painting). " Heat is used in firing pottery."

T. " Mention other processes of a similar kind to which it is essential."

J. " Heat is necessary in the making of glass and the burning of bricks."

T. nods to Henry, whose hand is up.

H. " Heat is used in getting metals out of their ores, in rolling steel rails, sheets, and plates. There is scarcely an important manufacturing industry in which it is not used in some of the processes."

T. " Very good. You generalized those facts well, for I am sure you could give many more particulars to justify it if we needed them. Now let us recall the gasoline engine, and see if it suggests any uses of heat that we can classify along with it."

T. nods to one after another. Steam engines are mentioned, and by a series of volunteer answers and appropriate questions, the fact is brought out that we can trace back our electric light and the power for motor cars to the heat of coal, burning under the boiler of the power house.

The word " industrial " is suggested as a second general descriptive term under which power, light, and chemical and physical uses in the house and factory may best be grouped in the outline. Thus by rapid questioning, by suggestive statements, and by occasional terse exposition, the teacher stimulates, guides, and directs the pupils in their discussion, until the material under I. *A*. of the lesson plan has been clearly brought out and made explicit. Step by step the material is organized and generalized as far as the pupils are prepared to do it for themselves. In the words of President Millis, " The pupil must be active. He must carry the ball. . . .

He must learn to do things for himself in a way he has adopted for himself." [1]

As the information grows and takes organized form, it is entered in the pupils' notebooks, the blackboard being freely used to guide them. Let the teacher beware, however, of dictating to the pupils an outline or a generalization, that they have not first worked out for themselves with his assistance in a manner somewhat like that which has been indicated. The temptation to do so in order to " cover the ground " is always strong and insidious; but in every lesson in science, — in fact in every lesson of any sort — *the teacher should constantly be aware that a general statement means nothing to any one unless it serves to call up in his mind a large number of images and memories of particular concrete facts that are included under it, and that have been repeatedly associated with it and with one another.*

For example, the general statement that heat is essential for cooking and for many other arts and manufacturing processes would be a meaningless string of sounds to a person who had never been inside a kitchen or shop or factory of any sort. On the other hand, the same statement would be meaningful to a girl who had spent considerable time in the kitchen, and who had looked in occasionally at a blacksmith's shop, seen a tinner mending a roof, a farmer's wife making soap, and a plumber wiping a pipe joint, and who had also spent two hours in visiting a rubber factory, or a modern steel plant. Having seen so much with her eyes, and having had these particular experiences of the outside world thoughtfully associated with the general statement, she would be able to supply somewhat more by reading and imagination; but the statement would never be as meaningful or suggestive to her as to a mechanically inclined boy who has neglected no opportunity to get into a factory and satisfy his curiosity as to how things are made there, and who has also been a con-

[1] Quoted by F. M. McMurry in *How to Study*, N. Y., 1909, p. 301.

stant reader of *The Scientific American* and *Popular Mechanics*. To such a boy the generalization would be almost self-evident. For him it would stand as a convenient symbol or abbreviation by which he might refer in thought or conversation to any or all of these particular uses of heat. But for the average high school student, either in the city or in the country, it is necessary to *develop* such a general notion or concept by discussing and making explicit a considerable number of particulars, which the students and teacher as individuals contribute to the general stock. No generalization should ever be sprung on a class until its members have had such particular knowledge as will make it meaningful. It should be given only when the students' minds are prepared for it, when they realize that it would be convenient, and are ready to frame it for themselves, — in other words, when they have built up the concept in their own minds, and want a name or symbol to represent it economically in thought and speech. If the teacher " gives it away " at the beginning the interest in the particulars will be lost, the zest of problem solving will be lacking, and what might have been a stimulating, life-giving discussion becomes only a dead and perfunctory *recitation*. There is a vast difference between teaching and " hearing recitations."

The lesson problem. — The statement of the aim, or the formulation of the lesson problem, was brought out in the preliminary work of the assignment of the lesson. The subject matter outlined under *general preparation*, in the case of this lesson plan, will take at least one lesson period, or possibly two or three, according to the character and intelligence of the class. However, each of the questions, *a, b, c, d, e*, under I. *A* is really a problem by itself, and constitutes a minor lesson unit; although it is a part of the more comprehensive main problem for whose final solution it is needed as preparatory material. Were it not for this fact, the preparatory step here outlined would be altogether too long. When the preparatory knowledge has been gained, a number of pupils may be called on to restate the main lesson problem, and the class should be guided in selecting the best statement. When this has been done it will become evident that the practical problem of finding the best way to build a fire in order to avoid smoke involves a selection among several possible ways, and that while a selection of methods might be made empirically by the " trial and error " method, an intelligent appeal to principles would result practically in the selection of just as good a method or better; and in addition it would result intellectually in the satisfaction of *knowing why* as well as *knowing how*.   Accordingly the problem becomes one of intellectual interest that grows in a natural way out of a practical interest.   It is now, " *Why* does the smoke go up the chimney? "   " What is the *cause?* "   To answer this the facts of experience must be examined in a search for principles, — hence the substep II. *A* of the lesson plan is needed.

Specific preparation. — This, although included in step II in the lesson plan, is logically a part of step I.   The " formal steps " are never adhered to in a good lesson.   The essential function of the preparatory step is the recalling and examining of facts while searching for principles or testing them.   It is the ordering, filling in, and making explicit of *apperceptive masses*.   Hence, the preparatory part of the teaching process will often be distributed through the lesson at various points, as it is here.   In fact, as has been said in the discussion of thinking, the thinking process is not a formal one.   Formal steps and logical rules are to be used as guide-posts to keep the thinking process from going astray. They cannot be successfully used as trolley cars to carry it to its destination.

In following out this part of the lesson plan the skillful teacher, by logically arranged questions and suggestions, will get from the pupils the steps of procedure in good fire building and at every step will ask, "Why?" "Why must the flues be clean, and the chimney fairly straight?" "Why must the ashes be cleaned out?" "Why must the match be applied to the shavings and fine kindlings at the bottom?" The questions *how* and *why* make the pupils *describe facts* and *seek for causes and principles*. The aim should be to *get to the bottom of things, or at any rate to complete the chain of efficient causes link by link as far as the pupils are able to go or as far as is needed for the solution of the main problem, and to make them do it by their own observation and their own reasoning*.

The search for fruitful ideas. *Reflection.* — With the facts and concrete principles fresh in their minds, the pupils are now asked to advance hypotheses, as to why the smoke and other products of the combustion move up the chimney. Probably all four of the suggestions under II. *B. a* will be advanced by them, and perhaps others also. Each of these in its turn should be developed and disposed of in a rational way. The first, for example, if advanced as a cause, may be shown to be merely a general statement of the particular fact. To say that the hot air and the smoke go up the chimney *because* hot air rises is to beg the question. If the pupils regard it as a general statement of ultimate fact, they may be greatly enlightened by the experiment suggested to test its generality. The teacher calls the attention of the class to a flask with a stopcock or pinchcock, which he exhausts with the air pump and counterbalances on a pair of scales. He asks, "Now if I allow hot air to flow into the flask will it push the flask up?" Opinions will probably be divided, some saying that the flask will be pushed up "because hot air rises," and some that it will be pushed down, because air is matter and must weigh something whether it is hot or cold. The teacher then takes the opportunity to say that such questions can be settled only by experiment. He makes it clear that, as the balance is in equilibrium, any movement up or down after the hot air is introduced must be due to the hot air itself, since all other possible causes of disturbance have been removed or counterbalanced. Then by means of a rubber tube, he connects the stopcock to an iron or copper pipe that is kept hot by a gas burner or other convenient means, and lets air flow slowly into the flask through the hot pipe. When the stopcock is again closed, and the rubber tube detached it will be seen that the flask descends, or, in other words, here is a case in which *hot air falls.* Hence the suggestion must be ruled out, since it proves to be neither a cause nor a statement of a general fact. Such a demonstration in testing a hypothesis experimentally is well worth the time it takes, from either the content or the method point of view. The other suggestions are taken up in turn and treated as indicated in the lesson plan under II. *B.*

The hypothesis. — By questioning and challenging, — avoiding " leading questions," and inciting them to do all they can do, — the teacher induces the pupils to reflect on the suggestions and analogies in II. *B. b.* 4, to formulate the idea under III. *A,* and adopt it as a hypothesis.

Developing and testing the hypothesis. — The suggestion under III. *B. a.* 1 may be examined by watching the overflow from a neighboring chimney, and seeing how the smoke spreads out and flows away at the top of the column. This is especially impressive when the air is calm. The experiments under III. *B. a, b,* and *c,* are best made by the pupils themselves in the laboratory. The necessary apparatus is very simple. In experiment *b,* one lamp chimney [1] may be heated by wrapping around it a rag wrung out of hot water, and the other cooled by wrapping around it a rag wrung out of cold water. The current may be reversed by cooling the first chimney and heating the second; or one chimney may be heated by placing within it a lighted candle, and afterwards cooled by substituting for the candle a few lumps of ice. The " convection tube " for *c* may be made from a lamp chimney,

[1] See Mann & Twiss, *Physics*, Chicago, 1910, Fig. 64, p. 111; Fig. 66, p. 114.

two corks, and two suitable lengths of glass tubing each bent into the form of a J and joined by a short rubber tube so that they form a branch leading out of the bottom of the chimney and into the top. This branch tube is heated by a small flame. This apparatus embodies the principle of the ordinary domestic hot-water tank with a side tube inclined upward and leading into the cook stove or furnace.[1]

The stages of reflection, adopting a hypothesis, and developing and testing it, correspond roughly to the second and third of the so-called "formal steps" of the inductive development lesson as described in books on methods of teaching. The second is sometimes called *presentation*, and the third, *analysis and synthesis* or *comparison and abstraction*.

Conclusion. — If the lesson has been successfully conducted up to this point, the pupils will be able to understand the following features of the process of convection, and to state them in response to terse questions.

1. The smoke and hot air rise in the chimney, because they are pushed up.

2. They are pushed up because the downward pressure due to the weight of the gases in the chimney is less than that of an equal column of the colder air outside.

3. The column of gases in the chimney weighs less than an equal column of the air outside because it has been expanded by heat, and part of it has overflowed above the chimney.

4. Hence since pressure in a fluid is transmitted equally in all directions at a given depth (Pascal's principle) the heavier air flows in beneath the lighter and pushes it up.

5. The moving force is equal to the difference between the weight of the gases in the chimney and that of an equal column of air outside, and exists as long as this difference in weight exists.

[1] Mann & Twiss, *Physics*, Chicago, 1910, Fig. 67, p. 115.

6. The same principle applies to *all* fluids, liquids as well as gases; and it applies *to fluids only.*

7. The conditions for rapid circulation are (*a*) that the difference in weight (hence temperature) be kept as great as possible, (*b*) that the hot column should have a path upward and as straight and free from impediments as possible, and (*c*) that no openings be allowed above the base of the hot column, excepting the vent at the top.

The final step in this stage of the lesson is to formulate a concise statement of the principle of convection currents that will include the essential and characteristic features of the process that has just been stated in detail. This is essentially a problem in English composition. Let the pupils each write a statement, and let their statements be compared and criticized in conference. Let the class finally select the best statement by vote. It should be essentially as follows.

Final generalization. — In the process of transfer of heat by convection in a fluid, one portion is heated to a temperature higher than that of the surrounding portions. It is therefore expanded, and a part of it flows away at the top. Since the remaining portion is lighter than the surrounding fluid, the latter, because of the greater pressure due to its greater weight, flows in beneath it and lifts it up. The lighter fluid flows away, carrying its heat with it; but when it has become cooled it contracts, becomes heavier, and sinks. Thus a circulation goes on in the fluid as long as a difference in temperature is maintained between its parts.

Application. — We now have a general principle under which we can bring the particular case of managing a fire and a chimney. The final thought process of applying this principle to the case in hand is *deductive;* while that of discovering the principle, including the preceding steps, was in general an *inductive movement.* The process of induction, however, as we have seen in this case, may include many minor deductive steps.   The development of an idea or hypothesis — the working out of its implications — is always deductive.   Analysis and synthesis, induction and deduction are correlative processes constituting parts of the general movement of thought. They are almost never formally separated in actual thinking. *They are separated only for convenience in studying or describing them as phases of the thinking process.*   In the application, then, the students are led to see that success in building a fire so as to keep the chimney from smoking depends on getting the chimney hot as quickly as possible; that this requires a hot fire; and that this in turn requires free access of air, so as to obtain complete combustion.   Furthermore, complete combustion serves to burn the smoke, hence the fire is to be laid loosely, with plenty of fine kindling, to make a fast-burning, hot fire.   If the chimney smokes badly it is because the air in it is colder than the air outside, and a draft is tending down the chimney instead of up.   This can often be obviated by pushing some shavings or paper up the chimney of a grate, or into the smoke pipe of the furnace through the check-damper opening, and igniting them before touching the match to the fuel on the grate.   This heats the air inside the chimney, and starts the draft upward before the fire is started below. It also serves to burn out any soot that may remain to clog the pipe or the chimney.

Further applications and related phenomena.   Association. — The main lesson problem has now been solved; and *in the process of solution a far-reaching general principle has been discovered by the pupils, because it was needed.   Under these circumstances it is more likely to be remembered and recalled when wanted for the solution of other problems than it would be if perfunctorily memorized, but in any case, unless frequently used, the principles would probably be forgotten, or remembered but vaguely.*   The way to fix a principle in the students' memories, and to have them appreciate how far-reaching and useful it is, is not to have them con it over from the book, but to have them first arrive at it inductively, through the process of solving a problem that suggests it, and then to have them apply it to the solution of a large number of particular problems and processes that come under it. This causes them repeatedly to make interesting association connections of such cases with the principle, and with one another. Thinking of the principle will then stimulate them to recall many particular cases that come under it; or, on the other hand, thinking of any one of the cases that have been thus mutually associated will stimulate them to recall other cases and the general principle.

When so associated with many of the phenomena of the world outside the schoolroom, the principle is likely to be suggested and recalled when needed for the solution of other problems, practical and intellectual, which are new to the pupils, but which have *elements of likeness* to those that they have previously solved with its aid. This process of *association, or correlation*, then, is a very important factor in *humanizing* the subject and making it interesting, so that the pupils will want to learn more of it; also it is the only correct psychological way to "store their minds with useful information."

Information so stored is likely to be useful because it is so associated that it can be recalled in many situations wherein it is likely to be needed. Thus there should be a thorough discussion of the management of cooking ranges, hot-air and hot-water heating systems, and ventilating systems in use in the home and in the school. Diagrams, illustrated advertising matter, lantern slides, models, — all should be freely used as aids to clear understanding; but above all, the appliances themselves should be examined and studied at first hand. In this work of correlation there should be a short, sharp review of the origin and nature of the various kinds of winds, such as land and sea breezes, mountain and desert winds, monsoons and cyclonic storms, with their useful effects in the distribution of heat and moisture, their destructive effects, and their controls of the activities of man and of living forms in general.

In like manner ocean currents should be briefly reviewed, and both winds and ocean currents should be compared with hot-air, hot-water, and steam-heating systems, and with the various ventilating systems. The fact should be clearly brought out that these artificial systems, in the house, office, factory, auditorium, and school, work on the same general principles as the larger movements of the air, water, and aqueous vapor over the whole earth.

The relation of winds and ocean currents to navigation, and the devices for using wind power, such as sails and wind mills, should be briefly reviewed; and it should be shown that the supplies of elevated water for our stores of water power originate in wind-driven clouds.

Attention should be called also to the fact that balloons, airships, and submarine boats depend for their action on *difference of average specific gravity*, just as winds do.[1]

Organizing and systemizing the subject matter. — Suggestions have already been made indicating that the subject matter should be arranged under various headings and subheadings, or classified according to relations that the facts and principles bear to one another. Particulars should be brought under general ideas, and these in turn under more comprehensive ones, which include them. No one order of arrangement is *the* logical one. *Any system of arrangement or organization is logical if it is economical and if the relations under which the parts are grouped are real and close. The best arrangement for teaching purposes is that which is most obviously and personally useful to the student, and which he can come nearest to making wholly for himself, as the product of his own thought.* The

---

[1] For examples of the kind of questions by means of which such correlations and applications may be drawn from the pupils, see Mann and Twiss, *op. cit.*, pp. 134–138 and 154–156.

scientist puts each new fact, phenomenon, or principle into its place in the general system as it is discovered and described; but it has first to be fully studied and its implications and relations worked out before its proper place in the system can be known. When so placed that it fits in intelligibly with all the rest, it is said to be *explained*.

The system of a science at a given time is not necessarily fixed and permanent. It is always that arrangement or form of organization that is most expedient, convenient, or fruitful at the time; and it is always subject to extension, modification, or rearrangement in order harmoniously to include newly discovered facts and principles. For example, the discovery of the law of evolution by Darwin and his successors revolutionized the system of classification of plants and animals, so that now the classification is based on the life histories of the forms and the various stages through which their embryos pass, beginning with the fertilized reproductive cell. In other words, comparative anatomy and comparative embryology, and the adaptation of structure to function, furnish the key to the present system of classification and description. Again, in 1888, Hertz discovered the long electromagnetic waves, which are started in the ether by the discharge of a Leyden jar, and the existence of which had been predicted mathematically by Maxwell, long before. This sensational discovery proved that light is essentially an electromagnetic phenomenon; and in consequence, it was followed by a reorganization of the subject matter of Physics, which placed all the facts and theories of light and electricity in close relation, and brought them together into one great domain.

As finding the place of a new fact or phenomenon in the general system is always the final step for the scientist in the treatment of a problem, so it should be for the student in the science class. Accordingly the logical position of a new fact should not be given by the teacher at the start, as so often it is, but should be found by the class after they have studied it. In the foregoing lesson the final step in organization consists in showing that all the phenomena included therein occur as the result of two universal agencies, — heat, which all comes ultimately from the sun, and gravitation, which exists as a " force " throughout the universe.

The plan suggested for these lessons on heat presents such a logical arrangement as a high school class might build up, with the aid of the teacher. The facts and principles are there organized on the basis of human needs and the means of satisfying them through the control of natural agencies. In other words, it is humanistic and concrete, rather than formal and abstract. Hence if the lesson is carried out in the spirit indicated, it will be interesting and meaningful rather than dry and meaningless.

The topical review outline. — An outline of the same content for the final review may be made more general, more abstract, and hence briefer as growing familiarity with the general ideas enables the pupils more readily to recall the details that come under them. For example, the subject matter that we have been discussing might be outlined as follows in a *topical review lesson.* Each pupil called on would place one of the sections on the blackboard, and fill in the details orally without referring to text or notes.

HEAT

A. Uses.
 1. Physiological. Necessary to life.
 2. Industrial. Chemical and physical processes, light and power in home, in factories, and on farms.
 3. Physiographic. Winds and ocean currents.

B. Sources.
 1. Animal heat.
 2. Sunshine.
 3. Burning fuel.
 4. Mechanical work.
 5. Interior heat of the earth.

C. PROCESSES OF TRANSFER.
  1. Radiation.
  2. Conduction.
  3. Convection.
     3^1. Conditions.
        3^{1a}. A fluid medium.
        3^{1b}. Maintenance of different temperatures in different parts.
     3^2. Causes.
        3^{2a}. Immediate. Difference in pressure in adjacent portions.
        3^{2b}. Proximate. Differences in specific gravity, — caused by local differences in temperature.
        3^{2c}. Ultimate. The sun's heat and the force of gravitation.
     3^3. Statement of the principle.
     3^4. Applications and correlated phenomena.
        3^{4a}. Heating and ventilating apparatus.
        3^{4b}. Winds and ocean currents : — kinds, and means for utilizing their energy.
        3^{4c}. The principle of flotation.
           Analogy with convection principle.
           Practical applications.

The abstract character of this outline when compared with the concrete fullness of detail covered by the lessons is striking. It would convey little meaning to the pupils, if given them *before* the lessons, but if used as a scheme of organization and topical review *after* the lessons, every noun and noun phrase in it becomes a symbol for a concept or general notion, under which many meanings have been linked together in the classroom. It serves as a brief group of symbols to be used for convenience in recalling any or all of a large group of facts and ideas through their relations to one another.

Danger of over-emphasizing organization.— It is easy to overdo this matter of logical organization, but so long as the work is done mostly by the pupils, and is never formally dictated by the teacher, less harm is likely to result from overdoing it than from neglecting it.

QUESTIONS FOR FURTHER STUDY

1. Work out a detailed lesson plan for presenting some subtopic in the science in which you are best prepared and most interested.

2. Do the same for a subtopic in the science in which you have the least preparation or the least interest.

3. Enumerate the reasons why the second task is more difficult than the first.

4. In which case are you likely to sense better the difficulties of the pupils? Why?

5. From which of the two tasks do you get the better understanding of the terms " apperception " and " apperceptive mass? "

6. Since doing the work called for in Question 2, have you modified your ideas as to what reasonably may be expected of your pupils? If so, describe the changes in your ideas.

7. Can you recall any cases wherein you were influenced toward forming habits of clear, consecutive, and independent thinking? Describe the mental habits of your teacher in such cases, as shown in his manner of presenting the lesson and guiding the discussion.

8. In a development lesson, to what extent are "leading questions" justifiable? If so, what principle should govern the frequency of their use? What intellectual danger lurks in them?

9. A teacher of science has the habit of writing the question, Why? on the board, and looking or pointing to it during the recitation when a pupil makes a statement without giving a reason for it. Is this a good device? Why?

REFERENCES

BAGLEY, W. C. The Educative Process. Macmillan, N. Y. 1908. 358 pp. $1.25.

BAGLEY, W. C. Classroom Management. Macmillan, N. Y. 1907. 322 pp. $1.25.

BETTS, GEORGE H. The Recitation. Houghton Mifflin Co., Boston. 1911. 120 pp. 60 ¢.

CHARTERS, W. W. Methods of Teaching. Row, Peterson & Co., Chicago. 1909. 255 pp. $1.10.

DEWEY, JOHN. How We Think. D. C. Heath. 1910. 224 pp. $1.00.

McMURRY, C. A. Special Method in Elementary Science. Macmillan. 1904. 275 pp. 75 ¢.

McMURRY, C. A. Elements of General Method. Macmillan, N. Y. 1907. 331 pp. 90 ¢.

McMurry, F.   How to Study, and Teaching How to Study.   Houghton
 Mifflin Co., Boston.   1909. $1.25.

Stevens, Romiett.   The Question as a Measure of Efficiency in Instruction.   Teachers College, Columbia Univ., N. Y.   1912.

Strayer, George D.   A Brief Course in the Teaching Process.   Macmillan, N. Y.   1912.   315 pp. $1.25.

Thorndike, E. L.   Principles of Teaching.   A. G. Seiler, N. Y.
 1906.   12 + 293 pp. $1.25.

G

CHAPTER VI

EDUCATIONAL FUNCTIONS AND VALUES OF THE SCIENCES

What scientific study should do for the pupils. — Because of both the content and the method of scientific study, we are justified in attributing to it certain important educational functions, and inferring for it some very high educational values.[1] Among the results that should accrue to high school pupils, as the outcome of pursuing scientific studies, the following may be named as the most important:

1. The formation of some useful specific habits, — through training, routine, rationalized practice.

2. The acquisition of useful information, — through methodical study, instruction, and drill.

3. The adoption of valuable ideals, or "emotionalized standards," — inculcated through the inspiration to be gained from the teacher, from the lives of great scientists, and from experiences of intimate contact with nature.

4. The acquisition of facility in the use of facts, ideas, and methodical thought processes, for the solution of problems, the overcoming of difficulties, and the accomplishment of worthy purposes, — through the mental discipline afforded by properly graded practice in the solving of scientific problems.

5. The development of taste, and power of appreciation, — to be gained through a clear apprehension of

[1] Cf. Bagley, W. C., *Educational Values*, N. Y., 1911, Chapter VII.

unity, adaptation, economy, order, and system in nature as interpreted by science.

6. The development of scientific or philosophic insights, perspectives, and attitudes of mind that serve as safeguards to the intelligent interpretation of contemporary life, — through acquaintance with systems of organized knowledge.

Relation of functions to values. — Thus science teaching has a *training function* in the formation of right habits; an *instructional function* in the storing up of useful information; an *inspirational function*, aiming at the inculcation of worthy ideals; a *disciplinary function*, resulting in the development of mental power; a *recreative function*, tending toward the development of refined tastes and powers of appreciation; and an *interpretive function*, aiming at scientific insight and such broad mental perspectives as are characteristic of a cultivated, well-balanced mind.

The general aim of education from the modern standpoint is the development in each individual of the highest type of personality, combined with economic and social efficiency. This aim takes account of individual differences and environmental differences. Its motto is " *the socially efficient individual*." On this basis the hope for outcome of the training function is the realization of utilitarian, economic, or vocational values, — " bread and butter values," so to speak, — which contribute to the ability of the individual to support himself and a family.

In the more narrowly vocational studies and trade studies, the aim is toward *direct* utilitarian value, — the specific kinds of motor skill needed in particular occupations, such as carpentry, electrical construction, plumbing, cooking, and the like; but the habits formed in science study are more *indirect*, more varied, and therefore of more general application. If the usefulness of these habits in life situations outside the school are clearly shown, so that the pupils realize their value as permanent acquisitions that will help them in their everyday lives in definitely apprehended ways, the pupils may form *ideals* of carrying these habits over into their everyday lives. Experiments have shown that without such conscious ideals such habits are not at all likely to be carried over in large measure.[1]

The instructional function tends toward utilitarian value, and also toward *preparatory value.* Much of the information gained in the study of physics, chemistry, botany, geology, and zoölogy is necessary in preparing for the higher studies needed in the professions of applied science, such as engineering, scientific agriculture, teaching, and medicine.

Both the training and the instructional function result incidentally in a certain amount of *conventional value.* Through these functions the pupil may acquire some of the habits, manners, and general information that constitute a minimum of conventional culture without which society will refuse to accord him respect, and the lack of which would stamp him as a boor, an ignoramus, and make it less easy for him to get on harmoniously with his fellows.

The remaining functions contribute to *socializing value*, because they enable the individual who has profited by them to contribute to social progress. They fit him to be a " soldier of the common good," to help in increasing the achievement of each for all and all for each, through the improvement of the environment of all and the personal worth of each.

Specific habits. — The following are some of the specific habits which pupils will tend to acquire through the study of any of the sciences under the direction of a good teacher. Since they are of kinds that will be useful in very many of the situations of everyday life, and in all kinds of occupations, they are of great general utility, and are important to every

[1] Cf. Bagley, W. C., *The Educative Process*, N. Y., 1905, Chapters VII and XIII.

individual. While the time and attention given them should not be allowed to become disproportionately great, no teacher should allow himself wholly to neglect them.

1. Careful observation of significant facts and phenomena, using hands, eyes, and ears before consulting books.

2. System, order, and neatness in the arrangement of apparatus and appliances for observational and experimental work.

3. Carefulness and skill in the manipulation of tools and appliances.

4. Careful measurements, according to correct methods.

5. Accuracy and methodical procedure in setting down, arranging, and tabulating data, and in making calculations.

6. Legible writing, clear, neat, and accurate drawing, correct spelling and punctuation, correct grammatical construction, clearness and conciseness in written and spoken English.

7. Good form and effective motor attitudes and expression in "making a recitation."

In the routine of studying a science in school all the various kinds of acts implied by the list just enumerated will be performed, either in the right ways or in wrong ways. Whenever an act or a thought occurs in response to a question, direction, suggestion, or act of the teacher, and it results in satisfaction, it is likely to be repeated under the same stimulus or a similar one. Every repetition of such a motor reaction or mental connection tends to make it recur automatically. *Hence, habits of some sort will inevitably be formed. Whether they are to be right habits or wrong habits will depend on the way in which the teacher conducts the work.*

The law of habit formation. — *Association.* — This is a special case of the more general *law of mental connections or association,* and is stated by Thorndike [1] as follows:

> " *The likelihood that any mental state or act will occur in response to any situation is in proportion to the frequency, recency, intensity, and resultant satisfaction of its connection with that situation or some part of it, and with the total frame of mind in which the situation is felt.*"

Application of the law of association in teaching. — Hence the teacher should see to it, when any of the things above referred to is done, that (1) the pupils clearly understand what is the best way and why it is best; that (2) he arouse in them such ideals of good form, efficiency, and professional pride, and get them into such a total frame of mind that they shall be anxious to do it in the best way; that (3) in the inevitable repetitions of the act they are not allowed to lapse into wrong ways, but are made to do it in the right way every time; and that (4) satisfaction shall always be connected with the right way and dissatisfaction with the wrong way until the right way becomes automatic.

Scientific information. — The content of the sciences is made up of facts, phenomena, and processes, laws and principles, hypotheses and theories, and fundamental generalizations, arranged and classified in accordance with their relations to one another, — particular under general, and these in turn under more general. The relations in accordance with which they are classified have to do with *time, space, quality,* — especially with reference to function or use, — with *quantity,* and with *cause, origin, or development.* [2]

Facts, phenomena, and processes. — These include what we learn through observation with our senses of things and their qualities, the events that occur or happen in connection

---

[1] Thorndike, *Elements of Psychology,* N. Y., 1905, p. 207.

[2] For examples of organization of subject matter for the purposes of the mature scholar, see the articles on *Science* and those on the various special sciences in the *Encyclopedia Britannica.*

with them, and the routines, or regular successions of occurrences in time. The student of physical geography and geology learns many useful facts about air, water, rocks, soils,
mountains, plateaus, plains, forests, rivers, and drainage,
about how they are changing and affecting one another,
what they were like in the past, toward what future condition
they are tending, and how they control and are controlled by
human activities.

The student of chemistry comes to know and understand
something of the constitution of substances; about oxygen,
hydrogen, nitrogen, carbon, iron, copper, and other elements
and their properties; about the composition and properties
of the compounds and mixtures into which they enter; about
the processes of combination, decomposition, metathesis,
electrolysis, and their relations to acids, bases and salts; about
bleaching and disinfecting agents; and about soaps, paints,
inks, oils, fats, and foods.

The student of biology learns many facts about animals
and plants, wild and domesticated; their structure and its
adaptation to the vital functions of growth, nutrition, respiration, and reproduction; their development and life history; how they get their food, their means of defense and
protection; how they coöperate in groups; how they are
beneficial or harmful to man; how he can best deal with insect pests and bird friends; and how he can care for his domestic animals and plants, and improve them by selective
breeding.

In the study of physics knowledge is gained of the conditions of temperature and pressure under which bodies exist
in the solid, liquid, or gaseous states; of what they do when
energy is imparted to them or taken from them; of how to
measure matter, force, and energy in its different manifesta-
tions as mechanical motion, heat, electrical currents, and
vibrations; of the phenomena of mechanics, heat, electricity
and magnetism, sound and light; of the processes of evap-

oration, condensation, precipitation, fractional distillation, conduction, convection, radiation; and the applications of all these and many other facts and processes in doing the world's work.

Ideas and meanings. Laws and principles. — In connection with the perception of facts, the student through his intellectual processes gets ideas as to possible meanings of these facts. He makes inferences and tests them. He finds that certain events always follow certain others, or that they occur together invariably under certain conditions.

Thus he becomes acquainted with certain laws and principles, or brief statements as to how and under what circumstances certain phenomena occur. For example, he finds that the leaves of plants are always arranged on their stems in one or more spirals. This is the law of arrangement of leaves, and he learns that it is a part of the more general principle in accordance with which all plants develop, so as to dispose their leaves and branches in such a manner that the latter shall all get the greatest possible amount of sunlight. He finds also that this is only a special case of the broader and more fundamental principle of adaptation, — that is, all living forms tend to develop in such a way that their structures are adapted to the functions to be performed by them, and that the whole organism becomes adjusted to its environment.

Hypotheses and theories. — The manner in which hypotheses are used in scientific work — how, when they have been thoroughly tested, they are received as theories, and how, if they suffice to explain all the facts, they are ultimately accepted as general laws or principles — has already been described in connection with the laws of motion and gravitation.[1] A single further instance will suffice here. Darwin started to solve the problem of the origin of species, and after examining a prodigious number of facts, adopted the hypothesis that

[1] *Ante,* p. 7 ff.

species originate through variation, adaptation, and natural and sexual selection in the " struggle for existence." The array of evidence in favor of this hypothesis was found to be so great, and the explanations of the negative instances [1] were so satisfactory and convincing, that when they were marshaled and brought forward by Darwin and Wallace, in 1859 in their published researches, the development hypothesis was almost immediately received as a theory by the scientific world. At the present time *the principle of evolution by variation and selection is an accepted fact*, although the theory as stated by Darwin and Wallace has received some important extensions in connection with the mutation theory of DeVries, and the inheritance theory of Mendel, and although many phases of the process are still in doubt.

An important part of the subject matter of science is made up of such theories and generalizations, of their history, and of the manner in which they assist in the simplification of the subject matters by explaining the facts that come under them. They have a high socializing and cultural value through their interpretive function.

Fundamental concepts. — Further simplifications are made of the subject matter of science by bringing its various departments under more and more comprehensive principles and fundamental concepts. All the substances and processes met with in physics, chemistry, astronomy, and physical geology are reduced in thought to *matter and energy*, and these in turn to *molecules, atoms, electrons, and ether* in various states of motion. All living matter is found to be composed of or elaborated from simple cells, of which the amœba is the type; and these are composed of protoplasm, which in its turn is a physical and chemical association of molecules and atoms, differentiated from dead matter by possessing a principle of life which science thus far has not successfully explained. Thus with the aid of these comprehensive concep-

[1] See p. 8, *ante*.

tions, all the facts of all the sciences tend ultimately to be brought into closer and more easily intelligible relations and classifications.

To one who has gone far enough in the sciences to grasp even partially these large ideas, the petty and trivial dissipations of life present few attractions; and on him small annoyances, prejudices, and hatreds can take little hold.

The choice of subject matter. — There are three conditions under which any part of the content or subject matter of a school study may be useful.

1. It must be capable of being made simple enough to be clearly comprehended by the pupil;

2. It must be knowledge that will help in the accomplishment of some worthy purpose;

3. It must have been frequently associated with the situations in which it is likely to be needed, or some part of them, or something like them, so that it can be recalled when the need for it occurs.

Were these three conditions always applied as criteria in the selection of the subject matter taught, much uninteresting and worthless lumber that is handed down from textbooks of an earlier day would be discarded from our lessons. Actual utility of this sort ought to be the sole test for the choice of subject matter, since there are such vast stores to choose from that no one can possibly learn it all, even should he so desire. To defend subject matter that cannot stand these tests by claiming that it is a means of mental discipline — of gaining power — is to ignore the findings of modern psychology. So far as mental power is dependent on information, it consists precisely in having at command, for immediate recall and use, information that will help to solve the various problems of everyday life, intellectual and social as well as physical, and especially such problems as have elements of more than ordinary novelty and difficulty in them. To claim that mental power results from the mere acquiring of information that cannot be so used is a direct contradiction of terms. On the other hand, even though the learning of contentless material were granted disciplinary value, there is a superabundance of useful material out of which just as good discipline can be got, provided the methods by which it is imparted are right.

Criteria for the choice of subject matter. — In making choice of content, therefore, we should select that which is comprehensible, and which has the greatest number of useful elements in common with the present everyday-life situations, interests, and knowledge of the pupils, and with the everyday-life situations in which they may reasonably be expected to take part when they become adults. Since the law of efficient recall is identical with the law of habit formation, we should connect this content with as many as possible of these situations, and do it as frequently, as vividly, and as interestingly as possible.[1] It is thus only that we can make sure that the knowledge gained shall be of useful sort, and that it shall be usable.

The mastery of content. — As has been shown [2] before, much of the content of the sciences is familiar to the active and enterprising boy and girl, but their concepts, gained empirically through untrained experience, are vague. The meanings grouped in them are disconnected and unsystematized. Such vague, indefinite products of experience are called *psychological concepts*.

The teacher's problem is to start with what the pupil knows about a fact or law — with his psychological concept — and help him to work out his ideas, to make them clear and explicit, to apprehend their relations, and to classify and arrange them accordingly. He must be supplied with new meanings from various sources, and in various ways, so that the contents

[1] See pp. 67 and 85, *ante.*
[2] *Ante,* p. 39.

of his concepts may be enlarged. He must be taught to define his concepts, and connect them in memory with the names, symbols, formulæ, definitions, or statements that are to stand for them. By such a process his vague psychological concept of tree, or mountain, or plain, or the law of the lever, or of the process of stream erosion becomes an explicit, organized, *logical concept*, and is connected in memory with a word or definition which serves to recall any or all of the many clear and useful meanings that are now grouped in systematic order under it.[1]

The learning of facts and laws, the building up of concepts, the mastery of principles are best carried on in connection with problems to the solution of which the knowledge is necessary or significant. The memory connections and associations thus made will be stronger just because of this necessity or significance; for if there is a strong desire or incentive toward reaching the solution, the information will be sought earnestly, it will be connected vividly with the other elements of the problem, and the connection will result in satisfaction if the knowledge proves to be helpful. Furthermore, frequency is secured by the repeated use of the fact or principle in different problems.

If an important principle is not successfully memorized in this way as an incident in problem solving, its utility may at least be made so apparent that the students will cheerfully submit to whatever formal drill may be necessary in order deliberately to memorize it for further use.

It thus appears that separate lessons will not often be necessary for the mastering of content and the mastering of method, but that the former is best acquired through the problem lesson, wherein lies the only road to a real hold on the latter.

Observations, reference reading, and collecting. — Beside the first-hand observation through which scientific infor-

[1] See Miller, *The Psychology of Thinking*, Chapters XV and XVI.

mation is gained in the home, field, and wood, on the stream or farm, in the factory, at the demonstration table, or in the laboratory, and beside the study of the textbook, the pupils may gain information from assigned readings in reference books, magazines, monographs, and reports. When such assignments are given out, the student should always be expected to make some definite and immediate use of the information gained, such as preparing for a debate, or a report to the class, or an abstract for the teacher's reference file. *It is not only useless, but is injurious to the mental habits of the pupils to assign them readings without some definite purpose. When such work is assigned, the teacher should see that it is done, and also that it is rewarded by proper extra credit or in some other way satisfactory to the pupils.*

Two important factors in gaining information are class excursions, and individual and school collections of specimens, photographs, pictures, clippings, or homemade apparatus. *The exploring, collecting, ownership, and the constructive and coöperative instincts are strong at the high school age, and they should be taken advantage of, and directed into scientific channels.* The difficulties in the way of doing something in this line are usually imaginary. Enthusiastic and ingenious teachers always find a way, while lazy and incompetent ones often spend more energy in inventing excuses than would be necessary in starting some of the work.

Inspiration and scientific ideals. — Ideals constitute the motive power for human endeavor. This is true for the adolescent no less than for the adult. Adolescence is the very time when the tendency toward idealizing is strongest. What the youths or maidens choose to do, how they regulate their conduct, depends, as far as their personal initiative is concerned, on what they think worth while. Hence the importance of recognizing the values of scientific ideals, and making every effort to realize them in the teaching process, can hardly be overstated. These ideals may be gained incidentally and unconsciously through practice in squaring conduct with them, through formation of the habits that they represent, and through learning by repeated experiences that the highest kind of satisfaction results in the long run from holding tenaciously to them.

Scientific study, if carried on in the true scientific spirit, compels sincerity, out-and-out intellectual integrity, uncompromising honesty, at every step. " What are the actual facts? " " What is the truth about them? " These are the sole ultimate questions of scientific study. To know the truth and put it into usable form is the only aim. Since honesty is of the very essence of scientific study, the student of science under good scientific instruction is trained day by day to habits of honesty, to the habit of seeking the truth, and he may therefore come to realize the general value in individual and social life of sincerity, honesty, and love for knowledge of reality for its own sake. He may subconsciously analyze out and generalize these ideals from the daily practice of these virtues in classroom and laboratory. Now although it is fair to count on much in the way of their subconscious acquisition, yet great opportunities for immediate motivation and the determination of future character will be lost unless the teacher constantly holds up the worthy ideals before the pupils, and occasionally points out their utility, both for accomplishing the scientific work immediately in hand and for regulating the conduct of a successful life. In doing this *the situations chosen as examples of such utility should always be specific and concrete, not general or abstract.*

Referring again to the law of mental connections, the teacher should understand that the only way to make sure that the ideal of honesty in the schoolroom shall be recalled and used in the various situations outside is to have the pupils associate it with a great variety of these situations with " frequency, vividness, and resultant satisfaction," and then to generalize it.

Prudish sermonizing is harmful. It defeats its own end, but *if the teacher loves the ideal and lives it himself, he will find multitudes of tactful ways, in addition to the powerful way of example, for quietly influencing his pupils to adopt it deliberately as a rule of life.*

Other important ideals that may be expected to accrue from the study of science by the scientific method are, (1) achievement, (2) industry, (3) " stick-to-itiveness," concentration of attention on the thing in hand, (4) efficiency, or accuracy combined with speed, (5) resourcefulness, (6) open-mindedness, (7) a logical, well-balanced mind, (8) hatred of narrowness and prejudice, (9) social service, and (10) the ability to present ideas clearly and convincingly.

Inspiration from literature. — There is much of nature inspiration in the works of the poets and essayists, such as Burns, Tennyson, Wordsworth, Shelley, Thoreau, Emerson, Ruskin, John Burroughs, and John Muir. If the teacher can occasionally quote from these, or if he will now and then assign passages to students to be quoted from memory, or read to the class, and if he interests the class in contributing to a card file of such quotations, he can do much toward realizing the inspiration and appreciation values of science.[1] If he is himself an enthusiastic reader of such scientific classics as Darwin's " Origin of Species," De Candolle's " Origin of Cultivated Plants," Kingsley's " Town Geology," and " Madam How and Lady Why," Huxley's lectures and essays, Shaler's " Aspects of the Earth," Faraday's " Chemical History of a Candle," J. P. Cooke's " The New Chemistry," Tyndall's lectures on heat, sound, light, and electricity and his " Forms of Water," Boys's " Soap Bubbles," and many others of the same sort which might be named, he is sure to catch the spirit and method of these great scientific teachers. His enthusiasm will spread among his pupils, and they will

[1] See chapter headings of Linville and Kelly, *A Text-book in General Zoölogy,* Boston, 1906.

want to read something of these fascinating books for themselves.

Inspiration and the teacher. — Among the sources of inspiration for catching this spirit and absorbing these ideals, the teacher is ever present and foremost. If he exemplifies in his own character and ambitions the qualities to be idealized; if he manifests a genuine, sympathetic, personal interest in his students, their work and their play, their trials and their successes, their hopes, and their present and future aims and ambitions; if he loves his subject but recognizes that he is primarily teaching boys and girls and developing character; if he realizes that his every action produces a reaction on their part, either beneficial or the reverse, then the pupils will respond to his appeals, and strive to realize the possibilities which they will feel that he divines in them.

Inspirational lectures. History and biography. — Some textbooks are inspiring and stimulating, and others are not. Inspiring textbooks should be chosen if possible, but there are other sources of inspiration which the teacher can command. He can give an occasional enthusiastic, inspirational lecture, illustrated with lantern-slides, pictures, and experiments, on the life, researches, and influence of a great scientist or teacher, such as Galileo, Newton, Harvey, Cuvier, Thomas Young, Franklin, Faraday, Tyndall, Lyell, Darwin, Huxley, or Agassiz, and can mention their self-denying labors and brilliant discoveries with appreciation whenever any of these are closely related to the lesson.

Occasional studies in the histories of the various sciences, illustrated by pictures, lantern-slides, and experiments, may be made sources of great power for motivation and inspiration, if used with discretion; and a collection of portraits of the great scientists clipped from magazines, photographed from books, or purchased from scientific publishers and apparatus dealers, will help in getting into something like personal contact with the heroes of science in whose books or in whose lives the pupils have become interested. Some of these portraits of great scientists, and the scenes of their youth and labors, as well as other pictures of scientific interest and artistic value, should be used to decorate the walls of the laboratory.

The artistic side of science. — Thus this inspirational work, besides inculcating worthy ideals which may be carried over by the pupils into their own studies and their everyday lives, may result also in developing a permanent taste for scientific knowledge, and permanent power of appreciation for the new discoveries and inventions that are constantly coming to light and modifying human thought and endeavor.

The artistic, the esthetic, the craftmanship side of science work should not go entirely without attention in the classroom. There is such a thing as a beautiful experiment, such as those that a skilled and artistic demonstrator with the lantern can make with prisms, with the color mixer, with the polariscope, or with the optical disk, and with microscopic projections of growing crystals, of surface tension phenomena, of spirogyra, living hydræ, daphniæ, and vorticellæ. These are fascinating, and if used as rare treats — the ice cream and strawberries of the course — will invariably provoke enthusiasm and fire ambition. There is such a thing as poetic scientific prose, such as may be found in any chapter of Tyndall's famous " Six Lectures on Light " or Russell's books on the rivers, lakes, and glaciers of North America, which cannot fail to be inspiring. There are some mathematical demonstrations in physics that are artistically clear and concise, and can be appreciated by at least a few; while if not given out as tasks but enthusiastically presented as examples of fine work, they will do the others no harm. The account of Sir Humphry Davy's research in the electrolysis of water is an example of masterly and artistic technique in scientific work which should appeal to esthetic appreciation, and cannot fail to widen the intellectual horizon

H

and educate the scientific tastes of the young student of chemistry.[1]

Inspiration and the gifted pupil. — Thus if there happens to be in the class a boy or girl with the native endowment for becoming a productive scientific worker or teacher, the inspiration emanating from the resourceful science instructor who is capable of using such means of motivation may result in helping such gifted youths to " find themselves " and to plan for the attainment of the kind of higher training that they must undergo in order to realize their best possibilities. *One of the most important functions of education is thus to seek out the exceptionally gifted, and direct their energies into the channels where they will be most effective for social progress.*

QUESTIONS FOR FURTHER STUDY

1. From a commonly used textbook in science or from one of the common syllabi of college requirements select the topics and laboratory work on some division of the subject. After each topic or exercise list the various educational values that may possibly be realized by good methods of teaching it.

2. For each kind of educational value assigned in the list (Question 1) outline briefly the procedure you would adopt in connection with teaching the topic or exercise in order to realize this value.

3. Choose any chapter of a science textbook; apply the criteria for the choice of subject matter suggested in this chapter, and state what parts of the subject matter should be discarded. Justify your decision in each case.

4. How would you arrange matters in order to teach the topics retained (Question 3) by throwing them into problematic form?

5. For some list of lesson topics make a corresponding list of assigned readings for library work, and show specifically how you would make the assignments definite as suggested in this chapter.

6. Outline specifically a plan for encouraging individual and school collections in connection with your favorite science.

7. Make a list of the books on science from which you can distinctly remember that you gained inspiration and ideals.

[1] In *Scientific Culture and Other Essays*, by Josiah P. Cooke. Appleton, N. Y., 1885.

8. Why is it of such immense importance to our national life that gifted children should be sought out and developed up to their maximum capacity?

REFERENCES

BAGLEY, W. C.   Educational Values.   Macmillan, N. Y.   1911.   267 pp. $1.10.

BAGLEY, W. C.   The Educative Process.   Macmillan, N. Y.   1908. 358 pp. $1.25.

BAGLEY, W. C.   School Discipline.   Macmillan, N. Y.   1915.   259 pp. $1.25.

COOKE, JOSIAH PARSONS.   Scientific Culture, and Other Essays.   Appleton, N. Y.   1885.

DARWIN, CHARLES.   The Origin of Species.   Appleton, N. Y.   1897. 2 vols. $4.00.

DAVENPORT, EUGENE.   Education for Efficiency.   D. C. Heath, Boston. 1909.   184 pp. $1.00.

DAVY, SIR H.   Decomposition of the Fixed Alkalies and Alkaline Earths. Alembic Club Reprints.   University of Chicago.   40 ¢.

FLEXNER, ABRAHAM.   A Modern School.   General Education Board, N. Y.   Occasional Papers, No. 3.   23 pp.

HALL, G. STANLEY.   Adolescence.   Appleton, N. Y.   1915.   2 vols. $7.50.

HANUS, PAUL.   Educational Aims and Educational Values.   Macmillan, N. Y.   1908.   211 pp. $1.00.

JAMES, WILLIAM.   Talks to Teachers on Psychology and Life's Ideals. Holt & Co., N. Y.   1899.   Chapters VII–XIV. $1.50.

MILLER, I. E.   The Psychology of Thinking.   Macmillan, N. Y.   1910. 298 pp. $1.25.

PEARSON, KARL.   The Grammar of Science.   Macmillan, N. Y.   1915. 2 vols.

ROWE, STUART HENRY.   Habit Formation and the Science of Teaching. Longmans, Green & Co., N. Y.   1909.   308 pp. $1.50.

SPENCER, HERBERT.   Education.   Appleton, N. Y.   1909.   301 pp. $1.25.

THORNDIKE, E. L.   Elements of Psychology.   A. G. Seiler, N. Y.   1907. 351 pp. $1.50.

THORNDIKE, E. L.   Principles of Teaching.   A. G. Seiler, N. Y.   1906. 12 + 293 pp. $1.25.

TYLER, JOHN M.   The Culture of Imagination in the Study of Science. School Review, Vol. 6, pp. 716–724, December, 1898.   Advocates teaching by the scientific method.

CHAPTER VII

Mental discipline.— According to modern psychology, mental discipline means a kind of training that gives one mental powers, aptitudes, knowledge of facts and general principles, and especially command of methods of procedure, so that he is mentally resourceful and is able to apply his mind efficiently and successfully to the pursuit of many kinds of study, or the solution of many kinds of problems, or the prosecution of many kinds of work that involve thinking.

It has been clearly shown both by many experiments and by studies of common experience that practice and training in any one subject or kind of activity do not ordinarily increase the ability of an individual in another subject or kind of activity in proportion to the amount of training.

In other words, mental connections, associations, habits, interests, abilities, are specific, although some are capable of functioning in a great variety of situations, and are therefore of very general value. Training clings to the content through which it has been gained. Practice in translating Latin improves the ability to translate Latin, but it does not proportionally increase ability to compute partial payments, or judge the value of real estate, or analyze ores, or raise good and abundant crops.

Notwithstanding the specific character of habits and intellectual functions, the possibility of the transfer or spread of training into fields other than those in which it is acquired is admitted by most modern psychologists; but it is certain that the extent to which such transfer may spread depends very largely on the kind of content with which the training deals and the way in which it is taught. Our present task is to find a principle that will help the teacher of science to convert this possibility into fact.

The so-called generalized habits, such as concentration of attention, methodical procedure, accuracy, open-mindedness, etc., are specific habits that can be used in a large number of different situations having elements of likeness to the situations involved in the training in which these habits have been gained, and requiring responses of a more or less similar kind.

Knowledge of many facts of physics, chemistry, geography, botany, etc., enables one to get on better in a great variety of activities in which knowledge that is identical with it, or like it in whole or in part, is needed as a basis for ideas in the solution of difficulties and the performance of tasks. It has been shown elsewhere that the method by which the scientific worker controls his thinking and carries on his researches is only a refinement and perfection, through scientific training, of the methods of thinking that are used by everybody who thinks effectively.

Thus it is evident that scientific training has elements of method that are common to all problematic situations in every field of activity. Also the subject matter of science contains many facts, laws, principles, and general concepts that have elements of content in common with a large variety of situations in many different fields. While the question as to how spread of training or mental discipline of general application can be obtained, and the extent of the spreading under varied circumstances, is far from settled, there is much of experimental proof, much of accumulated pedagogical experience that points toward some definite principles concerning this question; and there is a pretty general agreement of psychological opinion based on such evidence as to what these principles are.

Conditions limiting the transfer of training. — The principles to which we have referred may be stated thus :

(1) Training in one kind of activity may improve ability in other kinds of activity when the former has elements of content or elements of method in common with the latter.

(2) *Therefore the highest disciplinary value for general, nontechnical education is to be found in the studies and activities that have the maximum of elements of content and elements of method that are common to the greatest number of essential or important life activities, both individual and social.*

Applying the principles of transfer. — Hence in order to get such general discipline out of any particular study, the content selected for teaching must be that which has the greatest number of such common elements, and these must be mentally associated with as many as may be of such activities, and as frequently, vividly, and interestingly as possible.

Also whenever the methods used in the study are applied in whole or in part, with or without modification, to the solution of important problems or the performance of work important to the present or future life of the boys and girls, the teacher should make the pupils think how such methods apply, and what modifications, if any, must be made of them in order that they may be most efficiently used.

In connection with forming habits of associating school knowledge with life problems, the advantage of habitually acquiring such knowledge and of using it for accomplishing worthy things must be shown, so that an ideal of so acquiring and using concepts and principles may be built up and emotionalized.

How concepts of method are built up. — The most important phase of teaching with respect to mental discipline is the formation of *concepts of method.* These are built up just as other concepts are.[1]   A girl is set the problem of finding out whether an acid and an alkali combine in definite proportions and if so what kind of compound results.   She has at first a very vague idea of the best methods to be used in going about it.   But she weighs or measures out definite amounts of the acid and the base, and dissolves them in definite quantities of water.   She adds one solution, cubic centimeter after cubic centimeter, and then drop after drop, to a definite number of cubic centimeters of the other.   She learns that when there is a drop too little of one constituent the litmus or other indicator will have one color, and when there is a drop too much, another color.   She learns that the same proportions hold, no matter what are the actual quantities used.   She evaporates the neutral solution, crystallizes out the salt and identifies it with table salt, or potassium chloride, or saltpeter.   She weighs it and finds that it contains just the definite amounts of the acid and basic constituents that the original portions taken from the two solutions did.

After she has carried on all these operations methodically, accurately, and speedily with intelligent apprehension of what she has been doing; after she has methodically written up her methods, observations, and conclusions in her notebook; and after she has discussed them in the classroom and laboratory, and associated them with related phenomena of the laboratory and of the larger world outside, she has immensely increased the content of her concepts of the things she has dealt with.   She has explicit knowledge of old and new facts, and of one case of a new law.   Her ideas of the relations of these facts to one another have also become more clear and explicit.   The words " acid," " base," " salt," "alkali," "radical," " element " and the like now stand for larger, more explicit, and better organized groups of meanings.

[1] Cf. Heck, *Mental Discipline and Educational Values*, John Lane, N. Y., 1911, Chapters VI and VII.

But besides attaching more meanings to her concepts of acid, base, and the like, the girl has enlarged and clarified her ideas of method, order, accuracy, and system in carrying out the experiment, reasoning on the facts, and testing conclusions. In other words, she has done and thought many things that have added more meanings to her concept of method, and perhaps under the guidance of a resourceful teacher, has made association connections between the methods used in the experiment and other problems in cookery, pharmacy, and the manufacture of other chemicals in which the same or similar methods are used in whole or in part.   Thus if she has learned in such a practical way the meaning of "Stop! Look! Listen!" "Think before you act!" "Chemicals are dangerous when unintelligently used!" and if her concepts of nitroglycerine and mercuric chloride have sufficient useful content, then when she has become a wife and mother she will not clean a glycerine bottle with nitric acid, nor have about the house an unlabeled package of mercuric chloride tablets for baby to swallow.   If she wants to make biscuits she will remember the law of definite proportions, and will use suitable methods, and find out once for all the exact proportions of soda and cream of tartar to use.   She will learn the right oven temperature, and how to regulate it so that the biscuits will be light and wholesome, not tasting of either soda or acid.   And when her husband eats the biscuits and honey that she sets before him he will be glad that she studied pure chemistry, and learned to apply it in household economics.

Ideals as related to transfer of training. — If transferable discipline is to be given, not only must concepts of method be built up by explaining the best methods of scientific procedure in experimenting and thinking, but these methods must be organized and applied to many problems outside the classroom, and their advantages must be pointed out frequently and vividly.   Thus *conscious ideals* of recalling methods, of selecting those that are appropriate to whatever problem or task may be in hand, and of making such modifications of the known methods as are expedient in the case, will be built up and will have a tendency to function in the formation of habits of methodical procedure and systematic logical thinking on every task and problem.

Scientific habits of mind. — Among the higher habits which good science teaching ought to build is first, that of recognizing a problematic situation when it occurs, of analyzing out its specific factors, and bringing them under the appropriate categories. Is this a question of time and space relations, or of cause and effect, or of origin and development, or of quality, or of quantity? To use an extreme case, for example, one should be able to judge that the particular phase in which the moon happens to be has nothing to do with the growth of potatoes, but that their growth depends on the composition and texture of the soil, the kind of fertilizer used, the amount of available moisture, and the kind of care and cultivation they receive.

Important scientific habits have to do with collecting the facts, — habits of observing; of inquiring from experts; of consulting the right books, pamphlets, and reports; of handling card catalogues; of judging the relative worth of facts and the relative competency of authorities.

In learning science by the scientific method, one forms the habit of dismissing prejudices and holding judgment in suspension until sufficient facts have been examined; of reflecting on the facts in a search for a fruitful hypothesis; of developing and testing each hypothesis in turn, and selecting the most fruitful; of examining conclusions and testing them by observation and experiment to see if they square with all the significant facts of the problem.

The principles of scientific induction. — Logical methods are used in the search for causes, and as far as practicable the habit should be formed of applying such logical tests to all cases wherein causes are sought. The general principles on which these methods are based may be thus stated:

Whenever a certain occurrence may be due to a number of different supposable causes, and we can for conclusive reasons deny the possibility of causation to all of the number but one, that one must be the cause.

For example, if it has been proved that a certain kind of mosquito that has previously bitten a yellow fever patient has also bitten another individual, and the latter develops yellow fever, and if it can be proved that the infection could not have been communicated by any other of the supposable causes, then it has been proved that the bite of that species of mosquito is the sole and only cause of the infection. This statement is so simple that it seems axiomatic, but complete proof of this kind is very difficult to obtain, because it is usually very difficult to divine all the possible causes, and to find conclusive reasons for ruling out all but one. In very many cases we can only arrive at a conclusion which has a high degree of probability. Let us briefly consider the methods by which this is done.

The method of agreement. — Suppose that on the same day a number of persons become ill, and show all the symptoms of ptomaine poisoning. It is found that they all attended a certain picnic, and all ate ice cream, but that each of them refrained from eating one or two of the other kinds of food that might possibly have contained ptomaines. If the day were Friday the thirteenth, in " the dark of the moon," and there were thirteen at table, and if these circumstances were advanced as causes, we should at once rule them out as irrelevant for the good and sufficient reasons that numbers of cases are known where things have been done under these circumstances, and no harm whatever has come to the party, and furthermore no cases of harm occurring along with such circumstances have ever been recorded which might not more reasonably be attributed to other causes that intelligibly fit into our organized systems of demonstrated knowledge. Similarly we should rule out witchcraft, " the evil eye," and other superstitions as causes. Narrowing our consideration of facts to those that are relevant, and our ideas to those that are appropriate to the facts, we consider only the foods eaten. We reason that since all the ptomaine patients had eaten the ice cream, the ice cream is a possible cause; also since each of the other foods was *not* eaten by some member of the group, it could not have been the cause of his sickness. Therefore since the ice cream was the only supposable cause that was present with the illness of all the members of the group, we should infer with very great probability that it was the sole cause of the disaster.

This is a case of the use of the method of agreement, the principle of which may be stated thus:

> *Whatever circumstance is present in every observed case of the occurrence of a phenomenon is possibly related to its causation; and whatever circumstances may be eliminated without eliminating the phenomenon cannot be the sole cause.*

The method of difference. — Again suppose that all but one of the persons present at the picnic were found to have eaten the same bill of fare, and all became ill excepting one. If the fact developed that the one who was *not* poisoned was the only one who had *not* eaten the ice cream, then we should be warranted in judging it highly probable that ptomaine in the ice cream was the cause of the poisoning. This is called the method of difference, and its principle may be stated as follows:

> *Whenever the elimination of a single circumstance is accompanied or followed in a number of cases by the non-occurrence of any given phenomenon, that circumstance is probably related to its causation.*

The joint method. — This is a combination of the two preceding methods. The problem of locating the cause of a typhoid epidemic in a certain college town was solved in this manner.

The facts were found to be as follows. All those who developed the disease ate at a certain few tables. All supposable sources of the infection other than food and drink were disregarded, because it is well known that typhoid bacilli produce the disease only when taken into the digestive tract. The water, the milk, and the fresh vegetables were naturally suspected, because these have been found to be frequent sources of typhoid bacilli.

Fresh vegetables were at once ruled out because some of the houses where infection occurred and some where it did not occur were supplied with their vegetables from the same sources. There remained, therefore, the two rival hypotheses as to the water and the milk. Both the water and the milk supplies of all those who were infected came from the same sources; yet it was found that there were in the town many houses where the same water supply was used, but where the milk that was used came from other sources; and in these houses no one contracted the disease. The water supply was then eliminated from the possible causes, and the milk supply of the houses where the disease occurred remained the only object of suspicion. When these houses ceased to use milk from the suspected source, no new cases developed.

The facts may now be generalized as follows. While there were many points of agreement in the circumstances of those who had the disease, and many points of agreement among those who did not have it, there was one, and only one, circumstance that was present in the cases of all in the first group and absent in the cases of all those in the second group. That was the milk supply. Therefore if this statement truly embraces all the facts, the conclusion is certain and obvious. The milk was the source of the bacilli and causally related to the epidemic.

The principle of the joint method of agreement and difference may be stated thus:

> *If two or more cases in which a phenomenon occurs have in common one and only one circumstance which is absent from two or more cases in which the phenomenon does not occur, that circumstance is causally related to the phenomenon.*

The method of concomitant variations. — Some causes, such as gravity, heat, and life processes, cannot be conveniently eliminated by any grouping of observed facts, or by any experimental means similar to those described. For example, common observation tells us that a change in the volume of a given mass of gas invariably results when either its temperature or the confining pressure is changed. When the pressure is increased the volume is diminished, and vice versa; and when the temperature is increased the volume increases, and vice versa. In this situation, we at once recognize a problem. Is the change of pressure or the change of temperature the sole cause of the change in volume, or are they both independent causes, each of which may either increase the effect of the other or tend to nullify it? We cannot eliminate either of these hypothetical causes, but we can arbitrarily vary one and keep the other constant. If we keep the pressure constant and change the temperature by arbitrary steps, recording the corresponding changes in volume, we find on examining the figures that the volume increases regularly by $\frac{1}{273}$ of its volume at zero centigrade for every rise of one degree in temperature. Similarly, by keeping the temperature constant and varying the pressure we find that the volume diminishes in the same ratio in which the pressure increases, and vice versa. We thus find out that the temperature and volume vary *concomitantly*, as do also the pressure and the volume. Thus we can not only prove that both temperature changes and pressure changes are causally related to changes in volume, but we can also discover and prove the laws in accordance with which the variations occur.[1]

The principle of the method of concomitant variations may be stated in this wise:

> *Any phenomenon that varies in any manner whenever some other phenomenon varies in a particular manner is either an effect or a cause of the other, or is related to it through some fact of causation.*[2]

Besides being used commonly in experimental researches in chemistry and physics, this method is extensively applied to the investigation of statistics in economics and sociology. In the latter sciences the sets of numbers that are compared ordinarily represent phenomena that simply have happened and changes that are observed, measured, and recorded. They do not, as in physics and chemistry, represent variations that have been made to happen for the express purpose of investigating them.

The method of residues. — This method has already been described in connection with the discovery of the planet Neptune.[3] It is useful in cases where several agencies may be present, each producing an effect peculiar to itself. The principle is that:

> *When the effects of all agencies that are known by previous inductions have been balanced off or accounted for, the remaining portion of the total phenomenon must be due to some unknown cause or causes.*

This method does not necessarily determine what the cause is, but it serves to limit the field of inquiry so as to make it easier to hit on a hypothesis that can be tested out.

---

[1] See Mann and Twiss, *op. cit.*, pp. 84 and 319.

[2] See Jones, A. L., *Logic, Inductive and Deductive,* N. Y., 1909, p. 104. It would be well to read the entire chapter.

[3] Cf. pp. 8 ff., *ante.*

Transferable and nontransferable discipline contrasted.
— This explains why a person who is perfectly familiar with
the content of a subject is so ingenious, so fertile in ideas that
are helpful in solving problems in that subject. Knowing
familiarly all the different effects of the known causes, he is
able quickly to balance off these effects and mentally subtract them from the phenomenon. He is thus able to pick
out the unknown residue of the phenomenon and the few
remaining supposable causes and bring them together, so
that they stand out, as it were, in strong relief. Thus they
almost obtrude themselves on his attention.

The principle of the method of residues also accounts for
the fact already mentioned [1] that many persons who are
highly trained in one field of thought show poor judgment
and poverty of appropriate ideas in another subject in which
they are not trained. They have specialized narrowly in one
field and have not practiced themselves in carrying over their
methods and modifying them to fit facts and conditions in
other fields. Because they are unfamiliar with the content
of other subjects, they cannot quickly apprehend the relations and implications of the unfamiliar facts; and hence
they are not prompt and certain in ruling out inappropriate
ideas. For the same reason they are not fertile in fruitful
hypotheses nor resourceful in testing them out. *Their
training has not been broad enough in its associations to be
transferable.*

Relation of logical methods to science teaching. — It is not
claimed that the pupils should be formally instructed in the
logical methods that have been described above. With young
pupils such instruction would in all probability defeat its
own end. *What is both feasible and important is that the
methods should be well understood by the teacher*, and that whenever there occurs in the classroom or laboratory a case where
one or more of them can be used to advantage in making an

[1] *Ante*, p. 46.

inductive inference, the principle or warrant for such inference should be briefly and clearly pointed out. *By such use
and practice of this and other phases of the scientific method the
students' concepts of methods may be gradually built up and
made clear, and an ideal may be gradually instilled of systematically selecting, adapting, and using an appropriate method of
attack for every problem.*

The modern view of the nature of mental discipline. —
From the foregoing discussion we may infer that no matter
how great its specific value may be, the mental discipline
derived from the study of any subject can be of *general* value
only when it is transferable, — that is, when the knowledge
and skill acquired in the disciplinary process is such that the
person being trained can *use* it in many of the kinds of situations that occur in real life outside the schoolroom. The
essence of such transferable mental discipline lies in training
that has elements of content and elements of method that
belong, in whole or in part, to many life situations. Such
school training has possibilities of becoming transferable in
proportion (1) to the number and strength of the association
connections that are made between the content and methods
of the school training and the life situations outside the school
that have identical or similar elements of content or method,
(2) to the clearness and vividness of the concepts of method
that are gained by the students, and (3) to the motivating
power of the ideal of methodical procedure that they acquire.

Precepts for the conduct of transferable training. — From
the principles just stated we may derive some rules of procedure for the science teacher who wishes so to shape his methods
of teaching that his pupils may get transferable discipline
out of their study under his direction.

1. It is impossible to teach the whole of any science;
therefore a most careful selection of subject matter and
method must be made.

2. In making the selection the choice should fall on such elements of content and such elements of method as are useful in many situations of present-day life, and especially of the sorts of life that the pupils who are being taught are likely to live, now or later on.

3. The pupils should be caused to make association connections between these elements of content and method, as developed in classroom and laboratory, and the situations of life outside the schoolroom wherein such elements have significant counterparts.

4. Careful attention should be given to building up general concepts of method and ideals of methodical procedure for the conscious purpose of rendering the discipline transferable.

5. Whenever possible both subject matter and method should be presented by means of problems which are of such a nature that the pupils desire to attack and solve them for their own satisfaction rather than as perfunctory school tasks.

Developing powers of interpretation. — The interpretive value of science is closely related to the disciplinary value; and like this it is secured in very large measure by studying science according to the scientific method. The habits and ideals growing out of practice in organizing knowledge into systems, and practice in bringing particular cases and problematic situations under the general and special systems where in accordance with their relations they properly belong, are the fundamental elements of interpretive power. One who is trained in this way [1] will know how and where to look for the facts in any case, and what kind of principles to apply in dealing intelligently with them. He will know whether the matter in hand is a case for observation and experimentation, or a case to be settled by an appeal to authority, or whether

[1] See pp. 22, 44 and 76, *ante.*

I

it is simply a matter that goes back to a definition. Problems of interpretation are largely problems of deduction from known definitions, principles, and laws; or they may be problems of explanation, — that is, of identifying facts as cases or consequences of general principles or laws.

Again, to illustrate by an extreme example, a person with powers of interpretation would know that a case of lunacy cannot have anything to do with the moon, but is to be investigated in accordance with the principles of heredity, neurology, and psychopathology.

On the other hand, since the influences of the moon are comprehended under the laws of motion and the law of gravitation, he would know at once that the tides originate through the gravitation influence of the moon and sun, and that a question about a tidal phenomenon is not a psychological or ecclesiastical question. Hence, he would seek for the causes and laws of the tides under the principles of motion and gravitation.

He would know also that the problem of the effects on the human system of chemical preservatives in foods is not to be solved by the methods of pure chemistry alone, but that it is essentially a physiological problem, and must be investigated by biological methods primarily, and by chemical methods only secondarily.

Such acquaintance with systems of knowledge also gives one broad points of view and a judicial, open-minded attitude toward all questions. It gives him an appreciation of proportion, — of the relative importance of things, and therefore enables him to gain such intellectual perspectives that his judgments on any question are likely to be good judgments, so far as he permits himself to judge. One so trained and cultured will know also when his judgment is likely to be poor, and who the experts are whose judgment of the question is certain to be good. He will in such cases consult the experts and accept their conclusions instead of his own. For example, if he were a member of a committee of a chamber of commerce that was to investigate the question of a pure water supply and a sewage disposal plant, and to make recommendations to the city council, he would not trust his own judgment unless indeed he were an expert sanitary engineer himself. If he were not such an expert, but had good general powers of scientific judgment, he would use his abilities in the selection of an expert sanitary engineer, and would base his recommendations to the council on the facts of the expert's report and the inferences that might logically be drawn from them.

Some basic principles in science teaching. — It ought now to be apparent that a few simple principles are fundamental to the teaching of all the sciences, and should be borne in mind by teachers in order that they may guide themselves aright in the selecting and developing of their methods. These are here briefly summarized.

1. Children can be trained into efficient habits of thinking only by being made to think under guidance, day after day, and they can be made to think only by placing them in problematic situations.

2. The problems presented to them must be within the range of their needs and interests, of their concrete knowledge, and of their powers of abstraction at the particular stage of their development at which the teacher finds them.

3. Command of the technique of effective, rational thinking can be gained only by much practice in connection with numerous and varied problems, in each of which one or more of the various modes of methodical procedure characteristic of scientific problem solving is used. It cannot be gained by memorizing the finished products of thinking done by mature, experienced, highly trained minds.

4. In order to develop concepts of method, attention

must be directed to the method in many problems, and the common elements of method in the various modes of attack must be pointed out from time to time as the students advance in the subject. In connection with each problem, attention must also be called to numerous other problems among the various activities and processes which are going on outside the schoolroom, but within the scope of the children's knowledge, and to which a similar method is applicable.

5. The solution of every problem requires knowledge of a certain amount of the content of the subject, that is, of its facts, laws, concepts, and principles. This content or subject matter can best be acquired by the pupils, along with the methods, through the mental work that they have to do in solving the problems. When thus sought because it is needed in order to solve a problem that involves immediate interests and immediate needs this content is learned by the pupils under the circumstances that are most favorable for its retention, organization, and availability for later use.

6. The ability to recall and apply such information when needed will be in proportion to the number of times and the number of ways that it has been interestedly thought of and associated by the learner with the situations and activities of everyday life, and in proportion to the amount of elements that it has in common with such situations and activities.

7. In all this work, the advantages of methodical procedure and accurate knowledge should be pointed out to the pupils, and emphasized whenever these advantages can be made apparent; so that the young learners may become inspired with such widely applicable ideals of methodical procedure, of correct thinking, and of accurate, organized information, as may be carried over into all their other work.

8. As the pupils acquire new knowledge, they should be led to assimilate it with their previous knowledge (apperception), and to bring each new fact or principle under its appropriate heading (organization), as it is mastered, and finally, at the end of the course, to complete the process of organizing the whole into a logical scheme or system. As this process of systemization is always the last step in any stage of the work of the scientific investigator, so it should be the last in the classroom. Such work in organizing and systemizing the acquired subject matter should be done at the end of each lesson, each week, each term, or semester, and in the final review at the end of the course. The outlines or synopses should not be dictated by the teacher but should be made up by the pupils themselves with such assistance and suggestions from him as may be necessary.

QUESTIONS FOR FURTHER STUDY

1. Select any topic or laboratory experiment or field lesson as outlined in a science textbook, and list the elements that it has in common with various important life activities. List as many of these latter as you can think of.

2. Do the same for several other topics. On this basis should any of the topics be discarded? If so, suggest better ones to take their places, and justify the selection.

3. Briefly outline a part of a lesson plan in which the building up of a concept of method is provided for.

4. What would you do to build up an ideal of observing facts before consulting authorities? Of analyzing a problem before attacking it?

5. In the available books on scientific history and biography, find examples in which the various methods of scientific induction were used. Present brief abstracts of these to the class.

6. Are you conscious of having been able to transfer to any of your life problems some habit or concept of method that you acquired through science study in school? If so, give an account of it.

7. If not, can you think of a case where you needed such training, and might have got it if it had been provided for in some part of your

school science study where opportunity for doing so existed? If you have such a case in mind briefly outline it.

8. Can you think of any decisions of your own that might have been made more wisely if you had had better powers of interpretation? Explain them.

9. Does any one of the "basic principles" at the close of this chapter seem to you unsound or impracticable? If so, criticize it.

REFERENCES

BAGLEY, W. C.   The Educative Process.   Macmillan, N. Y.   1908. 358 pp.   Chapter XIII. $1.25.

COLVIN, STEPHEN S.   The Learning Process.   Macmillan, N. Y.   1911. 336 pp. $1.25.

HECK, W. H.   Mental Discipline and Educational Values.   John Lane & Co., N. Y.   1911.   208 pp. $1.00.

JONES, A. L.   Logic, Inductive and Deductive.   H. Holt & Co., N. Y. 1909.   304 pp. $1.00.

MANN, C. R. and TWISS, G. R.   Physics.   Scott, Foresman & Co., Chicago.   1910.   Revised Edition.   453 pp. $1.25.

MILLER, IRVING EDGAR.   The Psychology of Thinking.   Macmillan, N. Y.   1909.   303 pp. $1.25.

THORNDIKE, E. L.   The Principles of Teaching.   A. G. Seiler, N. Y. 1906.   12 + 293 pp. $1.25.

CHAPTER VIII

CLASSROOM AND LABORATORY INSTRUCTION

Current methods. — Three types of method have been commonly used in science instruction during the last ten or fifteen years, known respectively as the recitation, the lecture-demonstration, and the laboratory lesson. These are supposed to be closely correlated in a carefully worked-out plan; but unfortunately actual inspection of the work carried on in many schools leads to the inference that they are seldom so related. As witnessed in a large majority of the schools, the recitations represent reproductions seriatim of sections of the subject matter as given in the textbook; and the laboratory lessons are discrete units or tasks to be done. The latter too often have little or no direct logical relation to the former, and in very many cases not even a remote relation. Thus while the current theory of the three methods of instruction is correct, the actual practice is farther removed from the ideal than any one who has not witnessed the work in a large number and variety of schools could be made to believe.

The problem as the center of unification. — In the light of the principles at which we have arrived, the obvious remedy for this common fault is to organize the class work, the demonstrations by the teacher, and the laboratory observations and experiments about definite, well-chosen problems, after the principles of procedure exemplified in the lesson on heat that has been discussed in Chapter V.

No further argument should be needed to convince the reader that the problem should be the real unit in any science course that is designed to give training in the scientific method. Hence it is a pedagogical mistake to set up a recitation, or a lecture-demonstration, or a laboratory exercise as a unit of instruction unless indeed it consists essentially of a problem or a definite part of a problem which is to be completely worked out in the period given to the exercise. In the latter case the problem, not the recitation or laboratory exercise, is the logical and practical unit of instruction, as it should be. The aim of the student should be to arrive by correct scientific thinking and experimenting at the solution of a significant problem, rather than to recite a lesson or to " do a stunt " in the laboratory for the rather uninteresting purpose of getting a possible mark or escaping such disagreeable consequences as may be expected to follow a failure to satisfy the teacher's demands.

This difference in the attitude of the pupil toward the unit of instruction may seem to some to be of little consequence so long as the pupils actually do the required work; but it is really the condition that determines whether the work of the instructor shall be real scientific teaching or mere perfunctory school-keeping. It is the condition that determines whether the pupils are to get training that shall make them at home among scientific ideas and scientific or practical problems, or are merely to be crammed with words and processes that they cannot intelligently connect with things that are meaningful to them in life.

The class conference. — This term is to be preferred to the term " recitation." It represents more nearly the spirit in which the pupils and teacher should meet in the classroom and the purpose for which they come together. They should meet not in order to take turns in trying to remember and recite what they have all conned from the same textbook, but rather to confer with one another and with the teacher for the purpose of putting together their individual stocks of significant facts, and criticizing one another's ideas with reference to a problem in which they are interested and the solution of which they desire to find.

The term " conference " implies that the teacher should not be the only one who asks questions nor the only one who sets forth facts and ideas for the enlightenment of the others. In fact, some of the best class exercises the writer has witnessed have been those in which the pupils were fighting out a disputed question among themselves, one at a time against the pack, while the teacher stood, as it were, on the side lines and acted as umpire and referee. Too often the teacher monopolizes the spotlight in the center of the stage, tells too much, and asks four or five inconsequential questions when one incisive query would suffice. One concise, well-directed question or stimulating suggestion from a skillful teacher is often sufficient to start a discussion in which all the required facts and ideas are brought out by the pupils themselves.

The function of the teacher is to supply, by his own example, inspiration and stimulus for attentive, vigorous, consecutive, logical thinking and expression, and to see that all this activity is carried on by the pupils in an orderly and efficient manner. The pupils should be stimulated to ask questions of one another and of the teacher; and when a question is raised it should if possible be answered by the pupils rather than by the teacher. The things to be told by the teacher are those to which the pupils cannot find answers without too much loss of time. Such questions should be answered as concisely, as clearly, and as artistically as possible, and usually in such a way as to stimulate curiosity and provoke further study and inquiry. Ordinarily, altogether too little importance is attached by teachers to the function of inciting the pupils to raise questions and to answer questions that other pupils raise. Too often the classroom meeting consists merely of a succession of dialogues between the teacher on one side and various individual pupils on the other side, in which the teacher does most of the talking, and in which the remainder of the class show little or no interest for the reason that they know already very approximately what the substance of each dialogue is going to be. *The frequency and logical significance of the questions asked by pupils supplies one of the very best measures of the efficiency of a class conference.*

Some standards of good class work. — The following questions may well be used by a supervisor or inspecting officer in determining the quality of a class lesson:

1. Was the unit of instruction a significant problem, having a clear and definite relation to what the pupils already know and are to some extent interested in?

2. Is the lesson problem clearly and logically related to what has preceded it and what is to follow it in the course?

3. If the main lesson problem was too long to be solved in a single recitation period or a double laboratory period, was it split up into smaller parts or subsidiary problems, so that a definite unit or problem was completed during the lesson period?

4. Was the assignment of the lesson planned and made with care and forethought, so that the pupils understood definitely and clearly just what and how much was expected of them?

5. Did it provide for no more work than the average pupil might reasonably be expected to do in view of all other school tasks that had been assigned to him?

6. Did the teacher use definite and reasonably certain ways of assuring himself that each pupil had accomplished the work assigned to him?

7. Did the lesson problem and the teacher's methods make a successful appeal to the pupil's initiative and self-activity? In other words, to what extent did the pupils

adopt the problem as their own, so that every one was working and thinking on the subject all the time?

8. Did the pupils raise questions and objections, demand and supply evidence, and judge of relative values?

9. Was most of the talking done by the pupils or by the teacher?

10. Were facts and ideas significantly organized with reference to the problem?

11. Were hypotheses advanced by pupils? Were the hypotheses systematically tested and selected?

12. Were the pupils made to associate the facts and principles considered in the lesson with such situations of life as are found to have similar elements of content or method?

13. During the lesson did teacher and pupils use clear, concise, and correct English, and adjust their voices and enunciation to the size of the room, so that everything said was heard by all?

14. When the lesson was finished, was it evident that the essential points of the problem and the method of its solution stood out clearly, so that it should have been thoroughly comprehended by the pupils?

15. Did the teacher make the pupils apply the ideas brought out in the lesson in such a way as to show that they had gained intelligent practical command of them?

16. To what extent were the needs of the slower pupils and the exceptionally bright ones given intelligent attention?

17. What was done by the teacher toward the development of scientific concepts of method, ideals, attitudes, and habits of mind?

18. Did the attitude of the pupils toward the work indicate that the lesson was dead and uninteresting, or that it was stimulating and inspiring?

19. Was the teacher clear and logical in thought and speech?

20. Did he make use of concrete illustrative materials, demonstrations, and experiments in sufficient quantity and with sufficient skill to make the principles and relations clear?

21. Did the teacher show scholarship in the subject and genuine enthusiasm for it?

The extent to which these questions could be affirmatively answered would be an index of the efficiency of a class conference as part of a process of scientific training; and if every science teacher would keep them before him so that he might use them occasionally to estimate his success by self-examination at the end of a lesson, there would probably be a general and immediate improvement in science teaching.

The function of the laboratory. — When a botanist or zoölogist or geologist goes into the field he observes, measures, describes, and sketches, maps, or photographs those objects of his investigation which he cannot carry off with him to his laboratory. He takes with him only his pocket magnifying glass, his collecting kit, his field notebook, and a few other necessary instruments that are easily portable. When a chemist, metallurgist, or physicist goes to a mine or factory or power plant to make investigations and tests that must be made on the ground, he is often obliged to carry with him an outfit of instruments and testing materials and set up a temporary laboratory on the place; but, like the other sorts of scientists, whenever it is practicable he makes a field reconnaissance for observing conditions as they are, and carries the easily transportable objects of study to his laboratory.

The characteristic feature of the laboratory is the presence there of conveniences for observation and experimentation under specially arranged conditions, — in other words, of apparatus, machinery, and supplies of the special kinds that research experience has shown to be useful or necessary. The biologist has his dissecting tools, his microscope, and the materials and apparatus for making microscopic sections, slides, and photographs, and also the materials and appliances for the mounting and preserving of specimens for future study, reference, and comparison. The geologist and mineralogist have their microscopes, crushers, section grinders, and blowpipes; the chemists their glass and porcelain utensils, reagents, blast lamps, and balances; the physicists their special measuring and testing instruments of all sorts, such as balances, measuring scales, dynamometers, thermometers, barometers, electrical meters, photometers, and the like.

In addition to his apparatus, every working scientist has either in his laboratory or somewhere near and conveniently at hand, such books of reference, treatises, maps, charts, models, and classified specimens as are necessary for comparing the unknown with the known, and for finding the place of new facts in the scientific systems where they belong.

The laboratory therefore is the place where the scientist does his experimenting, measuring, and testing in order to find out those facts of his problems that he cannot find out elsewhere, or at least not so conveniently. He never works in his laboratory simply for the sake of " doing laboratory work," but always for the definite purpose of finding out some particular fact or relation that is necessary to be known in the process of testing out a hypothesis or solving a problem of pure or applied science.

The laboratory in teaching. — Thoughtful consideration of this relation between the professional scientist and his field and laboratory work ought to indicate clearly to the teacher what should be the relation between the pupil and the school laboratory. It ought to be evident that from his point of view the student should go there not to " do stunts," " perform experiments," " verify laws," fix principles in " the memory," get mental discipline, gain " power," or even to " get a concrete basis for appreciating the principles set forth in the textbook." In an ideally arranged course of science study he would go to the laboratory just as the scientist does, — *to find out at first hand by special appropriate observations and experiments certain essential facts of observation which he needs in the methodical investigation of a scientific problem, and which he cannot so conveniently or effectually find out elsewhere.* He may not be expected to discover there things that are new to the world, but the teacher's methods should be so planned and carried out that *he will find out things that are new to him* and in a way that will make them much more real and personal possessions than ever they could be if he merely had read them out of a textbook or heard them from the lips of the teacher.

In the ideal school laboratory, then, the students will observe, experiment, measure, consult and study reference books, maps, charts, or labeled and classified specimens in order to get first-hand information from nature, and to supplement it from the store of classified and organized knowledge which science has placed at his disposal. He will make in his notebook systematic notes, diagrams, sketches, tabulated measurements, and preparations of various sorts which express the facts that he has observed and compiled. All these things he will do, not as perfunctory tasks, but as parts of a methodical process of getting the answer to what for him is a practical or intellectual problem of a scientific sort. He differs from the scientist in that he is immature, his knowledge and scientific skill are limited, and he is not trained, *but being trained.* He has not reached the goal of his training, which is ability to think and investigate independently, but he is on the way.

This does not mean that every pupil can become a producer of scientific research work. Perhaps one in a thousand may; but the remaining nine hundred and ninety-nine should have as good and as thorough training in systematic thinking and procedure as the school can give them.

If they have also gained the conscious ideals of using methodical procedure and careful thinking that have been emphasized as a highly important part of scientific training, they may perhaps carry over this training into such problems of practical life as they are called upon to solve, and apply it successfully. Certainly they are less likely to do so if the important matters that have been mentioned are neglected.

Methods of laboratory teaching. — Hence the function of the teacher and the proper methods of laboratory instruction are clearly indicated. The teacher is the leader, inspirer, and guide. He passes from table to table, asking a question here, making a suggestion there, showing, by actually doing it, a fine bit of technique at one time, suggesting better form and expression for notes at another. Occasionally he calls the attention of the entire class to an important or peculiarly interesting phenomenon, a special point of theory or technique, a particularly meritorious bit of work by some student, or a mistake of one against which all need especially to guard.

In the laboratory as well as in the classroom the good teacher avoids too much telling, and often answers one question by asking another, or by directing the student to a reference book or map or museum specimen where he can get the required information for himself. He cites a principle to apply oftener than he tells or shows a pupil exactly what to do. He makes every individual stand on his own feet in observing, thinking, and experimenting so far as that individual is capable of doing so. By studying the pupils and the work, he knows when he should help a student and when he should allow him to blunder in order to find out how not to blunder again in a similar way. A common fault of teachers is either to give too much help or too little. Those who know their subjects well usually give too much help, and those who have imperfect command of the subject are likely to go to the other extreme.   Too many teachers know so little about their subjects that they don't see much in them to tell.

The wise teacher will make much of every good idea or piece of work from the pupils, and will be very sparing of faultfinding.   He will insist that every pupil complete the work that is assigned to him with as much thoroughness and excellence as he is capable of reaching in a reasonable amount of time.   The student who does faulty or careless work should not be punished or drastically criticized, but rather he should be required to repeat the work and do better.   The writer during a long teaching experience has never had the slightest difficulty in getting pupils of their own desire to repeat work that failed to meet his approval.   He never has found it difficult to get pupils to set up an ideal of good work which their own interest compelled them to make all reasonable effort to meet.

In this connection the teacher should remember that there are in every class wide individual differences in ability, and that the pupils of less than medium ability in any specific kind of activity may not be expected to produce a result equal in quality to the product of those whose inborn abilities or previous training have placed them above the average.   The ideal should be not " each as well as every other," but " each to the best of his ability."

It should not be necessary to caution the teacher that on the one hand a pupil who is naturally dull or slow should never be discouraged by having that fact impressed upon him, and on the other hand a pupil who has unusual ability should be made to recognize it and to realize that " To whom much is given, of him much shall be required."   Not only should better work be required of such pupils, but also extra work of a more difficult kind should always be available for them to do when they have finished the required work, and they should be stimulated to grapple with it.

Usually at the beginning of the period, or occasionally

during or at the end of it, the teacher will supplement the laboratory directions or the textbook by calling the attention of the entire class to matters that need fuller explanation, or by precipitating a conference or discussion on some hypothesis that needs particular development or on some facts that need to be generalized or associated with life situations outside the schoolroom. Occasionally he will show and briefly discuss, or have discussed, a lantern slide, picture, map, chart, model, specimen, piece of apparatus, or experimental demonstration which has an essential or interesting bearing on the problem in hand.

Efficient laboratory management demands that apparatus and materials be so methodically cared for and stored that the pupils may have them ready at hand at the beginning of the period, and a minimum of time be consumed in preparing to begin work.

When the materials are of such a nature that this is practicable they should be kept, methodically arranged, in drawers, lockers, or cases from which the students themselves can get them quickly, and to which they can quickly return them when they have finished their work. This is possible even with much of the apparatus used in physics; but in this subject some of the apparatus involves complications in setting up and arranging that would entail too much loss of time if it were not conveniently placed on the tables.

Student assistance. — Before the beginning of the period, in the time-consuming work of caring for, repairing, getting out, and replacing apparatus, the teacher should get as much help as is practicable from students. They will usually give it willingly if they are assigned to it in relays so that no one pupil has a burdensome amount to do.

It is a well-known fact that some boys will freely give large amounts of time to the making, repairing, or care of apparatus, and often gain much for themselves in pleasure and profit thereby, besides helping the class and teacher. This is true

K

of some boys who are especially poor in the abstract portions
of the class work.   The writer has often been successful in
getting such boys to do better class work, by enlisting their
help in this way and in experiments made before the class.
Such boys are usually conscious of their deficiencies in abstract
work and are secretly more or less humiliated in consequence.
If thus given an opportunity to express themselves through
their constructive and manipulative abilities, especially if
the teacher makes some unostentatious public expression of
appreciation for the value of their abilities and services, these
" practical minded " boys often gain confidence in their
abilities and are encouraged to see the value of the more
abstract work, and make greater efforts to master it.   *Success and a consciousness of growing power are the sharpest
spurs to further effort.*

Characteristics of a good laboratory exercise. — Much
time is wasted on laboratory exercises which have little significance to the pupils, because they have no easily perceptible
relation to the classroom problems and principles or to the
activities of the community.   Such for example are the formal experiments common in physics courses on the measurement of lengths, areas, and volumes, the determinations of
tensile strength and elasticity of wires, elastic and inelastic
collision, coefficients of expansion of metals when the amount
of expansion measured is less than a millimeter, electrical
resistance of wires, and specific resistances, when not needed
as information requisite to the solution of a practical problem.
So also are experiments given in chemistry to illustrate physical and chemical change, some of the more formal exercises
with topographic maps given in geography, and a good deal
of the drawing done in botany, physiology, and zoölogy.
Much of such work that is being done in the name of laboratory study is almost worthless.   The listless and unenthu-
siastic attitude of the students toward it should open the eyes
of the teachers to this and lead them to abandon such deaden-

ing work. Many teachers say that they require this kind of work from their pupils because the colleges demand it. This is not true. *Probably there is not a college anywhere in this country that would refuse to admit a student who is well grounded in the elementary principles of the science and who presents a good laboratory course in which such material is replaced by more significant kinds of laboratory work.* If there is such a one, the high school teachers and principals may conscientiously advise their students to go elsewhere.

The following criteria will be useful guides in the selection of laboratory lessons.

1. A project for the laboratory should provide the means of answering some question or questions that constitute essential steps in the solution of some problem that is significant to the students.

2. It should have some direct and clear connection with what immediately precedes and follows it in the course.

3. It should be one that compels careful observation, discrimination, and reflection, and that affords some opportunity for the development of skill and self-reliance in "putting questions up to Nature."

4. There should not be so many things to observe or do that mental confusion will result.

5. It should be so easy of manipulation that the poorest qualified of the students can do the work with fair success and reasonable speed.

6. It must be capable of being done by the students with a respectable degree of accuracy; and such reasonable accuracy should be insisted on, else the students will have no faith in it nor in what it is intended to teach.

7. Wherever practicable the parts of the experiments should be so arranged that the results obtained in them will check one another, thus enabling the students to judge their accuracy by the agreement among the results

themselves instead of by comparison with the results given in the books.

8. The reasoning involved in reaching the conclusions must be simple and direct enough to be made by the students themselves with but very little assistance.

9. It must involve no more operations than the average worker can finish without hurry and confusion in the laboratory period. If the period be but forty-five minutes long, the operations can, in some cases, be divided between two periods; in other cases the operations may be divided among the individuals of small groups of students and the results collated for each group and compared in the classroom.

Number of laboratory exercises per year. — There ought to be a sufficient number of these experiments so that when supplemented by those made at the demonstration table the main outlines of the subject as presented shall rest back on them or on principles that can be shown to rest back on experiments and observations of a similar kind. The minimum amount of laboratory work for each of the sciences according to prevailing ideals and standards is such as will require from thirty to thirty-five double periods a year.

Size of laboratory divisions. — There is a very general agreement among leading science teachers that for the best work there should not be more than twenty pupils in a laboratory division. Exceptionally able teachers successfully handle as many as thirty, but the latter number is considered the upper limit according to accepted standards of administration, for both recitation and laboratory sections.

Double periods. — In physics and in chemistry the double laboratory period has come to be considered as an essential feature. Though perhaps not so necessary it is also very desirable in the other science subjects. Nearly as much actual work can be done in a continuous period of ninety minutes as in three separate periods of forty-five minutes each. In many schools two double periods are given each week, throughout the year, to laboratory work, and three single periods to classroom work. In the opinion of the writer this is a larger proportion of the time than most teachers can profitably use for laboratory work, and the practice results in many cases in neglecting to have principles and applications thoroughly threshed out in class conferences and quizzes. Until the teaching becomes much better than it is now usually found to be, probably better results would be reached by having four single periods and one double laboratory period per week for each science.

Form of Notes. — The notes made by the student on his experiments should contain (*a*) a full and clear, but concise, statement of the problem that is to be solved or the question that is to be answered by the experiment, (*b*) a brief description of the apparatus and materials used, (*c*) an explanation of the methods of procedure, (*d*) a clearly tabulated statement of numerical data and results, (*e*) all the calculations that were used in obtaining the results, (*f*) the conclusions that were reached, (*g*) a brief discussion of such sources of error as are profitable for the student to consider. The students should be required to express themselves by drawings and graphs wherever such modes of description are obviously of service, but care should be taken that they do not get the idea that drawings and graphs are ends instead of means. The teacher should use good judgment as to the amount of time that a student should spend in drawing. Much time is often wasted in useless embellishment of notebooks. *Students should never be allowed to copy drawings from books. All drawings should be made from the objects themselves that are to be represented; and they should show clearly the particular features that are significant in the problem. Ordinarily a sectional diagram showing only the significant features is preferable to a perspective drawing.* Set forms for notes, containing blanks for the student to fill, are often found in laboratory manuals and direction sheets. These are ingenious devices for saving the teachers' and students' time, but they deprive the latter of the training that they ought to get in devising their own forms and arrangements, and in many cases also effectively prevent them from thinking. They are thus of doubtful value, if not positively pernicious. Notes of the best sort tell a straightforward story in the student's own language about what he wanted to find out, how he went about it, the steps by means of which he reached his answer, and what the answer was.

Laboratory notebooks. — The most generally convenient book for laboratory records is the letter-size loose-leaf type. This form of book enables the student to keep the notes used in all his different school subjects within a single cover, and is by far the most economical, since one cover only is needed for all subjects, and no paper or covers need be wasted.

The best form of cover is that with inside rings which spring open or shut by a single movement of the two hands.[1] A plain black linen binding is good, but canvas or buckram is more durable, and with reasonable care will last two years.

Paper of all grades, rulings, and sizes, punched ready for insertion, can be bought by the pound, with or without the covers, from any large dealers in paper or school supplies. The most convenient paper for general purposes is one that will take either ink or pencil marks and is " quadrille " ruled in squares of half a centimeter on a side. When written notes are made on these sheets, only the alternate lines should be used.

The quadrille sheets are alike convenient for writing ordinary paragraphs, making indented summaries and outlines, tabulating numerical results, making outline diagrams, and plotting graphs. For freehand drawings in biology and for

---

[1] One of the best of this type is known in the trade as the I. P. Number 6 (Irving & Pitt Co., Kansas City, Mo.).

some sketches and drawings in geography, unruled paper is, perhaps, preferable.

All the sheets should have a red ink margin at right and left and a double ruling to set off the heading at the top. One inch is a good width for the top and inner margins, and a half to three quarters inch for the outer margin.

For plotting graphs in physics many teachers prefer engineer's cross-section paper.

When the notes are to be handed in to the teacher, they may be taken out of the binder and placed, unfolded, in a stout manila envelope bearing the pupil's name and division.

Pupils usually want to make what they are pleased to call rough notes in a " scratch book," or worse still on loose paper, and to copy these into the permanent record at some later time outside the laboratory. This practice should not be permitted, as it makes for carelessness, loss of valuable data, and inefficient habits; and it wastes time. The teacher should insist that the pupil plan his notes before beginning the work, and make the permanent entries neatly and systematically at the time when the observations are made. *All notes that belong directly to the laboratory work should be made in the laboratory at the time when the work is done; and the sheets on which they are made should not be taken from the laboratory until they have been inspected, checked, and released by the teacher.*

Examination of notes. — Much time and trouble will be saved in connection with the examination of notes by the teacher and their correction by the students if the teacher can manage to examine them promptly and insist that the students make all required corrections with similar promptness.

With regard to the kind of notes to be made by the pupils, and the amount of time and care to be expended by the teacher in examining them, two principles should be kept in view : —

1. The notes should be made as a part of the process of

scientific problem solving, and should therefore be written up in the spirit of the scientific method.

2. The writing up of the notes inevitably entails the formation of habits of note making; and these habits must be either good or faulty according to the kind of practice that the teacher by his methods permits or enforces.

If these principles be accepted, the obvious duty of the teacher is to enforce good practice and thus secure the good habits, so far as possible.   Thus, he should insist on legible handwriting, good arrangement, correct spelling and grammar, and a reasonable degree of clearness and conciseness; and he should see that the data furnish conclusive evidence that the work which they represent has been well and methodically done.

If the classes are large, he must use a system of letters — not too many, such as W for wrong, S for spelling, G for grammatical errors, R for repeat, etc.   These are best placed in the margin in red ink, opposite the line where the mistake is.   The pupil should find and correct the mistake, bring the book to the instructor, and show him the correction.   The instructor may then check the marginal mark off with his initials or any chosen sign.   The check marks and also the mark of final approval can be most conveniently and quickly made with a rubber stamp.   If each exercise is graded *before* correction, and if correction is required to hold the grade, the pupils will be more careful not to make mistakes.

All this is grueling work for the teacher, but there is no escape from it if the pupils are to be properly trained.   The better the teacher is at inspiring his pupils with ideals of efficiency, the less arduous his work with the notebooks will be.

QUESTIONS FOR FURTHER STUDY

1. Make a list of the reasons why a class conference is better than a question and answer recitation for realizing the educational values of science study.

2. Which of the twenty-one standards of good class work enumerated in this chapter are easiest to apply? List them in the order of their practicability.

3. List these standards (Question 2) in the order of their pedagogical importance.

4. Select a list of laboratory exercises from some science textbook, and check those which can best be used so that the laboratory will perform the function indicated in this chapter.

5. In your school study of science were you ever called on to assist the teacher in experimenting? If so, how did this affect your attitude toward the work?

6. In a list of laboratory exercises from a current science book, select five that have in large measure the characteristics of a good laboratory exercise, as described in this chapter. Give reasons for your choice.

REFERENCES

ARMSTRONG, HENRY EDWARD. The Teaching of the Scientific Method. Macmillan, N. Y. 1910. 504 pp. $1.75.

BAGLEY, W. C. The Educative Process. Macmillan, N. Y. 1908. 358 pp. $1.25.

CHARTERS, W. W. Methods of Teaching. Row, Peterson & Co. Chicago, 1909. 255 pp. $1.10.

DODGE, R. E., and KIRCHWEY, C. B. The Teaching of Geography in Normal and Secondary Schools. Teachers College, Columbia Univ., N. Y. 1914. 30¢.

DODGE, R. E., and KIRCHWEY, C. B. The Teaching of Geography in Elementary Schools. Rand, McNally & Co. 1913. vii + 248 pp. $1.00.

ELIOT, C. W. Laboratory Teaching. School Science and Mathematics, vol. 6, November, 1906.

FITCH, J. G. Lectures on Teaching. Barnes, N. Y. 1891. 393 pp. $1.25.

GANONG, WILLIAM FRANCIS. The Teaching Botanist. Macmillan, N. Y. 1910. 439 pp. $1.25.

HODSON, FREDERICK. Broad Lines in Science Teaching. Macmillan, N. Y. 1910. 268 pp. $1.50.

LLOYD, FRANCIS E., and BIGELOW, MAURICE A. The Teaching of Biology. Longmans, N. Y. 1907. 491 pp. $1.50.

MANN, C. R. The Teaching of Physics. Macmillan, N. Y. 1912. 304 pp. $1.25.

School Science and Mathematics. Chicago, 2059 E. 72d Place. This journal contains many articles on all phases of science teaching written by experienced teachers. See indices of the various volumes.

SMITH, ALEXANDER, and HALL, EDWIN H. The Teaching of Chemistry and Physics. Longmans, N. Y. 1913. 377 pp. $1.50.

STRAYER, G. D. A Brief Course in the Teaching Process. Macmillan, N. Y. 1912. 315 pp. $1.25.

SUTHERLAND, W. J. The Teaching of Geography. Scott, Foresman & Co., Chicago. 1909. 312 pp. $1.25.

THORNDIKE, E. L. The Principles of Teaching. A. G. Seiler, N. Y. 1906. 12 + 293 pp. $1.25.

TYLER, JOHN M. The Culture of Imagination in the Study of Science. School Review, Vol. 6, pp. 716–724. December, 1898.

WELCH, W. H. The Evolution of Modern Scientific Laboratories. Smithsonian Report. 1895. Smithsonian Institution, Washington, D. C. pp. 493–504.

CHAPTER IX

Functions of the lecture-demonstration. — The ideals of science teaching that we have set up, are (1) that both scientific training and scientific information are best gained by the pupils through constant practice in the solving of problems that involve the content and method of the science to be taught, and (2) that the pupils can receive this training and gain the discipline which is especially characteristic of science only when they solve the problems themselves as far as possible through their own thought and activity. In view of these ideals the inference is obvious that the laboratory and the class conference are the most important means of instruction, and that the lecture method should be resorted to rather infrequently, and only with careful thought, planning, and preparation.

There are, however, two very important functions that the lecture demonstration may serve.

1. When any of the sciences is presented as a series of problems after the manner that has been described, there are gaps to be filled and information to be supplied in order that the subject may be adequately covered as a whole, in its broader outlines, so that unity and coherence of presentation may be preserved. Such information may be effectively presented by informal talks or lectures.

2. Accounts of new discoveries, classic experiments and researches, scientific information of local interest,

or of interest in connection with current events, may be presented occasionally by lecture and demonstration as a scientific treat for purposes of inspiration and motivation.

The technique of the lecture-demonstration. — These two functions of the lecture have already been discussed at length on pages 96 and 97 ; and but little need be added here.   A few hints, however, may be serviceable to those readers who are inexperienced in this mode of presentation.

1. There should be an abundance of concrete material for illustration, such as pictures, maps, models, preparations, or experiments.

2. There may be several experiments or preparations to illustrate or suggest one idea; but the same preparation should never be used to illustrate more than one idea at a given time.

3. The preparations and experiments should be arranged on the lecture table or a near-by table or shelves, in the order in which they are to be shown, so that each may be ready for use at the instant when it is needed; and the teacher should assure himself positively, by sufficient rehearsals and practice, that his experiments are going to work successfully.[1]

4. The teacher should never be " tied to his notes." He should know what he wants to present, and how he purposes developing it, well enough so that he needs no manuscript.   It is not usually worth time and trouble to memorize the topical outline of the lecture: there are many advantages in having that plainly written on the blackboard, where all can see it.   If this is not

[1] Nothing more severely discredits a science teacher in the eyes of his pupils than to have it said that his experiments do not work.   What must they think of a teacher who reprimands them for failing in recitation, or being awkward in the laboratory, and who "flunks" himself when they ask him a question or when he tries to show them an experiment?

done the teacher's outline, unless he has it memorized, should be written and spaced so that he can easily read it at a glance without bending over it or picking it up.

5. The lecture very seldom or never should be formal. The students should always feel free to ask questions provided these are pertinent and of general interest, and to approach the lecture table and group themselves around it if any of the demonstrations are of such a nature that they cannot be well seen from the seats.

6. The lecture should be a model for the pupils in clearness, vividness, and good form in presentation. It is well to outline at the outset the mode of approach and plan of development, to proceed slowly when important principles and generalizations are being stated, and to summarize conclusions carefully and deliberately at the end.

7. In the opinion of the writer, complete notes on the lectures that are given for inspiration purposes should not be insisted on, but occasionally the students should be encouraged to take notes of salient facts and important ideas as a basis for an account of the lecture to be written up later. The making of such lecture reports will give the students practice in an important kind of English composition; and in some schools, such work is examined by the English department and credited as work in composition, with excellent results.[1]

---

[1] Such coöperation between the English department on the one hand and the science and other departments on the other hand ought to be carried on in every school in order to insure the formation of good habits of writing and speaking English. If eight or ten lectures are given in the course of a school year, and if in connection with them the pupils are gradually instructed in good methods of taking notes and writing up accounts of lectures, those of them who afterwards enter college will not be so incompetent and so much at a loss when they come under the instruction of college teachers who still rely mainly on the lecture method. Even after it comes to be generally realized that the lecture method as a principal means of instruction is an inefficient survival from the times when books were scarce and printing unknown, the ability to take

8. The best way for the teacher to perfect his technique in oral instruction is to grasp every opportunity for hearing inspiring and lucid lecturers, and to take note of their methods of developing their subjects. He should by no means neglect reading the classic popular lectures and addresses of such masters of the lecturer's art as Tyndall, Helmholtz, Faraday, Lodge, Agassiz, Darwin, Huxley, Josiah P. Cooke, Ruskin, and many others, some of whose works should be found in every good library.

9. When the teacher is preparing a series of experiments to be made at the demonstration table in connection with either a lecture or a class conference he will miss valuable opportunities for intimate acquaintance with his students, and many chances to interest and instruct them, as well as much valuable help, if he does not enlist some of the students in the work of setting up and trying out the experiments. It is a splendid plan also to let individual students prepare and make some of the demonstrations before the class, and present the ideas that are to grow out of them. They may be asked to do this as a part of their assigned work or as volunteer work for extra credits.

10. In all demonstration and lecture work the aim should be, not amusement or pyrotechnics, but a clear and lucid presentation of the phenomena and their significant and human relations. Without arousing interest the teacher can accomplish little that is really worth while; *but fortunately natural phenomena are themselves*

notes and make abstracts of lectures or other oral communications will still be useful and worth some training. The lecture will always have its place both in colleges and outside of them; and there will always be a few specially gifted and inspiring lecturers who can on numerous occasions teach more effectively by the lecture method than by other means. Moreover there will always be occasions in the lives of many people when they need to take notes of instructions or bodies of information that are orally delivered.

intrinsically interesting to almost everybody if their meanings, interpretations, and relations to everyday life are made perfectly understandable, and if the learner is left with some of the thinking to do for himself.

Field observation. — The field excursion was first advocated as a means of instruction by Rousseau in the *Émile* [1] (1762), and first used in class teaching by Pestalozzi in his school at Yverdun in Switzerland, in the first decade of the nineteenth century.[2] It was soon introduced into Germany along with the Pestalozzian methods, and is now in general use in that country as well as in Switzerland and France. In this country, although it has been advocated with great unanimity by the highest authorities, and is regarded by them as indispensable in the study of geography at least, and as highly important in botany, zoölogy, and nature study, it has not as yet come into very general use.

Obstacles, and how to overcome them. — The principal causes for neglect of this important feature of science instruction are inertia or incompetence of teachers, failure on the part of teachers or their superiors to appreciate its importance, objections of parents, difficulties in providing time for the excursions in the school program, and difficulties in reaching the places where the observations are to be made. If the teacher through lack of interest and enthusiasm is unwilling to undertake the work, or if he is not competent to manage it, the principal or other authority who selects and controls him is at fault and should apply appropriate stimuli or replace him by one who is more enterprising or better trained and more able. If the teacher is enthusiastic, and realizes the importance of the work, and if he is competent to carry it on successfully he will surely find ways to overcome all the

[1] Cf. the first half of Book III for many suggestive ideas, that are worthy of critical study.

[2] See Holman, *Pestalozzi, an Account of his Life and Work*, Longmans, 1908. Every teacher of geography should read the account, p. 230 ff.

other difficulties to such a degree as to have a large majority
of his pupils participate in at least four or five field excursions
during the school year. By tact and perseverance he can
overcome the lack of appreciation of the parents or of his
superiors, find ways to suggest to the principal for managing
the difficulties of the program, or succeed in enlisting the
pupils in after-school or Saturday excursions. In small
towns and villages the difficulty of reaching places for field
observation and collection in connection with geography
and biology does not exist; and there is no trouble in gaining
admission to such small local factories, machine shops, plan-
ing mills, potteries, brickyards, water supply stations, telephone exchanges, electric lighting stations, bakeries, printing
offices, and the like as may exist in the locality, and in
which interesting and important applications of the principles
of physics and chemistry are to be found. In these localities
fields, woods, streams, farms, gardens, road or railroad cuts,
plains, or hills are always to be found within easy walking
distance; often weathering and erosion are going on at the
roadside or in a vacant lot within a stone's throw of the school
yard gate; plant and animal life are daily appealing mutely
to the attention of the pupils on their way to and from school.
It is true that large and spectacular factories and industrial
installations are not often located near village and township
high schools, but there is little excuse for not making the
pupils familiar with such local industries as do exist there.
The writer has visited many schools that stood in the very
midst of a rich variety of forms resulting from glacial and
stream processes, and on inquiring of the teachers as to the
kind and amount of field work that was done, has been told
either that there was no time for such work, or that there was
nothing of interest in the locality to be seen. Nothing but
textbook work was being done. The obvious reason was,
of course, that the teachers were incompetent to handle the
subject.

In many large cities the difficulties are real. Incompetent teachers and unprogressive administrative officials are less often found; but excursions usually involve long street car rides. Many students come from families where every extra car fare represents a sacrifice, and the long rides consume much valuable time. Nevertheless most of these students can earn, individually, the fifty cents to one dollar a year that is necessary for five or ten excursions; or the money for the class can be raised by an entertainment given by the school. Some of the pupils have music lessons or must work on Saturdays or after school, and such pupils must be excused from all or part of the field work; but these really constitute a rather small percentage of the whole, and the majority ought not to be deprived of field opportunities because this small minority cannot have them. If the city teacher has eyes that see he will often find field opportunities near the school and will at least use those which are available. Parks, gardens, hothouses, vacant lots, and neighboring factories afford opportunities within reach, and in most cities the open country or more distant factories can be reached in half-day excursions on Saturdays. There is sometimes a great deal of difficulty in getting into large manufacturing plants with pupils, but if the teacher or principal has influential acquaintances,—as he is likely to have through church relations, scientific clubs, or other civic and social organizations, some one or two of which he should connect himself with as a man and a citizen,— he will usually be able to get the desired permission through their influence.

In spite of all the difficulties, therefore, it ought, in any school, to be possible to have in every subject some field observation in which a considerable portion of the class can participate. In small schools where the localities are near at hand it ought to be possible to make short excursions during the double laboratory periods in regular school hours and to make longer ones if the laboratory or class periods

L

come last in the session. In such cases the attendance of
all should be required.

How to conduct excursions. — In this connection, the following suggestions growing out of the experience of the writer
and others who have handled large bodies of pupils in such
excursions will prove to be useful.

1. The maximum number of pupils that can be
conveniently handled by one teacher is ordinarily from
twenty-five to thirty-five. Exceptionally resourceful
teachers can handle a larger number and keep them at
the work, but inexperienced teachers would better
begin with groups of twenty or less.

2. The teacher should first make himself thoroughly
acquainted with the ground to be visited, with the route
and means of transportation, and with the special objects to be observed and studied.

3. The observations should be directed to specific
features or phenomena that are factors in some problem
or problems that have been set up in the classroom for
solution.

4. The field lesson should be carefully outlined in a
lesson plan that has been checked up by the teacher on
the ground, and the plan should be adhered to while
the class is in the field.

5. Mimeographed sheets should be provided beforehand containing questions to be answered from observation and reflection. They should also contain needed
directions, hints, or suggestions for making effective
observations, for recording results, and for collecting
specimens for individual or school cabinets. It would
be better to have these in the hands of the students a
day or two before the excursion is made. These sheets
are to perform the same function for the field work that
the laboratory manual performs for the laboratory work.

6. The field work should be explained and the field problems outlined in the classroom on the day before the excursion. The teacher should carefully refrain from answering questions that the pupils can answer for themselves as a result of the field study; but he should make sure that the students understand exactly what they are to look for and to do, exactly what rules of order and discipline they are expected to conform to, and exactly what is the nature of the problems that they are expected to solve in the field. If they are to make collections, they should be told exactly what kinds of samples and specimens they are expected to get and how they are to care for them.

7. On the way to and from the objective points the pupils may be allowed to enjoy the occasion socially in any way that is right and proper — the more they enjoy it the better; but when on the ground and while the work of observation, study, and note-taking is going on every one should be made to refrain from irrelevant social converse and attend strictly to business just as he would be required to do in the laboratory. They should be urged to control and direct themselves to the end that they get as much knowledge as possible out of the lesson, but when individuals fail in doing so the teacher *must* direct and control them. No one should be allowed to turn an opportunity for serious and profitable study into a riotous picnic. Sympathy for youthful instincts, good nature, a sense of humor, resourcefulness, and firmness are needed by the teacher to keep successful control on such occasions. These are qualities of personality that are indispensable in any kind of school work, and the person who does not possess them would better not try to teach at all.

8. When the classes are large, including several divisions, as in the great city high schools, careful organ-

ization is necessary. One teacher should be present for every group of from fifteen to twenty-five pupils; and each teacher should " know his sheep," be known by them, and be responsible for them. In such cases the teachers of the different sciences must coöperate and exchange assistance. Often teachers of other branches may enjoy " going along " and helping. It is a good plan also to organize the groups into teams with a student captain for each team, and get up a rivalry between teams as to which shall make the best score of facts and ideas. This plan will tend to hold the pupils in definite units which can be easily handled in the field. The different teams might each have a distinctive badge or colors and adopt as a name the name of some scientific discoverer. Since one of the most serious difficulties in field work management is that of the teacher in making himself heard by many or scattered pupils out of doors, it would be well for all the teachers to have bicycle whistles or horns, by means of which they can signal their pupils to come together for instruction. Occasionally the teacher who is leading the excursion will need to communicate with the whole class at one time or with groups at some distance, and for this purpose it would be well to provide a megaphone.

In the case of some especially bright, interested, and capable students, individual field work and collection should be encouraged; and such students should be given opportunity in the classroom to explain their work and exhibit their collections. This will add to the general interest and enthusiasm for such work, and will be especially good for the students who do it. It will be a pleasure to the teacher to invite such students to accompany him on his preliminary trips and it may often happen that he will get valuable information and assistance from them. The writer has found this practice to be of immense mutual profit to himself and many of his students, and has had abundant personal testimony from others to the same effect.

9. At the next class meeting after the excursion the problems, the observations, and their bearings on the solutions of the problems should be thoroughly discussed, and the information and conclusions should be organized; so that when the discussion has been concluded some definite things have been learned, and some tentative or final conclusions of a perfectly definite nature have been reached.

Reviews. — The great emphasis that has been placed upon the problem method in the preceding pages should not lead the reader to think that it is all-sufficient. This is far from the case. A working knowledge of the content of the subject is a necessary part of the ability which the successful study of any science ought to impart; and although it is claimed that both understanding of the concepts and principles of a science and the ability to recall them when needed are best acquired through solving significant problems, it should be clearly understood that knowledge once acquired is usually forgotten in large part, unless occasions for its recall occur at intervals, in order that the part that has been wholly or partly forgotten may be relearned. The purpose of the review, then, is to strengthen the association bonds that should be made permanent but which as yet are weak. Both pedagogical experience and the few experimental studies of memorizing and forgetting that have been made indicate that it is more economical to review or relearn frequently at first and then at greater and greater intervals than it is to try by many repetitions to fix the memory bonds permanently during the first learning period. Hence, the time-honored practice of reviewing in each lesson the most important facts and generalizations that were gained in the preceding lesson, and of providing at suitable intervals for the recall, and if necessary for the relearning, of that which is most likely to be forgotten, is fully justified. So far as our present knowledge of learning and forgetting goes, it confirms the very general opinion of successful teachers that frequent reviews are necessary.

The custom of conducting carefully planned formal reviews at the end of each week, each month, and each term, and at the end of the year, should be adhered to. The intervals need not be exactly those mentioned, but may preferably be adjusted to the minor and major logical divisions of the subject matter. Efficiency requires that we spend no time unnecessarily on that which is most easily and permanently remembered, or on formally reviewing that which is bound to be recalled anyway at sufficiently frequent intervals in consequence of being needed as bases for conclusions to be reached in later lessons. It requires us, rather, to select carefully that which most needs to be relearned; and to drill on that at intervals of increasing length until it is correctly recalled when required.

Functions of the review lesson. — Hence, the review lesson has two obvious functions: (1) *to find out what things have been wholly or partly forgotten and need to be relearned;* and (2) *to provide situations that will cause the students to relearn them.* Many teachers fail to plan their reviews with sufficient attention to these functions. A very common and very inefficient method is to hold a question and answer recitation in which nearly every detail of the lessons to be reviewed is called for in the order in which it was previously presented. This method results in a formal and uninteresting exercise which does comparatively little toward accomplishing the purposes mentioned. Interest is of capital importance in reviews as in all learning. If the act of recall gives satisfaction, the recall is likely to occur again; if it is accompanied by indifference or discomfort, the response is likely to be forgotten or replaced by some other response that brings more satisfaction or less discomfort. Several ways of making reviews interesting and profitable are here described.

The topical review recitation. — The importance of organizing the information gained through class conferences, laboratory lessons, and class demonstrations, and formulating it into a system has been thoroughly explained. Outlines and summaries of definitions and principles are concise expressions of such formulation, and it has been stated that these should be made at intervals similar to those mentioned as suitable for reviews. Systematizing and reviewing, then, should go on together. Let the pupils prepare for the topical review by making somewhat full and detailed outlines of the work of the past week, more general and less detailed outlines of the ground covered during the past month, and still more general summaries of the most important principles, laws, and definitions from the beginning of the year's work. Let them compare these, and discuss and improve them in conference. Then let them make rapid topical recitations, not always on the outlines just discussed, but usually on those that were presented and discussed in the last preceding review. Let the teacher direct one pupil to write on the blackboard an outline of the topics of the review, and fill in the more important details of one of the topics; and a little later on, after he has finished writing, let the teacher quiz him on some of the details, applications, or associated facts, principles, and concepts of that topic. While the first student is writing, have other pupils develop the important details of other topics that the first pupil has written or failed to write in his outline, and be cross-examined in the manner just suggested. Also have it understood that their fellow pupils are to ask questions and to challenge them to prove their statements. The more fully the pupils themselves are induced to enter into the spirit of this kind of quizzing the more interesting and vitalizing it will be. It ought to be possible to make this feature a contest of wits and to get into it much of the zest of a competitive game. The pupils may be encouraged to cross-question by giving each a score for every pertinent question that he asks, and if necessary scoring a penalty for each failure to ask a question or for each irrelevant question or quibble. When a student is making a topical recitation it is well to have him come out to the front and stand facing the class.

Types of topical organization. — The motive used in the organization of the review outline may be varied in several interesting ways. The usual textbook or treatise motive is that of organizing facts, laws, and concepts under some general principles or classes. For example, in physics the laws of machines and their applications are best organized under the work principle, the facts about fluids under the principle of Pascal and that of Archimedes, and so on; in chemistry the compounds of an element are usually described under that element; in physical geography, mountains, plains, plateaus, lakes, rivers, shore lines, etc., are usually the main rubrics under which the land forms and the facts and forces related to them are described; and in botany or zoölogy the various plants and animals are described with relation to the families or great groups, or with relation to anatomical structure or physiological processes. These traditional textbook and treatise methods of organization are not the only logical ones; and it is important that the pupils as well as the teacher should know this. Furthermore, variety in organization tends to make the subject more interesting, more suggestive in developing ability to judge and interpret, and more effective in recall, because of the greater number of association bonds by means of which a given fact or principle can be " fished up." [1]   In addition to reviewing the subject matter

---

[1] Cf. Thorndike, *The Psychology of Learning*, Teachers College, Columbia Univ., N. Y., 1913, Chapters I and X, and his *Principles of Teaching*, A. G. Seiler, N. Y., 1906, Chapter VIII.   Also James, *Principles of Psychology*, Henry Holt & Co., N. Y., 1890, Vol. 1, Chapters XIV and XVI.

under the usual headings, it may be reviewed in chronological order in connection with the discoverers and their work, or in connection with its most important economic and social uses in the home, local factory, municipal projects, and the like; or again in the case of physics or chemistry it may be reviewed by means of a series of numerical problems which demand the use of the various principles. Varying the motive in this way will tend to stimulate the interest of the pupils in perfecting their memory bonds so as to have the required knowledge at ready command.

For example, suppose that in physics the laws and properties of electric currents are reviewed, now under the headings, Sources (voltaic cells, thermoelectric cells, storage batteries, induction coils, magnetos, dynamos), Laws of Flow (difference of potential, laws of resistance, Ohm's law, laws of induced currents, laws of electrolytic conduction), and Methods of Measurement (galvanometers, voltmeters, ammeters, wattmeters, Wheatstone's bridge); again in connection with the work of Galvani and Volta, Sturgeon, Faraday and Henry, Maxwell and Hertz, Edison, Tesla, Lodge, Branley, and Marconi; again, through detailed consideration of the applications of electrical energy in the household (door bell, telephone, electric lights, cooking, vacuum cleaner, tracing the energy back to the power house, and the appliances used there), and finally by means of a printed or mimeographed series of drill questions and problems. Would not such a system of reviews be entered into with much more interest and better results in the formation of permanent memory connections than usually come from the dull and uninteresting reviews that are so commonly held?

Written reviews. — If ingeniously devised, these are especially useful in enabling both teacher and pupils to find out which of the desired association bonds are weak and which are well established; and they have the very great advantage that they may be so made out as to be easily scored. For example, consider the following question, " What kind of simple mechanical device would be of most assistance in getting (*a*) a heavy barrel into a wagon, (*b*) ten bales of hay into a loft, (*c*) splitting a log, (*d*) pulling a ship up to its dock, (*e*) drawing a bucket up from a well, (*f*) pressing the juice from apples to make cider, (*g*) lifting a stone flag from the sidewalk, (*h*) weighing a turkey, (*i*) working the rudder of a large boat? " and so on. Here each answer consists of a single name and can be scored one point. The expected answers to more complex questions involving several different ideas or bits of informatiom can be analyzed for scoring purposes into their component parts, each part being scored separately one, or two or more points according to its relative importance. The parts and the number of points assigned to each being announced to the pupils, they may exchange and score each other's papers, and competition for scores can be incited. For example, the next question might be to state the physical law for each of the devices suggested in the preceding question, and each law correctly stated might be scored two points. Or again, the next question might be to describe the necessary arrangement in each case in order that the force applied should be only one tenth of the weight lifted or the resistance overcome, neglecting friction ; and here two or more facts or relations are involved in each answer, so that each of these would receive one or more points.

Another kind of review is easier to devise and score, and is very economical with regard to time, but must be used with great care and caution and be followed up whenever necessary by cross questioning, lest it become a mere parrot repetition on the part of the pupils. In other words, the teacher must make sure that the pupils have the ideas for which the words, phrases, or sentences of their verbal responses are the mere signs. This exercise consists in presenting to the pupils a long list of the class names of objects or ideas, and requiring them for each name to give an example, or a definition of it, or to describe the characteristic form, or color, or function, or economic use, or geographical location, or any other of its class or individual characteristics that may be important to fix in memory. In this case the name constitutes the stimulus furnished by the teacher; and the kind of written definition, description, or named characteristic that is indicated by the teacher and is written down by the pupil is the pupil's response. Conversely any one or more of the characteristics may be given as the stimulus, and the name or some other characteristic required as the response. Zest will be added to the exercise and stimulus given for better preparation by the pupils if they are given a longer list than they can complete in the time allowed. If all start and stop together on the same signals, their scores will represent their relative efficiencies in recalling the response ideas when the stimulus words or ideas are given. A generous rivalry with one another may thus be excited; and better still, each pupil may be incited to try to beat his previous records. This procedure corresponds roughly to the practice experiments in controlled association, and in naming paired associates, as made in psychological laboratories, and is very favorable to intense application and retention.

Association tests as reviews. — Among the many modifications of the " controlled association test " form of review exercise the following are given, merely as a means of suggesting others to the teacher. *S* stands for stimulus, *R* for response.

1. *S*. Name of class. *R*. (*a*) Names of individuals; (*b*) definition; (*c*) color, form, location, etc.

2. *S*. Name of law. *R*. (*a*) Statement of law; (*b*) applications of the law.

3. *S*. Name of particular object. *R*. (*a*) Name of class to which it belongs; (*b*) definition of the class.

4. *S*. Seeing the object. *R*. (*a*) Its name; (*b*) class; (*c*) naming other objects of same class.

5. *S.* Statement of a problem.   *R.* Giving the law or principle for its solution.

6. *S.* Statement of a fact.   *R.* Giving the law or principle that " explains " it.

7. *S.* Naming or stating a principle.   *R.* (*a*) Giving evidences that led to its acceptance; (*b*) giving cases that come under it; (*c*) stating the deductions from the principle that apply to the cases named.

Review Matches. — Another form of review that has often proved to be interesting and effective is that of choosing sides, as in the old-fashioned spelling match, and putting the questions alternately to the two sides.   A good way is to have the individuals of one side take the even numerals in order, and the other side the odd numerals, and then let the teacher put the questions to the pupils in the serial order of their numerals.   If a pupil fails on a question, it is passed to the next number, who is on the other side; and if he also fails on it, it returns to the next number, who is on the same side. If a question is correctly answered, the next question is given to the next pupil, who is on the other side.   The side that makes the highest score wins.   In the traditional spelling match any one who missed a word was " spelled down " and retired from the contest.   This practice should not often be followed in the review contests, as those who most need the review remain idle during the greater part of the time and those who least need it do nearly all of the work.   This kind of exercise is not adapted to topical reviews.   The material must be in the form of clear, brief questions, to which concise and direct answers can be given.   Most of the kinds suggested for written reviews are suitable for this purpose. Printed or mimeographed review questions on which the pupils have studied in direct preparation for the contest are perhaps the best.   In order to arouse greater interest and secure more effective study, sides should be chosen before preparation begins.

Oral Quizzes. — The conduct of a class conference in which a problem is being worked out necessarily involves a certain amount of quizzing or cross examination of pupils, both for the purpose of bringing out facts that they know more or less intimately, but do not think of at the time that these facts are needed, and for the purpose of making them test out and prove their statements. When skillfully used in these ways, the quiz serves to bring out significant facts into bold relief so that their part in the solution may become clear, and to elucidate obscure points and fortify conclusions. It compels the student to examine carefully the grounds for his opinions and test the logical correctness of his thought processes, so as to eliminate unwarranted assumptions, hasty inductions, and false steps in deduction. The teacher should ply the questions rapidly, but not so rapidly that the students cannot hold the pace. It requires some experience and skill on the part of the questioner to know just about how much time he should allow a pupil to reflect before giving his answer. If he is not given time enough to apprehend the meaning of the question, he may become discouraged and disgusted; and if he is given too much time, he loses the stimulation of the pressure, and his attention wanders from the subject. Only by practice can the teacher learn to judge in any case just how long he should wait before passing the question to a volunteer. In general much less harm comes from pushing the questions too rapidly than from giving them out too slowly. If the pupils are habitually subjected to rapid-fire questioning, they will soon form the habit of preparing to meet the fire and of keeping their wits up to the pace. On the other hand if they are given all the time that they will take, they soon fall into habits of mentally loitering instead of " stepping lively " and may never learn to control their thoughts for steady and rapid thinking.

When a pupil makes a hasty induction, he should be compelled at once to check it by a further consideration of observed facts and previously established theory. When he makes careless deductions, he should be thrown back upon himself in order to make him prove his steps.

In effect the quiz should be constructive, not destructive, positive, not negative. If badly conducted, it will discourage the pupils and destroy their confidence in their ability to form opinions of worth, so that impatience and abandonment of effort are likely to result. This seems to be true of girls rather more frequently than of boys. If skillfully and tactfully conducted, the quiz will leave the pupil possessed of stronger confidence in the uniformity of nature's laws and processes, and in his own ability to judge facts, draw inferences, and reach valid conclusions. Having gone successfully through the ordeal, or even having failed himself and seen another go successfully through it, he will come to feel that the grounds for his opinions have been critically examined, that the inadequate and fallacious ideas have been ruled out and that the conclusions now reached stand on firm and proved foundations. It is a good plan occasionally to allow a pupil to be quizzed by another, or by several in turn, under the guidance of the teacher.

In reviews, when the pupil's response is a word, a definition, a law, a principle, a name, etc., the purpose of the quiz or cross examination is to find out whether the concept, of which the word, sentence, or phrase is the sign, really is present in the pupil's mind and has an adequate and accurate content. A volley of questions suitable in number and rapidity to the needs of the case should be aimed to develop any weaknesses that may exist in his concept and give him the chance to repair them.

Time and opportunity for the teacher. — No one acquainted with school work can doubt for a moment that the science teacher, if he plans and carries out his work day by day with some closeness of approximation to the thoroughness and detail of scientific organization and management that have been outlined in this chapter and the preceding one, will have enough to do. School authorities should understand that in order to secure satisfactory teaching of the sciences not only well-trained, competent, industrious, and enthusiastic men or women should be employed as teachers of these subjects, but also they should be given time and opportunity in the working hours for daily preparation, study, caring for, setting up, and making apparatus, and examining manuscripts and notebooks. *In a school that pretends to maintain a high grade of instruction no science teacher should be responsible for teaching more than an average of four classes per day of not more than thirty pupils per class.* If required to teach five classes, as is now common, the teacher cannot do the best kind of work for his pupils, and if he has to teach six classes or even more, as is very common in the smaller high schools, his work will be necessarily of a very poor grade, and his pupils will get the mere husks of the sciences that he tries to teach them. To give real scientific training under such circumstances is practically impossible. The time-worn district school notion that a teacher is not *working* unless he is "hearing a class" needs to be rooted out of our school systems, and the science teachers themselves should do what they can by tactful explanation and suggestion to educate the authorities above them on this point. Men and women whose ability and reputation are such that they are in a position to do so should refuse to accept engagements in which the number of classes they are expected to teach is so great that they cannot give the pupils genuine scientific instruction.

QUESTIONS FOR FURTHER STUDY

1. Give a subject for a lecture demonstration and justify the use of this method in preference to others for presenting the chosen subject.

2. Make an outline for your lecture with a list of the experiments, preparations, or illustrations that you would use in presenting it.

3. Justify psychologically each of the ten hints under the heading "Technique of the Lecture-Demonstration."

4. Criticize the propositions of Rousseau's *Émile*, referred to in footnote 1, p. 143. What do you think of Pestalozzi's methods of teaching Geography as described in Holman's book (footnote 2, p. 143)?

5. Make a list of places for possible excursions for studies in the various high school sciences that can be made in your home neighborhood. Briefly describe the possibilities of each locality for good instruction of this sort.

6. Discuss critically each of the types of procedure for review lessons advocated in this chapter.

REFERENCES

COOKE, JOSIAH P. The New Chemistry. Appleton, N. Y. 1891. 17 + 400 pp. $1.00.

FARADAY, M. The Chemical History of a Candle. Ed. by William Crookes. Harpers, N. Y. 1903. 223 pp. 75¢.

HELMHOLTZ, H. L. F. VON. Popular Scientific Lectures. Longmans, N. Y. 1891. 397 pp. 15¢.

HOLMAN, HENRY. Pestalozzi, An Account of his Life and Work. Longmans, N. Y. 1908. $1.10.

JAMES, WILLIAM. Principles of Psychology. Holt, N. Y. 1905. 2 vols. $5.00.

THOMPSON, SYLVANUS P. Light, Visible and Invisible. Macmillan, N. Y. 1903. 283 pp. 2d Ed., 1910. $2.00.

MICHELSON, A. A. Light Waves and their Uses. University of Chicago Press. 1903. 166 pp. 1.50.

ROUSSEAU, J. J. Émile. E. P. Dutton, N. Y. 1911. 444 pp. 70¢.

RUSKIN, JOHN. Ethics of the Dust. Dutton. 1908. 244 pp. 70¢.

THORNDIKE, E. L. The Psychology of Learning. Teachers College, Columbia Univ., N. Y. 1913. 312 pp. $2.50. (Vol. II of his Educational Psychology in 3 vols.)

THORNDIKE, E. L. The Principles of Teaching. A. G. Seiler, N. Y. 1906. 12 + 293 pp. $1.25.

TYNDALL, JOHN. On Sound. Appleton, N. Y. 1891. 420 pp. $2.00.

TYNDALL, JOHN. Six Lectures on Light. Appleton, N. Y. 1893. 272 pp. 15¢.

TYNDALL, JOHN. The Forms of Water. Appleton, N. Y. 1892. 196 pp. $1.50.

WRIGHT, LEWIS. Light. Macmillan, N. Y. 1882. 376 pp. $2.00.

See List at end of Chapter VIII.

CHAPTER X

EQUIPMENT FOR SCIENCE TEACHING

Rooms. — In large city high schools, where there are several divisions of students pursuing each of the subjects, a separate room or suite of rooms must be provided for each of the sciences. In small schools in villages and rural communities where there is but one division in each of the science subjects, it is usually inconsistent with necessary economy to provide more than one or two rooms to be devoted exclusively to the sciences. One may find many of the features of an ideal equipment, of rooms, furniture and fixtures, and apparatus, in any of a considerable number of the best city high schools; and he may see practically all of them by visiting a selected list of schools. Between the ideal equipment on the one hand and the meager, one-room equipment of the struggling high school in a small community on the other hand, every degree of compromise can be found. It is possible, for example, to have fairly good laboratory and demonstration work done in botany, zoölogy, or geography in an ordinary schoolroom equipped with the usual desks, if certain necessary equipment is added. In the case of physics and chemistry, where the classes are small, it is possible to carry on the class conferences and laboratory work for both subjects in a single room. A serious objection to this, even when the other difficulties have been successfully overcome, is that the corrosive fumes from the chemicals soon ruin much of the physical apparatus unless the latter is stored in a detached room. This expedient of course is not wholly effective and is also an undesirable one since *efficiency in class manage-ment requires that all apparatus should be stored as near as possible to the places where it is to be used.*

In small schools, however, it is rather common, and per-haps wisely so, to omit chemistry from the program of studies and restrict the science instruction to physics, geography, and botany, or to physics and a course in agriculture, in which a large amount of related biological and geographical sub-ject matter is introduced. For such a curriculum, one large room can be made to answer as a laboratory and classroom combined, provided there be adjoining it a room of sufficient size, say at least twenty feet by twelve, to serve as a stock-room and shop, where the apparatus used in all the kinds of work may be stored, and cleaned or repaired when this is necessary.

The ideal outfit of rooms for science in a large school includes laboratory, classroom, stockroom, photographic darkroom, teacher's office, and workshop for each depart-ment. It is obvious, however, that by locating the science suites near together, one workshop and one darkroom may serve for two or more departments or even for all, if the num-ber of teachers and classes in each department is not large. It is obvious also that a single room, if sufficiently large, may be made to serve as both stockroom and teacher's office or workroom, and perhaps for shop purposes also. It is far better, however, for the conservation of both the apparatus and the teacher, to plan the three separately. In schools that are well equipped with shops for manual training the greater part of the work of making or repairing apparatus can be done in these shops; but in a laboratory where many students are at work each day it is absolutely necessary to have conveniently at hand a workbench with tools for glass working, small quick repairs, soldering, etc.

Location of rooms. — Since direct sunlight is much to be desired for many experiments in physics and for projections with the *porte-lumière* or sun lantern, the physics classroom should be located on the south side of the building, preferably the southeast corner, with ample windows in the south wall, and at least an opening for the *porte-lumière* in the east wall. The room or rooms for botany and zoölogy should be located on the north side of the building in order that they may have the light of the sky from the north for work with the simple or compound microscopes. For this purpose direct sunlight is a nuisance, and white Holland shades for diffusing it are but a troublesome makeshift. The botany room should be at the northeast corner of the building, and preferably also would have windows in both north and east walls in order that the growing plants, which form an essential part of the equipment, may have the benefit of the morning sunbeams,[1] while the microscopes may still be lighted from the northern sky. The other science rooms, especially the geography laboratory and classrooms, should have south exposure.

Modern large buildings have one or more study rooms on each floor, large enough to accommodate all the pupils who are not in recitations, laboratories, gymnasiums, or shops, or on the playgrounds, at any one period. This plan is far better than either of the two which were in vogue until recently; namely, either that of having a single large study room for all, or that of having, at the same time, some pupils at recitations in the front parts of the rooms and others at study in the back parts of the same rooms. With the modern arrangement of a study room on each floor it is possible so to seat the pupils in the building that they may have all or nearly all their class and laboratory work as well as their "registration room" and study room on the same floor, or at any rate so that they will never have to climb more

[1] If there is a conservatory having sun exposure, opening from the botany room, as is now the case in a number of recently designed school buildings, this will not be necessary.

than one stairway in going from one class to the next. Due regard both for the physical welfare of the pupils, especially the girls, and for economy of time in shifting classes, demands that this problem should be carefully worked out in the planning and administration of the building.

Certain compromises are necessary in working out this problem. The chemical laboratory, even with the best facilities for ventilation, is a source of disagreeable gases, which are for the most part lighter than air, and therefore rise through the building. Consideration of this fact indicates the top floor as better for the chemistry rooms. On the other hand, if the chemistry rooms are on the first floor, the necessary plumbing arrangements can be much more easily and economically worked out than if the rooms are higher up. Furthermore, in order to secure the greatest stability and freedom from jarring for the benefit of galvanometers and similar delicate instruments a basement room, if adequately lighted, is advantageous for physics. For many reasons it is well to have the physics and chemistry rooms near together on the same floor. Again, it is well to have the zoölogy and botany rooms near together, and if a greenhouse has been built on the roof, the botany room should be on the top floor so as to be near the greenhouse.

To harmonize these various demands and at the same time arrange to have the pupils seated so far as possible on the floors where their laboratories and recitation rooms are, requires careful compromises and adjustments to which the science teachers and the principal should give their best thought. The problem becomes a much simpler one if the building is only two stories high, if an efficient separate motor-driven ventilation system is provided for the chemistry rooms, or if the building is amply provided with elevators, as every large building with three or more stories should be.

Size of rooms. — The sizes of the rooms must be determined by the maximum number of pupils in the class, and the plan of managing the instruction. For example, there are certain irreducible minima of floor and wall space required for pupils' working tables, demonstration table, apparatus cases and cabinets of drawers, blackboards, fume-hoods, doors, windows, and so forth. Obviously the room must be larger if designed to accommodate divisions of thirty pupils each than if designed to accommodate divisions of twenty-four pupils each; and other things being equal it must be nearly twice as large if it is to be used for both classroom work and laboratory work as it would need to be if designed for either purpose alone. A room thirty-two feet wide by thirty-six feet long provides about the lowest limit of floor and wall space for a combined laboratory and classroom for twenty-four students. Thirty-six by forty would provide more generously for apparatus cases, supply tables, and other desirable accessories in the room, and would greatly increase efficiency and comfort in carrying on the work. This allows for two rows of tables six by three feet each, three tables in a row, in the rear half of the room, and for three rows of tablet chairs or seats, eight in a row, and a demonstration table eighteen feet long and two and one half feet wide, in the front half of the room. A table six feet by three gives the minimum working space for four pupils, two on a side. There should be at least a four foot space, all around, between the walls and the students' tables and demonstration table; and if there are storage cases or cabinets, working or supply shelves, sinks or other furniture or fixtures next to the walls the same minimum space should be left clear between these and the tables. There should be a door opening outward into the hall at the front and at the rear end of the room. There are some advantages in smaller schools in thus combining the laboratory and classroom, but, especially in large schools, there are more advantages in having them separate but adjoining. In the latter case the rows of seats in the classroom may be placed on rising platforms each from four to six inches higher than the one in front of it, so that the students at the back of the room may look down at the demonstration table over the heads of those in front of them.   The seats and lecture table should, of course, be placed so that the light is received by the pupils from the left, or left and rear.   The plan of separating classroom and laboratory has the further advantage that ample cases for the storage of apparatus, books, charts, and other working materials can be built *in the room* without making the room too large. Immense amounts of delay and confusion are avoided by storing the apparatus as near as possible to the students' tables or demonstration table where it is to be used.

Planning the science rooms. — If rooms are fitted up for instruction in the sciences after the building has been completed, the disposition of the equipment must of course be adapted to fit the rooms as they are, and it is often very difficult to devise a thoroughly satisfactory arrangement.   In planning under these circumstances, or in fact in planning laboratories before the general plans for a new building have been drawn, it is best to determine as nearly as possible exactly what furniture and fixtures are needed to carry on the work, and what amount of floor and wall space will be needed for each, and then try various arrangements of it, in order to judge which arrangement is likely to be most convenient.   This can best be done by drawing, to scale, outline plans of the tables and cases on stiff cardboard, cutting them out, and shifting them into various relative positions. The outlines of the furnishings and the plans of the rooms should of course be drawn to the same scale.   If a new high school building is being planned, *the school architect should be required to call in the principal and science teachers and consult with them regarding the size, character, and location of the science rooms; and the latter should be ready to give the architect the best fruits of their knowledge and experience.*   Serious mistakes are often made by failure to do this; and science teachers often complain that they are handicapped because the rooms have been badly planned or their locations not chosen with reference to the needs of the particular kinds of instruction to be given. In this case the teachers are sometimes as much to blame as their official superiors. If competent and enthusiastic they should have definite ideas and plans, and should devise means of interesting the building committee and the architect in the information that they have to give. The writer has often heard teachers and principals complain that they were not consulted, but has known few school architects who were not glad to get from any source information that would help them in planning the best and most efficient buildings that could be erected for the amounts available. The science teacher who knows his business and cannot contrive to get himself consulted when his rooms are being planned must indeed be a rather timid and retiring person.

For a new building the ideal procedure is to determine the best locations for the rooms, bearing in mind the principles that have been mentioned, and also plan out the locations and arrangements of the furniture and fixtures for each room, and then to *draw the rooms around them*. The sketch plans thus made should be gone over with the architect and the essential features carefully explained. The architect can then take the essentials, and work them into his general plans for the building with as few and unessential modifications as possible. When his preliminary plans are ready, he should again go over them with the science teacher and adjust the conflicting demands as far as that is possible. This plan has been followed in many cases with most satisfactory results. If, as sometimes happens when new buildings are being designed, the science teacher is inexperienced and not capable of planning the rooms, the superintendent would do well to recommend to the board that they call in an expert science teacher from a neighboring city and pay him for his advice. Money spent for really expert advice would be saved ten times over.

Lighting of rooms. *Windows.* — Modern standards require that all rooms shall be lighted from left only, or in case of certain corner rooms from both left and rear, that the clear glass area of the windows shall be approximately equal to one fourth of the floor area, that the tops of the windows be within one foot (or less) of the ceiling, that the width of that part of the room which is occupied by pupils doing close eye work shall not be much greater than twice the length of the windows. In the best modern buildings the windows are massed into large units with wooden or iron mullions. The jambs, mullions, and sashes are beveled inside and out, so as to cut off the light as little as possible. The site of the schoolhouse should be so chosen that no building, hill, or other obstruction be nearer the windows of any story than a distance equal to twice its height above the floor of that story. Any part of a room is insufficiently lighted if a normal eye cannot readily read there a sample of print in diamond type number 1 from an optician's test card at a distance of fifteen inches. The minimum standard illumination by photometric test is about thirty candle meters, or approximately the illumination given by a thirty-two candle power lamp at a distance of $3\frac{1}{3}$ feet.[1] These standards should be met within reasonable approximate limits by every laboratory.

The windows of the laboratories that are exposed to direct sunlight should be equipped with spring-roller shades. These should be made of translucent material, either white or light gray or buff. They should be mounted on slats suspended by pulleys from the tops of the window frames, and inside the frames near the sashes ; so that they can be adjusted to any desired height,

[1] Instruments for testing the illumination of a room are Dr. Cohn's Licht Prüfer, sold by Fritz Tiessen, Adalbert Strasse 16, Breslau, Ger., price, 15 marks ; and Dr. Weber's Photometer. See Rowe, S. H., *The Lighting of School Buildings*, Longmans, 1904, and Kotelmann, *School Hygiene*, C. W. Bardeen, Syracuse, N. Y., 1899.

and to any desired length at the same time. Several excellent devices of this kind are sold by school supply houses.[1]

Shades for stereopticon work. — For the physics rooms, and for any other rooms in which a *porte-lumière* or a stereopticon is to be used, it is necessary also to have double opaque shades or curtains of enameled cloth. These should be mounted on spring rollers at the top of the window frames and should project over the inner faces of the frames at least three inches all around. They should slide in grooves a quarter of an inch deeper than this, in order that they may not be blown out by air currents, leaving crevices through which light may enter. The window frames in all the rooms where a stereopticon is to be used should be especially designed for this purpose when a new building is planned. Old window frames can usually be fitted with slats to provide these grooves for the curtains, but it is a troublesome job and ought never to be left for an afterthought if it can be provided for before the finishing of the building.

Electric lights. — There will be many occasions for artificial light, and this should be generously provided for. The wholesale impairment of children's vision because of negligence or niggardliness of school authorities in this matter merits and is receiving from physicians and sociological experts the strongest condemnation. The best lights, of course, are the modern tungsten incandescent lamps with " Holophane " reflecting shades for properly diffusing the light. The method of lighting by diffused reflection from the ceiling, which is now being used in hotel and public reading rooms, and which gives a daylight effect in all parts of the room, would perhaps be ideal for schoolrooms and laboratories, but would be very expensive as compared with the use of more widely distributed smaller units. Some hygienic experts are emphatically opposed to its exclusive use. Probably the indirect system will not be very generally used for

---

[1] The Draper Shade is one of the best. Sold by the Draper Sales Co., Spiceland, Ind.

some time to come; but it is to be hoped that a combination of the indirect and direct systems that will combine the advantages of both will ultimately be worked out and adopted, at least in those communities that are both able and willing to provide the best hygienic conditions for their children. An efficient direct system of lighting should provide for a fifty or sixty candle power lamp, or two thirty-two candle power lamps, for each working table accommodating four students. There should be a row of lamps, with reflectors, properly placed for lighting the demonstration table and the blackboard behind it, and a similar provision for lighting up blackboards or wall charts in other parts of the room. Suitable portable desk lights should be provided for the teacher's desk and for the demonstration table, and there should also be fixed lights for illuminating cases and cabinets which cannot be properly illuminated by lamps already provided for the other purposes. Such special lamps for temporary or occasional use, and each of the groups already mentioned, should be controlled by separate switches so that any detached lamp or any one group of lamps that happens to be needed can be lighted without lighting those which are not needed. The economy of electricity caused by this provision will, if the teachers are careful, save in a short time the extra cost of its installation.

Other artificial illuminants. — Next to electricity the best artificial lights are the inverted incandescent gas burners. There are also " Holophane " shades designed for these. In country high schools where there is neither a local electric plant nor a public gas plant, incandescent gasoline burners, acetylene burners or oil lamps are the only available sources of artificial light. Such a school ought to have its own gasoline gas plant, but very few of them do. The problem is how to get the best available sources of light and to distribute them in the most efficient manner according to the standards that have been described. Whatever the handicaps under which they are working, teachers should know the hygienic standards demanded by the needs of their pupils and use every available means to bring the school plant up to them as nearly as is possible.

Electric current for experimental purposes. — While providing for the electric lighting of the classrooms and laboratories, suitable wiring, switches, and openings should be provided for supplying current for the stereopticon and for other experiments in which electric current is needed. In cities where there is such a man, the science teachers should consult the illuminating expert of the local electric light company with reference to the problem of getting suitable distribution of current, and adequate light, efficiently distributed.[1] If this problem is left to architects and contractors alone it is almost certain to get a conventional solution that will be unsatisfactory for the school work.

Water, and fuel gas. — In addition to the provision for heating, ventilating, and lighting demanded by all schoolrooms, all the science rooms should be provided with running water and gas. These are indispensable for cleaning apparatus and for experiments in which water must be used or substances heated. In the physics laboratory gas, and in the chemical laboratory both water and gas must be distributed to each student at the working tables; and in both these laboratories wiring and openings for distributing to each student rectified electric currents of various voltages are also much to be desired, though not absolutely indispensable. In the laboratories for biology and geography it is not so necessary to distribute gas and water or electricity at the tables for students' experiments, but these should be provided at the demonstration tables and there should be

---

[1] The General Electric, the Westinghouse, and the Holophane companies furnish pamphlets giving valuable information on the distribution of light. The teacher of physics should make himself familiar with these.

abundant sinks and gas openings at other points according to the needs of the work.

Students' tables. — The minimum table surface for each student has already been indicated as thirty-six by eighteen inches. For classes in geography where charts and maps are to be worked over it is desirable to give the tables greater width. Four feet is, on the whole, about the best width. For biology, work tables having their tops in the form of an elongated isosceles trapezoid have many advantages. They are to be placed with their wider ends toward the windows. This arrangement obviously secures the nearest approach to an equitable distribution of the light from the windows. Such a table with sides nine or ten feet long and ends respectively two and a half and four and a half feet long will accommodate seven pupils; hence four of them will provide for twenty-eight pupils at one time. The floor space demanded by this arrangement is necessarily longer and narrower than that demanded for the same number of pupils by the rectangular tables with tops three feet by six. A floor space twenty-four feet by forty would provide ample room for these tables and the necessary demonstration and supply tables and storage cases.

For physics and geography, drawers in the working tables are not recommended. According to the writer's experience and observation they are a nuisance. They are also not very practical in the trapezoidal tables recommended for biology. In chemistry tables they are indispensable, and some teachers prefer to use for biology rectangular tables provided with them. The best tables are the simplest, made of the best seasoned lumber, with straight or slightly tapering legs, rails as narrow as is consistent with strength and stability, and having composite nonwarping tops of hard pine or maple wood not less than an inch and a half thick. The tops of the tables should never be varnished or polished, but should have a paraffin dressing ironed into them. For the tops of chemistry tables, though it is expensive, nothing is equal to " Alberine Stone."

For tables at which the most of the work is done standing, as in physics and chemistry, the best height is about three feet one or two inches, more or less, according to the prevailing or modal height of the pupils who are to use them. In designing laboratories, although this is seldom thought of, it would be well if at least one table were made lower and one higher than the others in order to provide for the comfort of those pupils who are below or above the modal height. Similarly, tables at which pupils are to work sitting should be from twenty-seven to thirty inches high, according to the size of the pupils.

Demonstration tables. — In every science classroom a demonstration table with a good-sized sink in it, with running water (hot as well as cold if possible), with several gas openings and electric connections, is indispensable. There ought also to be a similar table in every laboratory, which may answer for a demonstration table and supply table combined. The table should be two and a half feet wide, from three to three and a half feet high, and from twelve to twenty feet long. Most demonstration tables in high schools are both too low and too short. Many are also too wide. If too low it is a back-breaking affair. It is most comfortable for the teacher while demonstrating if its top is just a little below the level of the hip bone when he is standing erect, and it may be an inch or two higher than that without being inconveniently high. A demonstration table that is too short is a source of great inconvenience at times. There should be plenty of room in the top for a sink of generous proportions, for a clear space for the teacher's books and papers, and for all the apparatus that has to be used during the period for demonstrations. If the teacher is as enterprising as he should be in the way of making the subject concrete, this will sometimes be considerable; and the various pieces of apparatus must be arranged on the table according to the order in which the experiments are to come, with plenty of space between. Consequently inconvenience, loss of time, breakage, or imperfect perception by the pupils is likely to result, unless the table is long enough to provide abundant surface. If the table is more than twelve feet long it is best made in two parts with a two foot gap between, the gap being closed by a hinged cover, held up by bolts on the side opposite the hinges. This makes it possible for the teacher to get out quickly from behind the table into the midst of the room, without going around its ends; for it is necessary only to move aside whatever may rest on the cover, draw the bolts, let the cover drop down, and step through.

The space under the demonstration table should be filled with drawers and lockers of convenient sizes for receiving various small articles and supplies that are constantly being needed and should be always ready at hand, — such as corks, cork borers, rubber stoppers and tubing, files, pliers, supports, glass rods and tubing, rectangular blocks of different thicknesses for blocking up apparatus, etc. Drawers that are very wide or very deep are usually of little use on account of the difficulty in opening and closing them, and their tendency to become catchalls for useless junk. These drawers should be made as nearly dust-proof as possible. To this end the lowest ones should be several inches above the floor, and the table should have a dust-tight bottom just below them, otherwise the dust from sweeping will filter in behind the drawers and get into them. All tables and cases should have legs that support them at least six inches above the floor so that the floor under them can be easily swept, or they should be joined to the floors and walls so closely that no dust can collect under them or behind them. This is an important requisite of cleanliness and sanitation that is too generally neglected by carpenters and cabinetmakers. *There should always be sufficient " overhang " to the table tops, so that when the pupils or teacher stand against the tables there will be plenty of space for their feet underneath.* Otherwise great discomfort and inconvenience will result.

Students' and demonstration tables of good design and quality may be bought ready-made from several apparatus dealers, in some cases more cheaply than they can be furnished by local contractors.

Apparatus cases. — Cases for physical apparatus should be about eighteen inches deep, with adjustable shelves and glass doors, but there should be at least one section with opaque doors, for the preservation of instruments that are made of hard rubber or for other things that must be kept away from the light. The doors should be in pairs and close with spring locks. Sliding doors may be used where there is insufficient space for swinging doors. *The joints around the doors should be fitted with strips of soft felt to keep out dust.*

Cases for apparatus other than physical usually need not be more than ten or twelve inches deep. They should have adjustable shelves. Museum cases when designed to show minerals, shells, and other small objects in paper trays are usually made with some inclined shelves. They should be so placed that they may be well lighted. But cabinets of shallow drawers for this purpose are much more economical of space; and the drawers can be taken out and placed on the table when their contents are to be displayed. Cabinets of drawers are very convenient receptacles also for small pieces of apparatus and supplies used in the laboratories. The drawers should be twelve or eighteen inches long from front to back and of various widths and depths.

Drawers for herbaria and for the topographic map sheets of the United States Geological Survey should be made with hinged fronts that let down, so that any of the manila folders in which the plant specimens or maps are kept may be removed by sliding them out without lifting those above them.

Cases for wall maps and charts. — The cabinets in which

wall maps are sold in mounted sets on spring rollers are, in general, not to be recommended. The cabinets are too flimsily constructed to keep out the dust, and the map one wishes to use cannot be quickly and conveniently picked out from among the others. The large maps especially are much cheaper if mounted on ordinary rollers. It is well to have a strip of enameled cloth tacked or glued on to the bottom of each map, so that it will cover the map and protect it from dust when rolled up. They should be stored in a dust-proof case specially built for them. Such a case should be about six feet high, six feet wide, or as wide as the widest map, and about a foot deep, preferably with glass doors. Instead of shelves there should be rows of horizontal rods projecting straight forward from the back of the case. These rods are best made of stiff strap iron, bent at right angles so as to make feet by which they can be screwed to the back of the case. They should be bent slightly upward at their front ends, to keep the maps from rolling off. They should be about eighteen inches apart horizontally and six inches apart vertically. The rolled maps are plainly labeled on their ends and are laid on the rods according to some convenient system of classification, so that any particular one may be picked out instantly when wanted.

Display racks for wall maps and charts. — The best kind of rack for displaying maps is the simplest. This is made of a straight-grained strip of light seasoned wood five or six feet long, three inches wide, and five eighths of an inch thick. Large screw eyes are set into its upper edge near the ends and to these are attached by snaffle hooks a pair of strong soft cotton cords. The cords are reeved through screw eyes or pulleys projecting from the wall or ceiling. By means of an extra screw-hook or pulley the cord on one side may be carried over to the other side, so both cords can be held at the same time when raising or lowering the rack. A cleat should be conveniently placed for belaying the cords when the rack is in position. The lower edge of the rack may be supplied with screw-hooks at convenient distances along its length. When a map is to be shown the rings on its top strip are suspended on a pair of these hooks. If any of the maps are mounted on spring rollers, supports for the rollers can be screwed to the face of the strip.

Storage for pictures and lantern slides. — For storing mounted and unmounted pictures nothing is better than the cap-size vertical sectional filing cases, such as are furnished by the manufacturers of office supplies. The pictures are classified in manila folders which have tabs for labeling, and these are placed on edge in the filing drawers. Blank index boards are properly labeled and used to separate the different classifications so that any folder whose contents are wanted can be instantly picked out.

A single section can be bought having three cap-size filing drawers and four drawers for four and a quarter by six inch filing cards. These drawers can be used for either lantern slides or filing cards.[1]

Bookcases. — The same firms furnish the sectional book-cases, which are very useful for keeping the books of the department libraries. Sections may be added from time to time as needed for the storage of books or other articles.

Projecting lanterns. — No school can claim to be completely equipped that does not possess at least one projecting lantern or stereopticon and a *porte-lumière*. There are many types of these, and the choice must be governed by the purposes to which the instrument is to be put. The ideal would be to have a lantern for each department, but few school boards will be found that will permit such duplication. It is usually necessary, then, to select one that can be used for a variety of purposes. If it is to be carried from one room to another, the most important requisite next to working

---

[1] Among the best filing cases are those made by the Library Bureau, the Macy Company, and the Globe-Wernicke Company.

N

efficiency is that it be as light as is consistent with strength and rigidity. Few teachers are mechanical and electrical experts, and for this reason as well as for economy, the hand-feed arc lamp is preferable to the automatic.

The prime essentials of a lantern are a steady and powerful source of light approaching as nearly as possible to the condition of giving its light from a single point, a large and efficient condenser, and a good achromatic objective giving a flat, colorless field. The light-box is the next most important feature. It should be designed so as to keep the light from escaping into the room, and also so as to provide for ventilation and rapid radiation, in order that it may not be overheated. The stage should be so constructed that the centers of the condensing lenses, the object lenses, the slide, and the center of the source of light can easily be brought into the same line, which is called the optical axis, and firmly held there. The lamp should have adjusting screws for centering, extending outside the light box, by means of which it can be raised or lowered or moved from right to left. It should also be capable of sliding forward or backward, so that it can be accurately placed at the focus of the condenser. If the lantern is to be used for the projection of physical and chemical experiments it should have a large condensing lens. Also the stage should be considerably longer than is required for showing ordinary lantern slides and should be open, so as to afford plenty of clear space for lining up various lenses and other apparatus in the optical axis between the condenser and the objective. The optical axis should also be at least four and a half inches above the stage if all kinds of projection experiments are to be made with it. Electric current of at least sixty volts is necessary for operating an arc light lantern, and to secure the best results in lighting and freedom from noise the current should be a direct one. An alternating current, though inferior to the direct, is better than the remaining practicable sources.

The lantern should always be provided with a fuse block, carrying a fuse that will blow at thirty amperes or less, and the circuit which brings the current to it should be wired to carry safely more than that amount. The usual amperage for an arc lamp is nine to twelve, but for projecting opaque objects by reflection, twenty-five amperes are necessary for good results. The fuse at the lantern should always be chosen so that it will blow before any of the others between it and the point where the current comes into the building. A rheostat, preferably an adjustable one, to regulate the current, and a switch to control it, are necessary parts of the equipment.

The recently invented gas filled Mazda glow lamps with concentrated filament are proving themselves very satisfactory for most kinds of projection, require no skill for their management, and are very economical. These require no adjustable rheostat and work perfectly without noise on the alternating lighting circuit.

The only practical sources of light when electricity is not to be had are the calcium light, the alcohol mantle-light, and the acetylene light. The two latter are cheaper and easier to manage but far less satisfactory as to results than the first. From the standpoint of getting the largest and best pictures, the back of the room is the best place for the lantern and the front the best place for the screen. It is very convenient, however, when experiments or only one or two pictures are to be shown, to have the lantern near the demonstration table and the screen near the side wall. It is best, therefore, to provide connecting plugs at both places. An adjustable photographer's camera-stand or a permanent stand is needed for mounting the lantern when in use. The nearer the height of the lantern is to the height of the center of the screen, especially when the distance is short, the less distortion and imperfect focusing of the pictures there will be. The principle is that the screen and slide should be parallel, with both their centers in the optical axis. Hence if the lantern has to be tilted up, the faults can be corrected by tilting the lower end of the screen back at the same angle. The knowledge and technical skill required to operate a stereopticon with uniform success are considerable, but every teacher who aims to be an expert in his line ought to possess such power, and if he or she does not, should neglect no opportunity to acquire it from some one who has it. Much valuable information on the " art of projecting " can be obtained from the book of that name by Professor E. A. Dolbear,[1] from " Optical Projection " by Lewis Wright,[2] and from the catalogues of certain dealers.[3]

The *porte-lumière*, when direct and steady sunlight is available, is better and easier to operate than any lantern, and with the same grade of lenses much cheaper also. Its use is fully described in the books referred to.

The purchasing of apparatus. — The details that would be of service in making up the complete equipment of a modern high school would fill a good-sized book, and it is to be hoped that some competent person will sometime undertake the task of supplying such information. Only a few simple principles can be given here.

1. The teachers should thoroughly plan out their courses, and then determine what apparatus they need for carrying out the instruction with the number of pupils they have to teach. To order a lot of apparatus without knowing definitely what is to be done with each piece, and without a just allotment to the different portions of the subject, involves waste of both money and valuable space.

2. It is much better, if possible, to secure from the

---

[1] Published by Lothrope & Co.

[2] Published by Longmans, Green & Co.

[3] Notably T. H. McAllister, Philadelphia; The McIntosh Stereopticon Co., Chicago; Queen & Co., Philadelphia, and several other apparatus dealers who advertise in school journals.

board of education an annual or semiannual appropriation than to attempt to purchase a complete equipment
in one order. This will save many oversights and mistakes.

3. The teachers should find out by inquiry, if they do
not already know, what dealers are thoroughly reliable,
and deal with them only. Those whose agents endeavor
to sell to the board of education without first calling
on the teachers are to be regarded with suspicion.
So also are those who make their appeal for patronage
on the basis of underselling their competitors. " Complete cabinets " and " hundred dollar sets " are made
up to sell to schools where teachers know too little of
their subjects to make out their own orders. Dealers
of the highest standing advertise in *Science*, in *School
Science and Mathematics*, and in the special journals
devoted to the various sciences. Among these adver-
tisers it will not be difficult for the inexperienced teacher
to find out which firms have the reputation of furnishing the best materials for the various sciences, at fair
prices.

4. Much money may often be saved by importing
" duty free " through any one of the reliable firms who
do this work. When this is to be done the orders should
be made up several months before the articles will be
needed.

5. Competitive bids are required by law in some places,
and it is always well to get prices from more than one
firm, but it is not to be expected that acceptance of the
lowest bid will result in the most satisfactory purchase.

6. The science teacher should take advantage of
every opportunity that he may have to visit the factories of apparatus dealers, see what they have of interest to show, and get personally acquainted with them.

7. Raw materials, lumber, metals and wire, hardware,

tools, and many electrical devices can often, but not always, be bought to best advantage from local dealers.

QUESTIONS FOR FURTHER STUDY

1. Make a set of plans for the remodeling of the science room or rooms in your school.

2. If a new building were being planned for your high school, how would you go about securing the opportunity to help in getting things done right?

3. Make a set of plans for science rooms in a new building for your school, taking into account the necessary limitations, and providing for the best facilities that can be had under the circumstances.

4. How would you proceed in order to find out whether you could get more for the money by buying laboratory tables and cases ready-made or by having them built by a local factory or a carpenter and cabinetmaker?

5. How much of your proposed equipment of furniture could be made by the boys in the manual arts department as coöperative school projects? What educational advantages would come to the boys through such projects?

6. Secure catalogues from the leading dealers and prepare a report to your superintendent recommending the best lantern, giving the reasons for your choice, and including a table of comparative costs.

7. How could a lantern be made to pay for itself? Outline your plans in a report.

8. Criticize each of the seven suggestions made in this chapter as to the purchasing of apparatus.

9. Visit the science rooms of a neighboring high school and make a survey and report, applying the principles set forth in this chapter. State clearly the arrangements that are correct, and indicate those that are wrong, together with reasons, and with recommendations for the most imperative changes.

10. Go through the files of *School Science and Mathematics* and the reports of the National Educational Association and make an annotated bibliography of the most helpful articles on the planning and equipment of science rooms.

REFERENCES

The American School Board Journal, Milwaukee, Wis. This magazine contains many articles on school buildings of the best modern types, including plans, pictures, and descriptions. Consult the indices for the past five years.

AYERS, L. S., and AYERS, MAY. School Buildings and Equipment. Cleve. Ed. Survey Reports. Cleveland Foundation, Cleveland, O. 1916. 25 ¢.

BRIGGS, W. R. Modern American School Buildings. Wiley, N. Y. 1899. $4.00.

BRUCE, WILLIAM C. Leading American School Buildings. The American School Board Journal, Publisher, Milwaukee, Wis. Illus.

BURNHAM, W. H. The Ideal School House. World's Work, Vol. 2, pp. 866–871.

CLAY, FELIX. Modern School Buildings. Scribner's, N. Y. 1903. $10.00.

COHN, DR. HERMANN. Hygiene of the Eye. English translation, Simkin, Marshall & Co., London. 1886. A standard work giving much important information not found in most American books on school hygiene.

Commission of Oculists and Electricians. Report on Artificial Lighting and Color Schemes of School Buildings. Boston School Committee Document No. 14. 1907.

DRESSLAR, F. B. School Hygiene. Bull. 1910, No. 5. U. S. Bureau of Education, Supt. of Doc., Washington, D. C. 133 pp. 75 ¢.

DRESSLAR, F. B. School Hygiene. Macmillan, N. Y. 1913. xi + 369 pp. Illus. $1.25.

DRESSLAR, F. B. American School Houses. U. S. Bureau of Education Bull. 1910, No. 5. 127 pp. A very complete and authoritative monograph, profusely illustrated, with an extensive bibliography on school architecture and hygiene. The best for the general reader.

FARRINGTON, O. C. The Educational Value of Museums. Proc. Nat. Ed. Asso., 1902, pp. 765–771.

HOLLISTER, H. A. Public School Buildings and Their Equipment, with Special Reference to High Schools. Bull. Univ. of Illinois, Urbana, Ill. Vol. 6, No. 1, 1909.

HOLLISTER, H. A. The Planning and Construction of School Buildings. Bull. Univ. of Illinois, Urbana, Ill. Vol. 14, No. 8, October 23, 1916, 70 pp. Illus.

ITTNER, WILLIAM B. School Architecture. Proc. Nat. Ed. Asso., 1912, pp. 1207–1222.

KOTELMANN, LUDWIG. Tr. by Bergstrom, J. A., and Conradi, E. C. W. Bardeen, Syracuse, N. Y. 1899. 391 pp. Bibliog. $1.50. Light in School Rooms, Chapter II, is especially valuable.

MOORE, JOSEPH AUGUSTUS. The School House. J. A. Moore, 28 Conway St., Roslindale, Boston. 1905. $2.00.

Rowe, S. H. The Lighting of School Buildings. Longmans, N. Y. 1904. 94 pp. $1.00.

Shaw, Edward R. School Hygiene. Macmillan, N. Y. 1901. 260 pp. $1.00.

Wheelwright, E. M. School Architecture. Rogers & Manson, Boston. 1901. 324 pp.

Wheelwright, E. M. The Essentials of School Building. American Architect, Vol. 80, p. 28.

Whitney, E. R. Equipment of the Secondary School Laboratory. High School Bull. No. 7. The University of the State of New York, Albany, N. Y.

Wright, Lewis. Optical Projection. Longmans, N. Y. 1901. vi + 428 pp. Illus. $1.50.

Dealers in Science Apparatus and Supplies

The Alberine Stone Co., 223 E. 23d St., New York, and 306 Mercantile Library Bldg., Cincinnati, O. "Alberine Stone" for laboratory table tops, sinks, shelves, and fume-hoods.

The Bausch & Lomb Optical Co., 405 St. Paul St., Rochester, N. Y. Microscopes, projection apparatus, chemical and biological apparatus and supplies.

James G. Biddle & Co., 1211–1213 Arch St., Philadelphia, Pa. High-grade apparatus for physical measurements.

Biological Laboratory, Cold Spring Harbor, N. Y. Preserved materials.

Brooklyn Biological Supply Co., Brooklyn, N. Y. Living and preserved animal material.

The Cambridge Botanical Supply Co., 7 Lexington St., Waverly, Mass. Botanical materials and supplies.

The Central Scientific Co., 460 E. Ohio St., Chicago. Physical, chemical, biological, and geographical apparatus and supplies of all kinds.

Educational Department, International Harvester Co., Chicago. Charts and lantern slides on geography and agriculture, loaned for express charges to and from Chicago.

Eimer and Amend, New York. Domestic and imported chemicals, chemical and physical apparatus, microscopes, chemical charts.

E. A. Foote, Philadelphia, Pa. Minerals and rocks.

Geo. S. Gardner, 141 Clifton St., Rochester, N. Y. Gardner Season Apparatus.

The Geographical Supply Bureau, 111 Kelvin Pl., Ithaca, N. Y. Geographical lantern slides.

The Grand Rapids School Equipment Co., Grand Rapids, Mich. Laboratory tables, school furniture.

Henry J. Green & Co., Brooklyn, N. Y.   U. S. standard meteorological apparatus, barometers, thermometers, and optical apparatus.

The J. L. Hammett Co., Boston, Mass.   Maps and school supplies.

Henry Heil & Co., 210–214 South 4th St., St. Louis, Mo.   Chemicals and supplies.

Hopkins Seaside Laboratory, Stanford University, Cal.   Living and preserved marine forms.

E. E. Howell, Washington, D. C.   (Howell's Microcosm.) Geographical models, lantern slides, "The Washington School Collections" of minerals and rocks.

The Kewaunee Mfg. Co., Kewaunee, Wis.   Laboratory tables, demonstration tables, apparatus cases, etc.

L. E. Knott Apparatus Co., 79–83 Amherst St., Boston, Mass.   Physical apparatus, lanterns and slides, chemicals and supplies, biological and geographical supplies.

Kny-Scheerer Co., 404 W. 27th St., New York.   Science apparatus of all kinds, models and charts for botany, zoölogy, and physiology. Museum specimens, living biological material.

The Leeds & Northup Co., 4921 Stenton Ave., Philadelphia.   Electrical measuring instruments.

Leitz & Co., W. Krafft, Mgr., New York.   Leitz microscopes.

Leonard Peterson & Co., 1234–1248 Fullerton Ave., Chicago.   Laboratory tables and other furniture.

Library Bureau, Boston, New York, Chicago.   All kinds of furniture for libraries and museums.   Catalog L 1009.

The McIntosh Battery & Optical Co., 427 Atlas Block, Chicago.   Lanterns, slides, physical apparatus.

Marine Biological Laboratory, Wood's Hole, Mass.   Marine fauna, living and preserved.

A. G. Nystrom & Co., Chicago.   American and imported maps, globes, and school supplies.

James W. Queen & Co., Philadelphia, Pa.   Physical apparatus, projecting lanterns, chemical apparatus and chemicals, microscopes.

Rand, McNally & Co., Chicago.   Maps, all kinds.

Richards & Co., New York.   Chemical apparatus and supplies.

Spencer Lens Co., Buffalo, N. Y.   Microscopes, lanterns and slides, biological apparatus and supplies.

A. A. Sphung, North Judson, Ind.   Living land and fresh-water animals.

Standard Scientific Co., New York.   Apparatus, all kinds, lanterns and slides.

C. H. Stoelting & Co., 3037–3047 Carroll Ave., Chicago.   Science apparatus, all kinds.

Arthur H. Thomas & Co., West Washington Square, Philadelphia.
Laboratory apparatus, chemicals, supplies.

Ward's Natural Science Establishment, 84–102 College Ave., Rochester,
N. Y.   Museum specimens of all kinds.

Weston Electrical Instrument Co., 45 Weston Ave., Newark, N. J.
Standard instruments for electrical measurements.

Whitall Tatum & Co., Philadelphia.   Glassware, all kinds.

CHAPTER XI

College entrance requirements. — The high schools grew out of a popular demand for a kind of secondary education that would be better adapted to the needs of all classes than was that given by the academies and college preparatory schools; " but the high schools gravitated toward the colleges, as the academies had done before them." [1]   The teachers and principals gave their best energies toward the preparation for college of the small percentage of their pupils whose aim was toward a higher education.   Previous to the last decade of the nineteenth century every college set its entrance requirements in accordance with its own notions, without reference to those of any other college; and the high schools tried to meet them all, so that their graduates might pass the entrance examinations of the various colleges that they wished to attend.   The lack of uniformity in the preparation required by different students in the same school, and the conflict between the needs of those who were preparing for college and those who were aiming directly toward employment in the various occupations, brought about an intolerable situation for the high schools.   Greater uniformity in the administrative machinery that had to do with admission to the colleges, and a simplification of the means of adjustment became imperative. The movement toward uniformity began with the Report of the Committee of Ten of the National Educational Association

---

[1] Brown, Elmer E., *The Making of Our Middle Schools*, Longmans, Green & Co., N. Y., 1902, p. 373.

in 1893, gathered headway with the reports of the Committee on College Entrance Requirements of the same association in 1896 and 1899, and culminated in the organization of the College Entrance Examination Board in 1900.[1] The reports and syllabi published by these committees, and the bulletins of the College Entrance Board, of the various colleges, and of certain state departments of education, all of which have been based mainly on those reports, have in large measure shaped the curricula of the high schools and determined the character of the teaching.

Results of prescription. — As far as science is concerned the results have been both good and bad.   Among the good results are the establishment of the principles (1) that high school teachers should have adequate collegiate training for their work, (2) that laboratory work, field excursions, and some reference book work should be carried on in connection with each of the sciences, (3) that schools should be adequately equipped with laboratories, apparatus, and libraries for such work, (4) that double laboratory periods should be provided in the time schedules for the laboratory exercises, (5) that laboratory notes should be systematically entered in suitable books by the students, and (6) that the pupils should be taught not merely to memorize but to think.   Among the bad results have been (1) the tendency to cast all the instruction in one mold in the attempts to meet the specifications of syllabi and examinations, (2) overemphasis on the assimilation of subject matter, and the consequent undervaluation of the scientific method of study, by means of which the subject matter of science is best acquired, and (3), worst of all, discouragement of initiative on the part of school teachers and administrators because of the burdensome amounts of subject matter that were called for by these authoritative syllabi.   The tendency was rather toward cramming the pupils with facts and laws

[1] Cf. Mann, C. R., *The Teaching of Physics*, The Macmillan Co., 1912, Chapter I.

than toward putting them in situations that would necessitate thinking.

Reforms demanded. — The path for reform lies obviously in the direction of changes in the syllabi in consequence of which they shall contain a minimum of prescription and a maximum of suggestion, especially with regard to the use of the scientific method or problem approach in teaching, with regard to the organization of the subject matter about suitable problems for observational and experimental study, and as to utilizing the rich variety of practical applications of scientific principles and laws that may be found in all sorts of localities.

The introduction of such flexible and suggestive syllabi must be accompanied also by better training of science teachers themselves. Science teachers should not know less of their special subjects than they do, but they should be given a wider range of scientific knowledge, better training in the principles of the scientific method, and some special training in modern psychology as applied in the principles of teaching. The colleges must make themselves responsible for turning out teachers with this kind of training.

Along with more flexible syllabi and better training of teachers for intelligent experimentation on both subject matters and methods of teaching must come an attitude and a procedure on the part of both college professors and school administrators which shall make science teachers feel free to apply the method of intentional variation, testing, and selection to both subject matter and methods. In other words, teachers must apply the scientific method to the study of their teaching problems if science study is to do for their pupils what scientists and psychologists believe that it can do and ought to do. We must learn to teach science more nearly in a scientific — that is, in a psychological — way; and this we can learn only through a study of the pupils while engaged in the learning process, and by the use of observation, experimentation, and measurement. This means that a selected few of the best trained, most enterprising, and ablest secondary science teachers must become research students in experimental pedagogy, and that the results of their experiments must be published, critically reviewed, and put into the hands of all science teachers as suggestive material for their further guidance.

The program of studies in science. — Previous to the report of the Committee of Ten, the high schools and preparatory schools very generally attempted to give their pupils some insight into all the sciences; and since most of them were then working on the plan of a three-term year, the practice was common of giving one-term courses in any or all of the sciences, — botany, zoölogy, physiology, geology, and astronomy. Many of them also gave similar short courses in chemistry and physics, although, as may be seen from a report by Professor F. W. Clarke,[1] a few schools gave courses in physics or chemistry that extended through two or three terms. These short courses were open to serious objections; but they did serve two very important purposes that should not be passed by without comment. In the first place, they were necessarily superficial, because of the shortness of the time devoted to them; and they were therefore not very exacting. Hence, they allowed opportunity for the free and untrammeled play of curiosity, wonder, and imagination. Thus in the case of pupils who were unusually bright and inclined to be reflective as well as imaginative, they often proved to be very inspiring, and led to the establishment of permanent interests in the phenomena of nature, and in the methodical organization of facts in accordance with their relations to one another. Thus in very many cases they contributed largely toward laying a permanent foundation for culture and mental training to be gained later on. In the second place, they gave the pupils some little insight into all

[1] U. S. Bureau of Education, Bull. No. 6, 1880.

of these various sciences, and so were often effective in enabling individual pupils to find out to which of these realms of natural phenomena they were most strongly attracted by their native interests. It is to be feared that the tendency which was so strong during the period from about 1895 to 1910 — the tendency to restrict the opportunities for the study of science to intensive courses in only one or two sciences — was harmful because it cut off all the pupils from just this opportunity. United States Commissioner of Education P. P. Claxton puts the matter thus:

"Among the subjects that I should include in the course that everybody in the high school should study, would be astronomy. The interpretation of the grandeur and magnitude of natural laws as they appear in astronomy, and as they were revealed to me through my study of astronomy, has made an indelible impression on my life. As I think of the textbook which we used, Steele's *Fourteen Weeks in Astronomy*, I cannot feel but that our modern textbook writers have much to learn from the example which this book set. Any one who can write a modern series of science textbooks, and can put into them the charm and point of view that was put into this book of Steele's will win great honor, and also a fortune that will enable him to endow institutions of learning.

"Most of us have not the ability to give the children a genuine love of learning science, but it is an ideal toward which we should continually strive. I found, when I first studied science in a disconnected and probably superficial way, that after a while there would suddenly come over me an appreciation of the fuller significance of what was being taught. In the meantime I had been in contact with the things under discussion, the natural objects or events upon which the teaching was based, and my science course was correlating and interpreting these things, of which I had been only partly conscious. All science teaching must grow out of contact with real things and from the casual and disconnected observation and study of nature.

"The boy or girl needs to be made to discover that he knows already what is being taught. He needs to be made to go farther on to appreciate the value of correlating his knowledge and of cultivating the ability to apply it to his future experience. As a boy, I have myself seen my father at his grindstone; and as he held the axe, and I supplied the power to turn it and poured the water over the stone, I have watched the peculiar smooth way in which the water flowed over the edge of the axe; I have swung a pail of water at arm's length; and I have listened to the whistling sound as I twirled a horse-chestnut at the end of a string. It is out of such experiences that the teacher should build a science course and develop a child's appreciation and love of science.

"There is another thing that I must say at this time. The science teacher and every high school teacher should forget that there is such a thing as a college. I believe that it is true now as it used to be some years ago, when I was in more intimate contact with the details of the college requirements in physics, that the specific requirement for entrance is sixty laboratory experiments — sixty mystic units like the chips with which a child plays and builds one on top of another, until the last chip is put in place and the whole structure falls into an incoherent mass; and I suppose that year after year we have been trying to build up this tottering pile of sixty units without the reinforcement of contact with real things, and without any reference to what is in the minds of the children.

"Go out and bring together a few things that have reality and let the pupil see if they are in harmony and conform to some fundamental laws; and then I would have you go one step farther and point out to them how these principles may be put into practical use. There may be persons who are interested in learning things for the sake of knowledge; but I cannot see why we should learn anything unless we purpose to put it to some practical application." [1]

The Committee of Ten, however, gave fixed expression to a feeling that had been gaining ground, that there was in these short science courses little of the patient observation, experimenting, and measuring that is characteristic of science, and that more sustained study in a few lines would be better. The Committee therefore advocated courses extending throughout a school year in each science that was taught. It favored chemistry and physics for the last two years in the order named, placing physics in the fourth year, because of its alleged greater difficulty and because of

[1] Proc. N. E. A., 1914, Ann Arbor, Mich., 1914, p. 769 ff.

the supposed need of more previous mathematical training. A course in physical geography was recommended for the first year as an introduction to the other sciences; and physiography and meteorology were to be offered as more advanced phases of earth science and were to be elective in the last year. These subjects were favored as offering an excellent opportunity for the correlation and organization of the scientific knowledge gained in the other courses.

Botany and zoölogy were also to be offered as electives in schools where the number of teachers and the number and variety of pupils made it practicable and desirable.

The practical result was that year-long courses in chemistry and physics, with laboratory work, became quite general; and intensive abstract study on the one hand, and the laboratory work in them on the other, were often overemphasized at the expense of thorough organization. However, botany and physical geography held their own quite widely as half-year courses. A little later the National Education Association's Committee on College Entrance Requirements, responding to the pressure from the zoölogists and botanists, recommended, among the subjects "proper for secondary schools" and acceptable for college entrance, the following subjects in the order named, —

"First year, physical geography; second year, biology or botany or zoölogy, or botany and zoölogy; third year, physics; fourth year, chemistry."

As to physics and chemistry this recommendation has been almost universally followed, while one or another of the four kinds of biological courses mentioned is pretty generally found in the first or second year. In the first year it is common to find physical geography, either extending through the year or limited to a half year and followed by physiology, agriculture, or botany, or preceded by a half year of elementary or introductory "general science." Astronomy as a high school subject has well-nigh disappeared from the high schools, as

o

has geology also; but certain phases of these subjects, and a good deal of what is most valuable in meteorology from the standpoint of young students, are retained in connection with physical geography or with " general science " courses. Furthermore, agriculture has come to be recognized as a valuable science, or as a vocational subject, in many rural and village schools.

Four years of science study. — It is the firm belief of the author that every four-year high school should provide for a four-year course in science.   Because of their great value, when well taught, for culture, for those types of mental discipline that offer possibilities of transfer to the problems of domestic industrial and civil life, and especially because of the practical utility of the knowledge to be gained from them, the demand for scientific studies of one fourth of the time of most of the pupils does not seem excessive.   Even though this demand may imply some reduction in the time given by various groups of students to foreign language, to formal English study, and to formal mathematics, yet for the large majority of pupils predominance should be given to science along with social and vocational studies.

Curriculum making. — In small high schools serious difficulties are encountered in making workable curricula and time schedules that will include the minimum number of units of scientific, social, and vocational studies, and yet provide for desirable amounts of foreign language, English, and mathematics.   Nevertheless it is possible to surmount these difficulties in a four-year high school employing only three teachers.   This may be done in such small schools by combining classes of the eleventh and twelfth grades, or of other contiguous grades, and alternating certain subjects in pairs. For example, physics may be taught to pupils of both the eleventh and the twelfth grades during one year, and chemistry to the same pupils during the following year.   A program of studies and a time schedule based on such a scheme has been devised by the author and published elsewhere.[1] It provides offerings of twenty-two units, only fifteen of which need be taught in any one year. The offerings include four units of science, four of social studies, four of vocational work, three of English, three of mathematics, and four of foreign language.

In large high schools, where several recitation divisions must be made for each unit, and where a large teaching force must be provided, the difficulties involved in providing a flexible program are not so great; and it is becoming customary to provide many curricula in order to meet the needs of groups of students having various types of aims.

Order of studies in the science program. — The best order for the different science studies has never been tested out and determined. That it ever will be so tested out or indeed that there is any one order that is demonstrably best for all schools is very unlikely. Nearly every teacher likes to have his own special or favorite subject placed in the fourth year, or as high in the course as possible, because with maturer pupils he can go farther into it, and put it on a basis of more finished organization. He is likely also to want it placed in the fourth year, so that the pupils, as he usually presumes, will have a working knowledge of the other sciences and training in their methods that will give them the ability to do more exacting work with less preliminary teaching. Thus, since every science contributes somewhat in both content and method to every other, the advocate of any one science can argue about as cogently as the advocate of any other in favor of having his own science placed last in the course. On the basis of the former argument physics seems to have a slight advantage in claiming the last year, while on the basis of the latter argument geography and the biological sciences seem to have a little stronger claim than the others, since geography may serve as a means of organizing and correlating

[1] Ohio High School Standards, Bulletin Ohio State Department of Public Instruction, Columbus, 1917.

the others, and advanced knowledge of botany, zoölogy, human physiology, and general biology presupposes considerable knowledge of both physics and chemistry. On the other hand, in view of the fact that there is a steady process of elimination going on in the high schools, so that approximately 37 per cent of ninth grade pupils drop out of school before reaching the tenth, 29 per cent of the tenth before reaching the eleventh, and 33 per cent of the eleventh before reaching the twelfth,[1] the argument is often heard from the advocate of a favorite science that his science, being the one of most universal utility, should be placed lowest in the curriculum in order that more of the pupils may have the benefit of it. On this basis, hygiene and biology would seem to have slightly the strongest claims for the first year, with general geography or physics as a close second.

Apparently the only solution of the question of relative position that could be fairly satisfactory from all points of view would be found in giving throughout the elementary grades lessons involving such facts from each of the sciences as are comprehensible and useful to the pupils of the various ages, and following in the high school with courses in biology, general geography, physics, and chemistry. If the teaching below were efficiently done teachers of each science in the high school could count on some elementary knowledge of the other sciences to build on, and every child eliminated from school would have had opportunity to learn some of the important facts of each of the sciences. A further improvement on the most general practice might be made by carrying the first two sciences parallel through the first two years, and the last two on a similar basis through the last two years. Thus in the first year the biology course would run three days per week and the general geography course two days per week; while in the second year the former would be given on two

---

[1] Calculated from figures given in Strayer and Thorndike, *Educational Administration*, Macmillan, N. Y., 1913, p. 13.

days and the latter on three days per week. A similar alternation would apply to physics and chemistry; and with careful planning the courses in the paired sciences could be made to correlate closely with one another, so that each would help immensely in the understanding of the other.

This plan of parallel courses, however, could not be used in the smaller high schools where, in order to economize in teaching force, the classes of two contiguous years are combined for alternating the studies, by taking one of the studies together in one year and the other in the next year.

The " project teaching " plan. — Another plan that is receiving serious consideration at this time, especially at the hands of the Sub-Committee on General Science of the National Commission on the Reorganization of Secondary Education, is to abandon, for the first one or two years, the strict organization of the sciences according to their content, and to teach facts, laws, and principles from all the sciences in connection with a series of " projects " growing out of the direct and immediate needs and interests of the pupils. According to the plan proposed the project would be the basis of organization for the scientific facts and principles that were needed in carrying it out. For example, if the project were the raising and marketing of an acre of potatoes, the students would study the physics and chemistry of the soils and fertilizers, the topography and drainage of the ground, the rainfall and weather conditions, the structure and physiology of the potato plant, the development of varieties by breeding, the physical and chemical effects of tillage, the insect enemies and the appropriate insecticides, the bird enemies of the injurious insects, the cooking and the food value of the potato, the nature and uses of potato starch, the marketing of the potatoes, and so on.

Thus the students at each stage would see the use of every scientific fact that they learned, *and would learn it because they wanted to make use of it.* They would learn many facts and principles of geology, geography, physics, chemistry, botany, and physiology, and would also be carried into the fields of arithmetic, bookkeeping, and elementary economics, developing skill in the former and a permanent interest in the latter.   The making of a chicken house and the raising of a brood of chickens would present to them the necessity of acquiring many more scientific facts and principles which, under a skilled teacher, would gradually become classified, organized, and correlated, as project after project was carried out.   The projects need not be agricultural and they need not be so extensive as the ones cited.   These are mentioned only as illustrations for making the proposed method clear.

It would require a remarkable teacher to carry out such a scheme.   However, one can scarcely doubt that if it were carried out even with very moderate success, there would be such a hunger and thirst for further scientific knowledge among those youngsters that not even the sixty mystic experiments in physics that are so picturesquely excoriated by Commissioner Claxton could spoil it.   Then in the last two years the way would be clear and easy for carrying out good courses in any two of the sciences, physics, chemistry, biology, or geography.   The choice of the two sciences would be indicated by the needs and interests of the majority of the pupils and of the community where the school was located.

It is altogether probable that such a program will be attempted in many schools within the next decade, and will be watched with interest by all progressive enthusiasts for the spread of scientific knowledge and training.   Some reactionaries are accustomed to hurl at those who are trying to apply modern psychological knowledge to the problems of science teaching the sneering accusation that they are " trying to emasculate science " because of their attempts toward fitting it to the needs and interests of real boys and girls instead of parceling it out in the traditional abstract doses to hypothetical manikins.   It is fairly certain that the results of such experiments will demonstrate that these reactionaries are striking at men of straw which they themselves have set up.

Best present order. — In the meantime the order, biology and general geography in the first two years and physics and chemistry in the last two years, is likely to be the most successful, because it has come very generally to prevail, and the best textbooks on these subjects that are now on the market are planned with this order in view. There is therefore no good reason for advocating any radical changes from it in schools where the project plan is not to be experimented on.

Future modifications. Junior and senior high schools. — Nevertheless it would seem to be very desirable to have the plan of two-year parallel courses in paired sciences carried out in a number of schools, as it has been with success in Europe, in order that results might be compared and its relative value determined. The changes necessary to carry out this plan would not involve serious difficulties, nor would they be likely to produce bad results. This mode of time distribution is one of the proposed features in connection with new plans, just now being tried out, for reorganizing the curricula and changing the year grouping of the pupils, so as to include the seventh and eighth grades with the high school.

With the coming of these "intermediate" or "junior high" schools and the junior colleges, the time span for possible high school studies is going to be lengthened; and the curricula are going to be very materially enriched. Science is sure to participate largely in this expansion. Such enrichment will probably come largely through adding such 2 or 3 hours-per-week courses as have been indicated.

QUESTIONS FOR FURTHER STUDY

1. Discuss the topic, "College domination *vs.* college leadership."
2. Might the advantages that were secured by the short science courses prevailing before 1895 be secured through the introduction of

lessons from these sciences carried on through the elementary grades above the fifth?

3. Which would be better in a high school science, to cover thoroughly all the matter in the book, through crowding on the pressure, or to secure intensive work in the solution of comparatively few interesting problems, and for the rest touch the high places in a leisurely manner, seeking to infect the pupils with a permanent interest in the science?

4. Which of the two methods (Question 3) do you think would be more likely to arouse permanent interest? Why?

5. To what extent do you think Commissioner Claxton's statements are sound? In what particulars, if any, would you disagree with him?

6. What possible substitutes exist or can be found, in the case of the boys and girls in a large city, for Mr. Claxton's varied boyhood experiences on the farm?

7. Would you stand firmly for four years of science in the high school for every pupil, knowing that some non-science units would thus be crowded out? Or would you put all or part of the sciences on the elective list? Give your reasons.

8. What do you think of the plan of carrying 3-day-per-week subjects for a longer time instead of 5-day-per-week subjects for half a year?

9. What do you think of the feasibility of teaching science through projects? Make a list of some projects that you think would be suitable; and enumerate the scientific principles and other scientific information that would be gained through them.

10. What are the arguments for the "six-six plan" or the "six-three-three plan" of reorganizing the high schools? What advantages would these plans secure for science instruction?

REFERENCES

BROWN, E. E.   The Making of Our Middle Schools.   Longmans, N. Y. 1903.   547 pp. $3.00.

Committee of Ten.   Report on Secondary Studies.   American Book Co., N. Y.   1894.

CUBBERLY, E. P.   Public School Administration.   Houghton, Mifflin & Co., Boston.   1916.   471 pp. $1.75.   (Chapter XVIII.   The Courses of Instruction.   Adjustments and Differentiations.   Pp. 294–324.   With bibliography.)

DAVIS, C. O.   The Subject Matter and Administration of the Six-Three-Three Plan of Secondary Schools.   Bul. Univ. of Mich.   N. S.

Vol. XVII, No. 9. Sept., 1915. Ann Arbor. 35 pp. with bibliography.

FLEXNER, ABRAHAM. The Modern School. General Education Board. N. Y. 1916. Occasional Paper, No. 3. 23 pp.

JOHNSTON, C. H. Curriculum Adjustments in a Modern High School. School Review. Vol. XXII, No. 9. Pp. 577–590.

JOHNSTON, C. H., and Others. High School Education. Scribner, N. Y. 1912. 546 pp. $1.50. (Chapter IV. Pp. 67–105 by C. O. Davis, on Principles and Plans for Reorganizing Secondary Education.)

JOHNSTON, C. H., and Others. The Modern High School. Scribner, N. Y. 1914. 839 pp. $1.75. Chapters V, VI, VII, and VIII, by Josselyn, Kingsley, Carlton, and Scott. Pp. 164–244. Should be carefully read.

MANN, C. R. The Teaching of Physics. Macmillan, N. Y. 1912. 304 pp. $1.25. Chapters I, II, III.

MONROE, PAUL (Editor). Principles of Secondary Education. (Chapter XXI by David Snedden, on The Reorganization of Secondary Education. Pp. 745–74.) Macmillan, N. Y. 1914. 774 pp. $1.90.

CHAPTER XII

BIOLOGY

Biological problems. — Plants and animals may be either useful or harmful to man and his activities. They are sources of manifold utilities. Their life activities present features of dramatic interest, for they are often compelled to engage in fierce competition in the hard struggle for existence, — to fight, as it were, for their lives in the midst of a hostile environment. Their activities bear many obvious analogies to those of the human body. Like the human body a plant or an animal is a living, working machine, whose parts are adapted both in form and structure to perform certain functions in the service of the whole.

They thus present a multitude of problems that are of immediate and intense human interest, if approached from the side that is suggested by such human relations and analogies as have been mentioned. Biological study therefore affords interesting and absorbing opportunities for acquiring information that is useful to everybody in many fields of thought and work. Not only that, but it enables the teacher who has broad biological points of view to lead his pupils in directing their own thinking in the biological field, and also their interpretations of human activities, from these illuminating and suggestive viewpoints.

Points of view from biological study. — One gets a certain point of view when he has come through first-hand observation to know that every living plant or animal is made up of cells which are themselves living individuals like the amœba or the unicellular plant. He has gained a broader outlook when he realizes that the necessity of adaptation to more complex and difficult situations is accompanied by division of labor, by differentiation of functions, so that special groups of cells are modified in form, structure, and distribution, with the result that each group performs some one of the specialized activities that are necessary to the survival of the organism in its more complex environment. He can see farther still if he gets the notion that there is in plant and in animal life a series of great groups beginning with unicellular forms, and continually increasing in complexity by such divisions of labor and speciali-zations of organs. If, through observations and experiments which he makes himself or sees the teacher make, he learns of the responses that plants make to the stimuli of light, gravity, moisture, soil, pressure or atmosphere, to other plants, and to insects; if he notes the general process of adjustment of which these responses are the elementary factors; if he gets even the most elementary notions of development, of variation, of elimination and survival, of mutations and inheritance, as factors in biological evolution, he gains an outlook on life as a whole that will make more meaningful everything that he afterwards learns about living things.[1]

The evolutionary point of view that one almost inevitably gets from biological study is invaluable in gaining a broad outlook on all questions involving achievement and progress. Improvement in economic status, in social, industrial, and political relations, in art, in education, and even in ethics and religion, is an evolutionary process. It proceeds by variation, selection, and elimination, by continuous adjustment, by the survival of the fit. Biological study leads naturally to such a point of view, and tends to open-mindedness, patience, and

---

[1] In this connection caution is necessary. The reader should study care-fully the discussion by Professor Bigelow as to how far the teaching of evolution should be carried in secondary schools. Lloyd, F. E., and Bigelow, M. A., *The Teaching of Biology in Secondary Schools*, Longmans, N. Y., 1904, p. 286 ff.

toleration in dealing with the conditions that one meets with in life.

Further, if the student learns the meaning of biological observations, experiments, descriptions, and interpretations, and perceives the relations of form and structure to functions, he will get the experimental and interpretative point of view, and perhaps habits of attacking his problems in a methodical way. He may perhaps come to prefer first-hand knowledge to book knowledge in some limited field at least. He will not, probably, be able to make discoveries, nor can he hope to settle the mooted questions of biology; but he will be able to find out for himself some things that are new *to him*, and to get some clear notions as to how biological questions should be attacked. Particularly, he can be taught the meaning and use of a control experiment,[1] and how to tell a good experiment from a bad one from which no logical conclusions can be drawn.

Principles to be observed in a biological course. — There are certain biological and pedagogical principles that should be prominent in the mind of the teacher in shaping and conducting a course in either botany or zoölogy or human biology. It is not necessary, nor perhaps even possible, that every pupil in a high school class should master these principles in such a thorough way as to be able to follow out all their implications or to give an extended, connected, and logical account of them. If they could all do that, they would be competent to write a textbook or treatise on general biology. What is necessary is that the teacher, through laboratory courses in biological studies extending over at least two years, should have gained a fair working knowledge of these principles himself, and should have formed habits of organizing biological facts with their aid. He should be able habitually to bear them in mind while

[1] That is, two experiments are run side by side, in which *all* the conditions excepting the one under investigation are as nearly as possible exactly alike. In elementary work, this type of experiment is altogether too generally neglected.

shaping his courses, planning his lessons, and carrying on his teaching, so that every opportunity that is practicable may be given his pupils to gain clear conceptions of these principles and to acquire the breadth of view that is sure to result from such conceptions.

1. *Development of the type concept.* — When we speak of *the* frog or *the* common buttercup (*Ranunculus bulbosus*), ordinarily, we do not mean any particular individual, nor do we mean all the animals or all the plants of the species named. Rather we mean any one that is *typical* of the whole species or group to which it belongs. A thousand individuals of a given species collected at random will be alike in certain characteristics, but will vary among themselves in many minor ways. If we could measure the amounts of each of the qualities or characteristics in which they resemble each other and find the average amount of each, we should find that in each of these common characteristics the great bulk of the samples would be near the average, and that those which deviated most widely from the average in the amount of each of these common qualities would be relatively very few. If then we wanted a specimen that would stand as a fair representative or type of the species, we should pick one that was near the average. This is what is meant by a typical individual of a species. When a biologist describes a species, he describes what he estimates is a typical individual of that species. So whenever a species is thought of, these individual differences or variations should be thought of also. Now the individuals of any species that are near the type resemble each other more closely than they resemble those of any other species. In the same way, species which resemble each other more closely than they resemble other species are grouped in larger divisions called " genera." On a like basis genera are grouped into families, families into orders, and so on. For convenience in study, an individual of a species may be taken as a type form of a genus or of a family. The student, after studying

the type in sufficient detail, can then learn in what important respects the representatives of the related genera or families differ from this type, and thus get a relatively large amount of information in condensed form.   It is obvious that this type notion is of immense importance to the student; and the teacher should be at some pains to have it grow up naturally in connection with whatever samples of biological material the pupils are dealing with.   They should get the notion not only of a typical plant or animal, but of a typical seed, leaf, or other organ of either plant or animal.[1]   It is only by forming type notions through the careful study and comparison of a relatively small number of types that anything like a general survey of living forms can be made.   Biological teaching therefore must perforce be carried on through provision for comparative study of type forms.

2. *The comparative principle.* — This brings us to the next principle of biological study, the development through habit formation of a comparative attitude on the part of the pupil. Having made himself acquainted to some extent with a grasshopper, for example, the pupil is led to compare its near relatives, the cricket or katydid, with it, so that he knows the qualities of structure, physiology, habits, and life-history which they have in common, and also the important ways in which the other two differ from the first as a type.   Again, making a study of the crayfish with regard to structure, physiological processes, habits, life-history, and so on, he compares the lobster and crab with it after the same plan that he pursued with the grasshopper and its near relatives.   He is then in a position to compare the crayfish as a type of all crustaceans with the grasshopper as a type of all insects, and learn in what ways the crustaceans differ from the insects, and why they are grouped together as arthropods.   He will accomplish this more easily, and will remember characteristics better as he goes along if he uses the type and comparative notions

[1] Cf. Lloyd and Bigelow, *op. cit.*, p. 126 ff.

from the first. In other words, the crayfish will mean more
to him *while he is studying it* if he has a clear notion of the
grasshopper at the time, and is working with the comparative
attitude. He will then be looking for the resemblances and
differences; and hence every characteristic of structure,
function, behavior, and life-history will mean more to him than
it would if he had no comparisons in mind.

3. *Classification.* — The next principle follows quite naturally from the second. By noting resemblances and
differences in the process of comparing types, the pupil
arrives in a perfectly natural way at the principle of classification, and gets a first-hand appreciation of its economy
and value as a means of organizing and rendering intelligible a mass of facts which otherwise handled would be
chaotic.

4. *Form and structure as related to function.* — In form and
structure, the animal as a whole, and its organs as working
parts of it, are adapted to the activities in which they engage,
the functions that they are called upon to perform. No child
who has tried to capture a grasshopper in the field will have the
slightest difficulty in grasping the notion that one of the grasshopper's necessities is to escape his enemies, that his ability
to hop quickly, or to fly, enables him to do so, and that his legs
and wings are admirably adapted to provide him with this
ability. Here then is one of the countless starting points for a
lesson problem. What is the mechanism of the grasshopper's
leg that enables him to star in the standing broad jump?
Why can he jump so much farther in proportion to his length
than the best boy on the track team can jump? When this
problem of the relation of structure to function has been solved,
others present themselves in profusion. What is the structure
of the wings and body, and the arrangement of the muscles,
that enables them all to coöperate so efficiently in balancing
and flying? On what does the grasshopper feed? How are
the mouth parts adapted to eating? How is the food digested?

How does the insect breathe? Has he a nervous system, and
if so, what is it like? How is it adapted to the functions that
it has to perform? Is it more or less complex than the human
nervous system? Is this difference related to the difference
in the complexity of the work that it has to do? What enemies
and other agencies work destruction among grasshoppers and
thus tend to keep them from destroying our growing grain?
These questions indicate clearly that the right method of
approach is not to study morphology or physiology or ecology
separately, but to study them together by working out problems on a type. They indicate also that in biology as in
all other sciences the joint activity of the teacher and pupils
in field work, in laboratory work, and in class conferences is
unified in the problems.

5. *Adjustment, division of labor, and coöperation.* — Life
involves a continuous process of adjustment to environment.
If the environment of the organism is simple, the adjustment
processes are simple, and few specialized organs are found
to exist. If the environment is complex or difficult, necessi-
tating many adjustments, more parts or organs are necessary
and the organism is found to be complex. There is division
of labor and specialization of groups of cells adapted to perform the various kinds of adjustments both among the working
internal parts of the living machine and in the organs by which
it responds to stimuli from without. Thus we have the
principle of adjustment correlating with the principles of co-
operation and division of labor on the physiological and ecological side, and with the principle of adaptation and differentiation of parts on the morphological side. Physiology and
ecology then represent the dynamic phase, and morphology
(including anatomy, histology, and classification) represents
the static phase in the study of the same life process, —
adjustment. Out of this relation comes another important
principle in biological pedagogy, *study structure and function
together, as related to adjustment, in one type, and compare with*

analogous adjustments and the structures and functions related thereto in other types.

6. *Continuity of life, — life history and race history. —* Each plant or animal type has a life history. From the union of two reproductive cells and the fission of the new cell thus formed until the new individual dies it goes through a cycle of changes from a simple to an increasingly complex condition. Some of the individuals before they die reproduce their kind and hand on to their progeny their race characteristics; so that the life of the race of organisms as a whole is continued. In the history of the races of plants and animals some species as species have become extinct, and are known only by their fossil remains; and others have survived, and exist at the present time. Just as there is a life history for the individual of a species, so for the race there is a succession of changes from simple and undifferentiated forms to complex and highly specialized forms. These changes constitute a race history which can be more or less clearly traced in the successive relationships that the later groups bear to the earlier.

7. *The theory of evolution.* — Thus life, which is limited in the individual, is continuous in the race, and in the struggle for existence those qualities tend to be handed on which have survival value — that is, are advantageous to the individual with reference to adjustment to its environment and the preservation of its life. If the individual lives and reproduces its kind the qualities that are most advantageous to adjustment may be transmitted to its offspring and give them a better chance to survive and transmit it to their progeny; and if the individual does not live and reproduce its kind any quality that may appear in it as a variation cannot be transmitted through it to the race. So survival is connected with advantageous adjustment to environment; and a process of natural selection goes on whereby the best adapted survive. By variation and selection through successive

P

generations, the races of organisms have become adjusted to varying conditions; and newer and more complex forms have resulted.

The young student cannot follow all the evidence in favor of organic evolution, nor go very far into the theories concerning its various factors, nor debate the questions which biological specialists have not been able to settle among themselves; but his attention can be called to the most obvious facts and relations that point in the direction of progress by variation and selection; and he can thus get a broad notion of the evolutionary process. The important rule for the teacher is *to refrain from dogmatizing or quoting authorities, and restrict himself to citing facts, both for and against any statement of theory, and lead the students to maintain an open-minded attitude and get their own point of view.*[1]

General method in biological study. — The preceding principles furnish the basis for a general method in teaching biology. Start with problems that involve the study of a type plant or animal. Study it as a whole, with reference to its general form and structure as related to the work that it has to do. Note its differentiation into parts and the work to which each essential part is adapted. Make comparisons showing the clearest analogies in the case of other types, carrying the comparisons far enough to give a general idea of the plant or animal as a working machine or organism with coöperating parts.

In the case of plants, continue with a similar study of the parts in a somewhat more intensive way, paying special attention to the comparison of similar organs, such as roots, stems, leaves, flowers, and fruit. Study their forms and structure with relation to their functions. When occasions occur, direct attention in different groups of plants to the organs that have a common origin, but are adapted to different uses

---

[1] Read Professor Lloyd's statement, Lloyd and Bigelow, *op. cit.*, p. 136 ff., and compare it with Professor Bigelow's, p. 286, previously referred to.

(homologous organs) and those that have similar uses, but different origins (analogous organs).

Sometimes it is better to let the students observe the structure of an organ and then ask them to find out what it is good for, how it is adapted by its structure to do the things it has to do, and finally what other functions are performed by organs of similar origin both in the plant that is being studied and in other plants also.

At other times, and probably much more frequently, better results will be obtained if the teacher explains some phase of the work that the plant has to do, such as respiration or absorption or reproduction, and then sets up for the pupils such problems as finding out which organs perform the work, what features of their structure are essential to the work, what the origins of these appropriate organs are, and what kinds of organs do this same kind of work in plants of other groups.

In animal biology, after a good idea of the working organs as organs has been gained, proceed with a somewhat more intensive study of a suitable type such as a perch, a crayfish or lobster, or a grasshopper. Let the purpose of this more detailed study be to obtain a knowledge of the general physiological processes in animals, and the adaptations of structure to functions both external and internal. To this end the structures and organs that are adapted to the performance of each kind of important work in the type animal that is being studied should be compared as to make-up and origin with those of the higher animals, and particularly those of man. For example, the breathing apparatus of a frog or a bird should be compared with that in mammals and man, for the sake of the light which it throws for the student on the physiology and hygiene of respiration in man. On the other hand, it should be compared with that of the perch, the crayfish, and the insect, for the sake of the insight into the biological principles of adaptation and development that such comparisons afford.

Typical animal studies should also be made from the standpoints of ecology and behavior, of life history, and of economic and human relations.

After a very few types have been studied thus intensively from the standpoints that have been mentioned, continue the study with types from the other great groups, making the work more extensive and less intensive. Put increasing stress on comparison of types and especially on ecological, economic, and human relations, and steadily diminish the stress on details in anatomy and physiology.

In emphasizing the practical and pedagogical utility of study by types, the author must not be understood as advocating the exhaustive study of a few types by the method of verification that was in vogue fifteen or twenty years ago. Nor is he advocating an exhaustive study of many types, all by the problem method, and each with reference to anatomy, physiology, ecology, etc. The point that he wishes to make clear is that if the student knows well at first hand one plant or animal of a given great group he will then be able to take in from the teacher, from books, and from charts and lantern slides, a large amount of comparative information about near relatives of the type and also about typical representatives of other great groups. For example, knowing the grasshopper well at first hand, he can organize about his knowledge of this insect a large amount of similar but mostly second-hand information concerning crickets and katydids, walking-sticks, etc., and also much concerning the resemblances and differences that would be noted when comparing the grasshopper with the crayfish or lobster, with the salamander or frog, with the earthworm or with the clam, as representatives of great groups that are more or less widely removed from the insects in the animal scale.

In all comparative work lead up to the classification concept, and give practice in classification whenever opportunities come in naturally, and where the classifying helps in the organization of the information that is being acquired. It is undesirable to make classification a principal end; but where the teacher has opportunity he should give the pupils a start in collection, classification, and identification, and encourage those few who have special taste and aptitudes in this line to carry on elementary taxonomic studies for themselves.

Incidentally throughout the group studies the teacher should point out, for observation, facts that have a bearing on the evolution concept. There are many such facts whose meaning can be clearly and easily grasped.

In studying the physiological processes, compare these processes not only in the field of plants or animals, but also correlate in plants and animals and in human physiology.

It is doubtful policy to use for laboratory studies preserved starfish and sponges from the seashore in inland classes to the exclusion of forms that may be gathered by the pupils themselves near their own homes. Make the largest possible use of local and living material and of local human and economic relations that is consistent with the broader aims of the course.

Broader aims of the course. — These aims should be: (1) to give the pupils information of such biological facts and principles as are most directly and obviously related to human welfare and to right living; (2) to give them training in methods of gaining for themselves information in this field of knowledge; (3) to give them opportunity to get an elementary grasp on a few of the great biological principles, and the methods of organizing biological knowledge; (4) to arouse in them an abiding interest in plants and animals, for the sake of the pleasure and intellectual profit and culture that such an interest offers for the employment of leisure out of doors.

Special methods. — The special methods must always be worked out by the individual teachers each for his own school, and tested and improved by trial and success. The best way for a beginner to acquire effective special methods is to master the principles and notions of general method, study and compare the presentations of the various textbooks and laboratory guides, study and compare critically the various syllabi with reference to local conditions, and read from year to year the pedagogical literature that is available on the subject.[1] Lloyd and Bigelow, and Ganong, whose books should be owned and studied by every biology teacher, discuss laboratory methods and equipment as well as general and special method in botany, zoölogy, and human physiology, with sufficient detail to meet the needs even of inexperienced teachers.   With such books available at a price within the reach of any teacher it would be presumptuous in the writer to undertake an extended discussion of special methods and the selection of subject matter even if not forbidden by the space limitation prescribed by the purpose and scope of this book.

Correlation of botany, zoölogy, and physiology. — For a course of one year in biological study there are three plans from which to choose : (1) a half-year of botany, followed by a half-year of zoölogy, closing with a brief survey of human physiology [2] ; (2) a year of botany only ; or (3) a year of zoölogy only.   From the standpoint of a well-balanced curriculum for

[1] Especially Lloyd and Bigelow, *op. cit.;* the current and many of the back numbers of *School Science and Mathematics*, particularly the St. Paul Report of the N. E. A. Committee on Biology of July 9, '14 printed in Vol. 15, 1915, pp. 44–53 : The Report of the Botanical Society of America on Botany in Secondary Schools, in *School Review*, November, 1908 (Vol. 16, p. 594) : Ganong, W. F., *The Teaching Botanist*, Macmillan, 1910 : The Report of the American Society of Zoölogists on Zoölogy for Secondary Schools, College Entrance Board, Sub-station 84, N. Y., Document 48 : and the Definitions of Units in Botany and Zoölogy in the *Report of the Commission on Accredited Schools of the North Central Association of Colleges and Secondary Schools*, Chicago, 1910, price twenty-five cents, which may be obtained from the Secretary, Principal Henry E. Brown, Kenilworth, Ill.

[2] For excellent outlines of such a course, worked out in a single textbook, see Hunter, G. W., *Elements of Biology*, and *Civic Biology*, American Book Co., 1907 and 1914; Peabody, J. E. and Hunt, A. E., *Elementary Biology*, Macmillan, 1913; and Bigelow, M. A., and A. N., *Introduction to Biology*, Macmillan, 1913.

the purposes of general education the author agrees with a number of leading biologists in favoring the first plan. In case the second is adopted he believes that sufficient botanical details should be excluded from the course to give time for frequent comparisons of animals with plants to make their common physiological resemblances and differences clear; and in case the third plan is adopted he believes that a similar comparative use of botanical material should be made; and that in either of the three plans the broader correlations of plant, animal, and human physiology should be made at every point where they will be clear and illuminating.

QUESTIONS FOR FURTHER STUDY

1. What sorts of economies in learning may be effected by the use of the type concept? The comparative principle? How are they related to each other and to the principle of classification?

2. What economies in teaching may result from teaching structures in their relations to functions?

3. How may the principles of adjustment, division of labor and coöperation, and race continuity be used to make biological study more interesting?

4. Make a brief written statement as to how far you would carry the idea of evolution in your teaching.

5. Would you begin to teach the theory by starting with "Most biologists believe . . . etc."? If not, how?

6. Examine three of the latest textbooks in biology, and decide which of them you could do the best teaching with, giving the principal reasons for your decision from the standpoints (a) of subject matter and (b) method.

7. Supposing it impossible, because of time limitations, to realize all the "broader aims of the course" in biology, on which of the aims would you concentrate your efforts?

8. What is your opinion as to the desirability of correlating botany, zoölogy, and human physiology as suggested for all biological courses? Do you think it practicable? Why?

9. Examine the North Central Association units in botany and zoölogy, the College Entrance Board units, and the St. Paul Report of the N. E. A. Committee on Biology. To what extent do the syllabi

presented in these documents agree in spirit with the constructive suggestions made in this chapter?

10. In what respects do these syllabi agree in fundamental pedagogical doctrine? In relative emphasis on the various fundamental principles of biological science?

11. What differences in attitude toward the social and human aspect of biology do you note in these syllabi? To what extent do you attribute these differences to the differences in interests among the persons composing the majorities of the committees that formulated the syllabi?

12. For each of the syllabi, if there seems to be too much suggested for a year's work, indicate the things that in your opinion might be eliminated with the least loss.

13. If obliged to choose only one of these proposed courses for the science curriculum of your school, which would you choose? Give your reasons.

14. In what ways might "civic biology" be correlated with "community civics"?

REFERENCES

BIOLOGY

Treatises and Advanced Textbooks

ABBOTT, JAMES F. The Elementary Principles of Biology. Macmillan, N. Y. 1914. 329 pp. $1.50.

CALKINS, GARY N. The Protozoa. Macmillan, N. Y. Illus. 8vo. $3.00.

COULTER, J. M. Fifty Years of Darwinism. Holt, N. Y. 1909. 274 pp. $2.00.

CAMPBELL, D. H. Plant Life and Evolution. Holt, N. Y. 1911. (Am. Nature Series.) 360 pp. $1.60.

DARWIN, CHARLES R. The Origin of Species. Appleton, N. Y. 1885. $2.00. 2 vol. 1897. $4.00.

DARWIN, CHARLES R. The Variation of Animals and Plants under Domestication. J. Murray, London. Appleton, N. Y. 1890. 2 vols. $5.00.

EGGLING, OTTO, and EHRENBERG, F. The Fresh-water Aquarium, and its Inhabitants. Holt, N. Y. 12mo. $2.00.

HENDERSON, LAWRENCE J. The Fitness of the Environment. Macmillan, N. Y. 1914. 317 pp. $1.50.

HUXLEY, T. H. The Crayfish. An Introduction to the Study of Zoölogy. Appleton, N. Y. 1879. 371 pp. $1.75. This is a classic that should be in every library.

KELLOGG, V. L. Darwinism Today. Holt, N. Y. 1908. 403 pp. $2.00.

LLOYD F. E. and BIGELOW, M. A. The Teaching of Biology. Longmans, N. Y. 1907. 491 pp. $1.50.

METCALF, MAYNARD M. An Outline of the Theory of Organic Evolution, 2d Ed. Revised. Macmillan, N. Y. 1914. 204 pp. $2.50.

PARMELEE, MAURICE. The Science of Human Behavior, Biological and Sociological Foundations. Macmillan, N. Y. 1914. 443 pp. $2.00.

PUNNETT, R. C. Mendelism. Macmillan, N. Y. 3d Edition. 1911. 192 pp. $1.25.

RICHARDS, Ellen H. Sanitation and Daily Life. Whitcomb and Barrows, Boston. 1907. 60¢.

SEDGWICK, W. T., and WILSON, E. B. General Biology. Holt, N. Y. 8vo. $1.75.

SEWARD, A. C., Editor. Darwin and Modern Science. Cambridge, Eng., University Press. Putnams, N. Y. 1909. 595 pp. $5.00.

SPENCER, HERBERT. Principles of Biology. Appleton, N. Y. Rev. Ed. 1899. 2 vols. $4.00. A classic of philosophical biology.

THOMSON, J. ARTHUR, and GEDDES, PATRICK. Darwinism and Human Life. Holt, N. Y. 1911. 245 pp. $1.50.

THOMSON, J. ARTHUR. Evolution. Holt, N. Y. 1911. 256 pp. 75 ¢. (Home and University Library.)

WALLACE, ALFRED RUSSEL. The World of Life. Chapman and Hall. London, Eng. 1911. 400 pp. $3.00.

WALLACE, ALFRED RUSSEL. Darwinism. Macmillan, N. Y. 1899. 16 + 494 pp. $2.25.

WALTER, HERBERT E. Genetics, an Introduction to the Study of Heredity. Macmillan, N. Y. 1913. 264 pp. $1.50.

WILSON, EDMUND B. The Cell in Development and Inheritance. 2d Ed. rev. and enlarged. Macmillan, N. Y. 1914. 483 pp. $3.50.

Elementary Textbooks and Manuals

BIGELOW, M. A. and A. N. Applied Biology. Macmillan, N. Y. 1911. 533 pp. $1.40.

BIGELOW, M. A. and A. N. Introduction to Biology. Macmillan, N. Y. 1913. 415 pp. $1.10.

BAILEY, L. H., and COLEMAN, W. M. First Course in Biology. Macmillan, N. Y. 1908. 224 pp. $1.25.

HUNTER, G. W. Civic Biology. American Book Co., N. Y. 418 pp. $1.25.

HUNTER, G. W.   Laboratory Problems in Civic Biology.   American Book Co., N. Y.   1916.   283 pp.   80 ¢.

HUNTER, G. W.   Essentials of Biology, Presented in Problems.   American Book Co.   1911.   5 + 488 pp. $1.25.

HUNTER, G. W., and VALENTINE, M. S.   Laboratory Manual of Biology. Holt, N. Y.   1906.   12mo.   60 ¢.

HUXLEY, T. H., and MARTIN, H. N.   Course of Practical Instruction in Elementary Biology, rev. by Howes, G. B., and Scott, D. H. Macmillan, London and N. Y.   1892.   279 pp. $2.60.   Type studies of plants and animals.   A book that was influential in shaping the trend toward type studies in biology.

PARKER, T. J.   Elementary Biology.   Longmans, N. Y.   1889.   503 pp. $2.60.   (Plant types and animal types from amœba to dogfish.)

PARKER, T. J. and W. N.   An Elementary Course in Practical Zoölogy.   Macmillan, London and N. Y.   1900.   608 pp. $2.60. (Anatomy, histology, embryology and physiology of the frog, and the animal types of Parker's Elementary Biology with the addition of some vertebrate types.)

PEABODY, J. E., and HUNT, A. E.   Elementary Biology, Plant, Animal, and Human.   Macmillan, N. Y.   12mo. $1.25.

SHARPE, RICHARD W.   A Laboratory Manual for the Solution of Problems in Biology.   American Book Co.   1911.   352 pp.   75 ¢.

SMALLWOOD, WILLIAM, REVELY, IDA L., and BAILY, G. A.   Practical Biology.   Allyn & Bacon, Boston.   1916.   421 pp. $1.25.

Biography, History, and Travel

AGASSIZ, E. C.   Louis Agassiz, His Life and Correspondence.   Houghton, Mifflin & Co., Boston.   1885.   794 pp. $2.50.

ALLEN, GRANT.   Charles Darwin, His Life and Work.   Longmans, London and N. Y.   1888.   206 pp.   Twentieth Century Pub. Co., N. Y.   30¢.   A short biography by a clear and stimulating writer.

CLODD, EDWARD.   Pioneers of Evolution.   Appleton, N. Y.   1897. 6 + 274 pp. $1.50.

DARWIN, CHARLES.   Journal of Researches during the Voyage of H. M. S. Beagle around the World.   Appleton, N. Y.   1893. 10 + 517 pp. $2.00.

DARWIN, FRANCIS.   The Life and Letters of Charles Darwin.   Appleton, N. Y.   1888.   2 vols. $4.50.

GEDDES, P.   Chapters in Modern Botany.   Scribner, N. Y.   1893. 201 pp. $1.25.

GREEN, J. R. History of Botany 1860–1900, being a continuation of Sachs's History of Botany, 1530–1860. Clarendon Press, Oxford, Eng. 1909. 543 pp. $3.15.

HUXLEY, LEONARD. The Life and Letters of Thomas Henry Huxley. Appleton, N. Y. 1901. 2 vols. $5.00.

LOCY, W. A. Biology and Its Makers. Holt, N. Y. 1908. 469 pp. $2.75.

NICHOLSON, H. A. Lives and Labors of Leading Naturalists. Chambers, Edinburgh. 1890.

PACKARD, A. S. Lamarck, the Founder of Evolution, His Life and Work. Longmans, N. Y. 1901. 451 pp. $2.40.

SACHS, J. Tr. by Garnsey, H. E., and Balfour, I. B. History of Botany. Clarendon Press, Oxford, Eng. 1890. 568 pp. $3.25.

THOMSON, J. ARTHUR. The Science of Life, an Outline History of Biology and its Advances. Blackie, London. Crown 8vo. 2s. 6d. Herbert S. Stone & Co., Chicago.

VALLERY-RADOT, RENÉ. Tr. by Mrs. R. L. Devonshire. The Life of Pasteur. Constable, London. 1911. McClure, Phillips & Co., N. Y. 2 vols. Doubleday. $3.00.

WALLACE, ALFRED RUSSEL. The Malay Archipelago. Macmillan, N. Y. 1906. 515 pp. $2.00.

WALLACE, ALFRED RUSSEL. Natural Selection, Tropical Nature, and Other Essays. Macmillan, N. Y. 1891. 492 pp. $2.00.

WALLACE, ALFRED RUSSEL. Island Life. Macmillan, N. Y. $2.00.

WRIGHT, HENRIETTA CHRISTIAN. Children's Stories of the Great Scientists. Scribner, N. Y. 1888. $1.25.

BOTANY

Treatises and Advanced Textbooks

ATKINSON, G. F. A College Text-book in Botany. Holt, N. Y. 1905. 2d ed. 1908. 737 pp. $2.00.

BAILEY, L. H. Cyclopedia of American Horticulture. Macmillan, N. Y. 4 vols. $20.00.

BAILEY, L. H. Cyclopedia of American Agriculture. Macmillan, N. Y. 4 vols. $20.00.

BAILEY, L. H. Standard Cyclopedia of Horticulture. Macmillan, N. Y., 1914. 6 vols. $36.00.

BAILEY, L. H. Botany for Secondary Schools. Macmillan, N. Y. 1913. 460 pp. $1.25.

CAMPBELL, D. H. A University Text-book of Botany. Macmillan, N. Y. 1902. 579 pp. $4.00.

CHAMBERLAIN, C. J. Methods in Plant Histology. University of Chicago Press, Chicago. 1901. 159 pp. $2.25.

CLEMENTS, F. E. Plant Physiology and Ecology. Holt, N. Y. 1907. 315 pp. $2.00.

CLEMENTS, F. E. The Genera of the Fungi. N. W. Wilson & Co., Minneapolis. 1909. 227 pp. $2.00.

COULTER, J. M., and CHAMBERLAIN, C. J. Morphology of Angiosperms. (Pt. II, Morphology of the Spermatophytes.) Appleton, N. Y. 1903. 348 pp. $2.50.

COULTER, J. M., and CHAMBERLAIN, C. J. Morphology of Gymnosperms. University of Chicago Press. 1910. 458 pp. $4.00.

COULTER, J. M., BARNES, C. R., and COWLES, H. C. A Textbook of Botany for Colleges and Universities. American Book Co., N. Y. 1911. Vol. I. Pt. 1, Morphology. 8 + 294 pp. $1.25. Pt. 2, Physiology. Pp. 295–484. $1.25. Vol. II. Ecology. Pp. 485–964. $2.00. Illus. Authoritative, clear, readable.

CURTIS, C. C. The Nature and Development of Plants. Holt, N. Y. 1907. $2.50.

CURTIS, C. C. Textbook of General Botany. Longmans. 1897. $3.00.

GANONG, W. F. The Teaching Botanist, 2d ed. Macmillan, N. Y. 1910. 459 pp. Illus., w. bibliographies. $1.25.

GANONG, W. F. A Laboratory Course in Plant Physiology. 2d ed., extended to form a handbook of experimentation for educational use. Holt, N. Y. 1908. 265 pp. $1.75.

GANONG, W. F. The Living Plant; a description and interpretation of its functions and structure. Holt, N. Y. 1913. 478 pp. $3.50.

GANONG, W. F. A Text-book of Botany for Colleges. Macmillan, N. Y. 1916. 401 pp. $2.00.

GREEN, JOSEPH REYNOLDS. Introduction to Vegetable Physiology. Blakiston, Philadelphia. 1900. 459 pp. $3.00.

JOST, L. Lectures on Plant Physiology, Tr. by R. J. H. Gibson. Clarendon Press, Oxford, Eng. 1907. 546 pp. $6.75.

MACDOUGAL, D. T. Practical Text-book of Plant Physiology. Longmans, N. Y. 1901. 352 pp. $3.00.

NELSON, A. New Manual of Botany of the Central Rocky Mountains. (A revision of J. M. Coulter's book of similar title.) American Book Co., N. Y. 1910. 646 pp. $2.50.

PEIRCE, G. J. Textbook of Plant Physiology. Holt, N. Y. 1903. 291 pp. $2.00.

ROBINSON, B. L., and FERNALD, M. L. A Hand-book of the Ferns and Flowering Plants of the Central and Northeastern United States and Adjacent Canada, being the seventh edition of Gray's New Manual of Botany. American Book Co., N. Y. 1908. 926 pp. $2.50.

SMALL, J. K. Flora of the South Eastern United States. J. K. Small, N. Y. Botanical Garden, N. Y. 1903. 1370 pp. $3.60.

SORAUER, P. Tr. by Weiss, F. E. A Popular Treatise on the Physiology of Plants. Longmans. 1895. 256 pp. $3.00. " An admirable treatment from the practical viewpoint."

STEVENS, W. C. Plant Anatomy. Blakiston, Philadephia. 1907. 349 pp. $2.00.

STRASBURGER, E. Tr. by W. Hillhouse. Handbook of Practical Botany. Macmillan, N. Y. 1893. 425 pp. $2.50.

STRASBURGER, E. Tr. by Lang, W. H., Noll, F., Schenck, H., and Karsten, G. A Textbook of Botany. Macmillan, N. Y. 1908. 4th Eng. Ed. 1912. 746 pp. $5.00.

WARMING, E., and VAHL, M. Tr. by Broom, P., and Balfour, I. B. The Ecology of Plants, an Introduction to the Study of Plant Communities. The Clarendon Press, Oxford, Eng. 1909. 422 pp. $3.25.

Elementary Textbooks and Manuals

ANDREWS, E. F. Botany All the Year Round. American Book Co., N. Y. 1903. 302 pp. (With Flora, $1.50.)

ATKINSON, G. F. Botany for High Schools. Holt, N. Y. 1910. 493 pp. $1.25.

BAILEY, L. H. Lessons with Plants. Macmillan, N. Y. 1899. 491 pp. $1.10.

BAILEY, L. H. Botany, an Elementary Text for Schools. Macmillan, N. Y. 1902. 355 pp. $1.10.

BERGEN, J. Y., and CALDWELL, O. W. Practical Botany. Ginn, Boston. 1911. 545 pp. $1.30.

BERGEN, J. Y., and CALDWELL, O. W. Introduction to Botany. Ginn, Boston. 1914. (Similar to Practical Botany, but briefer.) (With Flora and Key, $1.40.)

BERGEN, J. Y., and DAVIS, B. M. Principles of Botany. Ginn, Boston. 1906. 555 pp. $1.50; and its accompanying Laboratory and Field Manual of Botany. 1907. 90 ¢.

COULTER, J. M. A Text-book of Botany. Appleton, N. Y. 1905. 365 pp. $1.25.

COULTER, J. M. A Text-book of Botany. Appleton, N. Y. 1900. (The author's Plant Relations and Plant Structures bound in one volume.) 348 pp. $1.80.

PHYSIOLOGY

Advanced Textbooks and Manuals

HOWELL, WILLIAM H. A Text-book of Physiology for Medical Students and Physicians. Saunders, Philadelphia. 1911. 4th Ed. 998 pp. $4.00. (Highly authoritative, clear, and comprehensive, with copious references to the best literature on the subject.)

MARTIN, H. NEWELL. The Human Body, Advanced Course. Holt, N. Y. 1896– . 685 pp. $2.50. Standard college text.

SCHAFER, E. A., Editor. A Text-book of Physiology for Advanced Students. 2 vols. Young J. Pentland, Edinburgh and London. Macmillan, N. Y. 1036 pp. $18.00. Full and authoritative, especially strong on physiological chemistry and with authoritative bibliography.

VERWORN, M. Tr. by Lee, F. S. General Physiology. Macmillan, N. Y. 1899. 615 pp. $4.00. Plant and animal physiology treated.

Elementary Textbooks and Manuals

COLTON, B. P. Physiology, Experimental and Descriptive. Heath, Boston. 1897. 399 pp. $1.20.

FITZ, G. W. Principles of Physiology and Hygiene. Holt, N. Y. 1909. 347 pp. $1.12.

FOSTER, SIR M., and SHORE, L. E. Physiology for Beginners. Macmillan, N. Y. 1894. 247 pp. 75 ¢.

HOUGH, T., and SEDGWICK, W. T. The Human Mechanism. Ginn, Boston. 1907 and later. Vol. I. Elements of Physiology. 328 pp. $1.25. Vol. II. Hygiene and Sanitation. 231 pp. $1.25. Also published in one volume.

HUXLEY, T. H. Lessons in Elementary Physiology. Amer. Ed., Rev. by Lee, F. S. Macmillan, N. Y. 1900. 577 pp. $1.10.

MARTIN, H. NEWELL. The Human Body. Briefer Course. Rev. by Fitz, G. W. Holt, N. Y. 1898. 408 pp. $1.25.

PEABODY, J. E. Laboratory Exercises in Elementary Physiology. Holt, N. Y. 1902. Rev. 79 pp. 60 ¢.

PEABODY, J. E. Studies in Physiology, Anatomy, and Hygiene. Macmillan, N. Y. 1903. 332 pp. $1.20.

PYLE, W. L., Editor. Manual of Personal Hygiene. W. B. Saunders Co., Philadelphia, Pa. 1916. 543 pp. $1.50.

WALKER, J. Anatomy, Physiology and Hygiene. 2d Ed. Allyn & Bacon, Boston. 1900. 490 pp. $1.20.

Zoölogy

Treatises and Advanced Textbooks

ADAMS, CHARLES C. A Guide to the Study of Animal Ecology. Macmillan, N. Y. 1913. 183 pp. $1.25.

BAILEY, F. M. Handbook of Birds of the Western United States. Houghton, Mifflin & Co. Boston. 1902, 1908. 514 pp. $3.50.

CALKINS, G. N. The Protozoa. Macmillan, N. Y. 1901. 347 pp. $3.00.

DOWNING, E. R. Some Data regarding the Teaching of Zoölogy in Secondary Schools. School Sci. and Math., Vol. 15, Jan., 1915, pp. 36–43.

JORDAN, D. S. Manual of Vertebrate Animals of the Northern United States. McClurg, Chicago. 1894. 3 + 375 pp. $2.50. Useful for identification of the vertebrates.

KINGSLEY, J. S. Elements of Comparative Zoölogy. Holt, N. Y. 1904. 212 pp. $1.35.

PACKARD, A. S. Zoölogy (Advanced Course). Holt, N. Y. 1886. 721 pp. $2.40.

PARKER, T. J., and HASWELL, W. A. Manual of Zoölogy. Amer. Ed. 1900. Macmillan, N. Y. 563 pp. $1.60. Good on classification.

PARKER, T. J., and HASWELL, W. A. Text-book of Zoölogy. Macmillan, N. Y. 2 vols. 2d revised ed. Illus. 8vo. $9.00.

THOMSON, J. ARTHUR. Study of Animal Life. Scribner's, N. Y. 1906. 369 pp. $1.50. Contains important bibliography.

THOMPSON, J. ARTHUR. Outlines of Zoölogy. Appleton, N. Y. 3d Ed. 1899. 819 pp. $3.50.

Elementary Textbooks and Manuals

COLTON, B. P. Zoölogy, Descriptive and Practical. Parts I and II in one volume. Heath, Boston. 1887 and later. $1.50.

DAVENPORT, C. B., and G. C. Introduction to Zoölogy. Macmillan, N. Y. 1902 and later. 34 + 413 pp. $1.10. Contains key and description for identification, also reference list of books.

DAVENPORT, C. B., and G. C. Elements of Zoölogy. Macmillan, N. Y. 1913. 508 pp. $1.25.

JORDAN, D. S., and HEATH, H. Animal Forms. Appleton, N. Y. 12mo. $1.10.

JORDAN, D. S., and KELLOGG, V. L. Animal Life. Appleton, N. Y. 1900. 329 pp. $1.20.

JORDAN, D. S., KELLOGG, V. L., and HEATH, H.   Animals (the two preceding in 1 vol.).   Appleton, N. Y. $1.80.
JORDAN, D. S., KELLOGG, V. L., and HEATH, H.   Animal Studies. Appleton, N. Y.   1903.   448 pp. $1.25.
LINVILLE, H. R., and KELLY, H. A.   A Text-book of General Zoölogy. Ginn, Boston.   1906.   451 pp. $1.50.

CHAPTER XIII

BIOLOGICAL EQUIPMENT

Method of selection. — A great deal can be done in elementary biology with relatively inexpensive equipment; yet teachers of biology should aim to have as much and as good illustrative material and apparatus as the school and community can afford. Care should be taken, however, that no money be wasted in things that will not be used. In general, the best plan for providing an outfit is first to select the textbook and laboratory manual that are to be used for the course, then to go through it carefully and decide on the demonstration and laboratory experiments that are to be made. Some of those in the book will probably be omitted, and others not in it will be added. When this has been done the list of equipment for the demonstrations to be made by the teacher should first be made out; then the list of appliances to be used in common by the pupils. Before doing this, the teacher should make a careful study of Chapters VI and VII and Part III, Divisions I and II in Ganong's *The Teaching Botanist*, and of Lloyd, Chapter VIII and IX, and Bigelow, Chapters VII and IX, in Lloyd and Bigelow's *The Teaching of Biology*. The appendices I–IV of Peabody and Hunt's *Elementary Biology* will also be exceedingly helpful, whether that book or some other is the one selected for class use. If a year's course in botany is to be given, the teacher before ordering equipment for the laboratory should read carefully Part I of Ganong's *Plant Physiology*,[1] and Osterhout's *Experiments with Plants*.[2]

[1] Henry Holt & Co., N. Y., 1908.
[2] The Macmillan Co., N. Y., 1905. $1.25.

Student's individual equipment. — For each pupil's individual use, the instruments needed are for the most part few and relatively simple and inexpensive. A good hand or pocket lens of two powers (4 to 9 or 6 to 12 diameters), a scalpel or a sharp pocket knife of good quality, a pair of forceps, and two dissecting needles, constitute the irreducible minimum for botany. The dissecting needle can be made by sticking a large sewing needle into the butt of the wooden stalk of a cheap penholder. A good oil-stone should be always at hand in the laboratory so that instruments can be sharpened by teachers or pupils at any time. It is desirable to have in stock a few of the high grade lenses known as doublets and triple aplanats for examining specimens that require considerable magnification, a good working distance, and a large flat field.

For work in zoölogy and physiology, several pairs of bone-forceps and a few cartilage-knives will also be needed.

Dissecting microscopes. — Better than the magnifiers are the various forms of dissecting microscopes, one of the best types of which, when economy is necessary, is the well known Barnes form. This type has been improved by the Spencer Lens Company by cutting out the base block on the two sides of the inclined mirror below the glass stage, so as to admit light from the sides as well as from the front, and by providing a space for keeping dissecting instruments, which opens from the back of the base-block. Equipped with two doublet lenses magnifying six to twelve diameters it is listed at $3.25. It is desirable to have one of these for each pupil.

Compound microscopes. — It is easy to over-emphasize work with compound microscopes, so that time is spent with them that might better be used otherwise. It should be remembered that interposing between the young pupil and the object of observation a complicated tool requiring skill in its manipulation, before he has formed the habit of first seeing all he can see with his unaided eyes or with a simple lens, is likely to confuse him, dampen his enthusiasm, and make him dependent on the teacher. Nevertheless the fact remains that no school, however small, can be considered adequately equipped for biological work unless the equipment includes at least one good compound microscope. The cheap instruments that are often sold by dealers in general school supplies are usually worse than none.

A standard form of instrument, with inclinable stand, perforated or "handle" arm, milled heads for coarse and fine adjustments, iris diaphragm, circular dust-proof double-nose-piece, vulcanite-covered stage, two objectives (16 m.m. and 4 m.m.) and two eye-pieces (4 and 8) can be bought of any of the leading makes for about $33.00. The favorite foreign makers are Zeiss, and Leitz; and standard American makers are the Bausch and Lomb Optical Company of Rochester, and the Spencer Lens Company of Buffalo. These firms are known everywhere as being absolutely reliable.

The ideal class equipment would include one such microscope for each pupil in a division, but when economy is necessary, the work can be managed so that it may be carried on efficiently with one instrument for each two, three, or even four pupils.

When microscopes are ordered for a school, the teacher should see to it that at least one instrument is included which is, or can be, equipped with a substage and Abbe condenser, a high power objective, and other accessories for advanced work, and which will therefore be available for such work and study by himself or for occasional exhibition demonstrations. It will then be possible to add such accessories as a camera lucida, mechanical stage, and so on as they are found to be needed and as funds become available. It is very desirable for his teaching that the teacher should be doing some advanced study; and the school board should encourage him, when it can, by providing the facilities, within reason. On the same basis it would be justified in providing the school with a good camera and a dark-room, if the teachers know how to use them, for the betterment of their teaching. Along with the microscopes, of course, there should be a supply of slides and cover-glasses, a hand microtome, section razor, and razor strop. If the teacher has had training in the technique of sectioning, staining, and mounting materials for permanent slides he should provide for a minimum outfit of paraffin oven, paraffin, turn-table, stains, media, and chemicals for this purpose. It is of great advantage to the class for purposes of accumulating demonstration slides, for inspiring the pupils, and for inciting them to further study, that the teacher do some of this kind of work; but he should possess himself of some knowledge and skill in it before ordering an outfit. The best way to get such knowledge and skill, if he does not already possess it, is through laboratory courses in the summer sessions of colleges or universities.

Homes for living plants and animals. — The biology room should by all means contain some living plants and animals; and therefore a small greenhouse opening from the botanical rooms is a desideratum which in fact is found in a few schools. As a substitute for this, plants may be kept on racks provided near the windows, or better still in a Wardian case, such as is described in Ganong's *Teaching Botanist*, p. 124.

A cheap vivarium, or live-cage, for small animals may be made by combining a large cylindrical galvanized iron pan, such as is sold for catching the water from refrigerators, with a cylinder of the same diameter, made from galvanized iron wire netting, and fitted with a circular cover of the same material. The cylinder and pan may be fastened together with soft copper wire.

As cheap substitutes for aquaria, battery jars or large candy jars may be used; but a good sized rectangular aquarium with glass sides and metal frame is not excessively expensive, and is always a center of great interest for the pupils. A good place for the aquarium is at one end of the teacher's demonstration table adjoining the sink where water supply and drain pipe are near at hand. A long table at the side of the room near the laboratory tables is almost a necessity as a temporary place for supplies; and on this, vivaria, breeding cage, and other things of that sort may find a place. Aquaria, vivaria, breeding cages, Wardian cases, insect nets, and all kinds of naturalists' supplies may be purchased from the firms listed in Chapter X.

General apparatus and supplies. — For dissecting-pans, tin or enamel or granite ware pans with sloping sides, about 6×9 inches at the top, and $1\frac{1}{2}$ to 2 inches deep, may be bought from the hardware dealers or department stores. For pinning down the objects, a piece of cork carpet may be cut of such a size as to fit tightly into each pan at the bottom; or smaller pieces may be held down by strips of sheet lead.

For specimen jars, clear glass patent fruit jars or glass stoppered salt-mouth bottles may be used. Jars of many sizes and styles made especially for preserving specimens are sold by dealers in biological supplies, and listed in their catalogues. They also sell glass-covered boxes and frames for preserving and exhibiting dry specimens, such as insects and plants. These are made of pasteboard or thin wood, and with glass or celluloid in the covers. If a few of these are ordered from the catalogues, it will be seen that they are of simple construction, and others can easily be made by teacher and pupils.

Test tubes, pipettes, and medicine droppers, Petri dishes, glass and rubber tubing, chemicals and other utensils can be bought from the regular dealers, and are best ordered at the same time with similar supplies needed for the chemical laboratory.

For the preservation of bulky physiological material such as bones, hearts, lungs, kidneys, etc., obtained from local butchers, an ordinary garbage can containing formalin solution is very convenient.

Wall charts. — Besides the abundant laboratory material

both living and preserved that may be collected by teacher and pupils, or purchased from dealers, many excellent visual aids in botany, zoölogy, and human physiology are sold in the form of charts. Such are the sets of botanical charts of Kny, Peter, Jung, and Frank and Tschirch, the zoölogical charts of Leuckart-Chun and of Jung, and the charts and manikins in human physiology, of Bauer, Fischer, and Kolb, of Kunrad, Eckhardt, Frohse, and others. All these are made in Germany and may be imported duty free or bought from stock of the Kny-Scheerer Company and other dealers. Such charts should be carefully selected, if possible with the advice of experienced experts.

Models.—Besides the charts an extensive line of models exists, selections from which may be imported duty free or bought from the dealers' stocks. Among those most needed for the efficient illustration of human physiology, are models of the heart and lungs, section of head, digestive system, eye, and ear.

Animal preparations. Human skeletons. — Beautiful and ingenious animal preparations in great variety are sold, and if the school can afford to develop the museum idea to some extent a few of these would be of great interest and value. They are fully illustrated and described in the Kny-Scherer catalogue. Some of the best of these are : type collections of vertebrate skeletons ; half-skeletons, showing one side stuffed and the other side with the bare skeleton ; jars containing specimen series showing life histories of various typical animals ; frames showing life histories of insects, examples of mimicry, noxious and beneficial insects, protective coloration, insect types, and collections illustrating various phases of economic biology. If a few of these are accumulated from year to year the pupils, under proper stimulation by the teacher, may become interested in making and mounting similar collections, such as are within the range of their resources and ingenuity. A good rule in this connection is "After getting a start do not buy anything that you can get the pupils to make."

For the teaching of Physiology, an articulated human skeleton is much to be desired, for it is only with the skeleton that the uses of the bones as levers and their adaptation for the attachment of the tendons and ligaments can be made clear. Such a skeleton can be bought for from thirty-five to forty-five dollars.

Microscopic slides and lantern slides. — Collections of typical microscopic slides are sold by the dealers, showing plant and animal tissues, parts of the smaller insects, bacteria, and the like; and a limited and judicious selection from these is a good investment. Lantern-slides are obtainable in great variety, and in many respects are superior to the wall charts, less expensive, and easier to store and handle. Such slides are not only very useful in teaching, but are also great aids in creating community interest in the school when used along with its other facilities in developing the school as a social center.

Government publications of interest to schools. — The United States Department of Agriculture, and the United States Fish Commission, publish a multitude of reports, bulletins, circulars, and monographs, some of which are of great value in the teaching of practical biology. The teacher should write to the U. S. Department of Agriculture, Division of Publications, for lists of the publications of the Divisions of Entomology, Biological Survey, Animal Industry, Forest Service, and Plant Industry, and of the Farmer's Bulletins that are of interest to schools in the teaching of zoölogy, botany, and agriculture. Write also to the Superintendent of Documents, Government Printing Office, Washington, D. C., for lists of publications for sale, particularly such as are of interest to high school pupils and teachers.

The Yearbook of the Department of Agriculture and many of the other publications that are charged for otherwise may be obtained free by addressing a request to a congressman of the district where the school is located, and giving titles of publications wanted. Address the United States Fish Commission at Washington for a list of its publications. The Agricultural Experiment Stations and the State Departments of Agriculture of various states also publish reports and bulletins, lists of which may be obtained on request; and most of these are free. The agricultural extension departments of several state universities send out free literature to schools in their respective states. Lists of the publications of these departments may be obtained by applying to their respective directors.

Argument for biological equipment. — Usually it is not difficult to secure appropriations for equipment for the teaching of physics and chemistry; but school board members often object to expenditures for biological material. This is largely due to ignorance of its advantages. If the teacher would take the trouble to make the acquaintance of board members and explain to them how the desired material is to be used, he would seldom fail to get a sufficient appropriation for making a beginning. It should then be possible to get the pupils so enthusiastic that other appropriations would come with less difficulty. The expense for even a generous outfit is small in comparison with the cost of a school building, and it ought to be possible to convince men of fair intelligence that a school without apparatus is like a factory without machinery, that equipment is just as necessary for teaching as a place in which to teach, and that most of the apparatus when once bought is as permanent as the building itself. The author, during a long career as a high school teacher of science, experienced little difficulty in getting all the facilities for teaching that he wanted, and it is his belief that where a suitable minimum of equipment is not found in a school, its absence may almost always be attributed to lack of initiative and competency on the part of the teacher. It may be admitted that there are schools, communities, and administrations that so limit and hamper a teacher as to make the building up of a good science equipment almost impossible; but on the other hand it may be asserted that a competent teacher will not remain long in such a school. In fact he ought not to do so, for if he has ability he should go where he can use it to accomplish something.

QUESTIONS FOR FURTHER STUDY

1. Make out a minimum list of biological equipment for such a school as that in which you are teaching or expect to teach.

2. Supposing your school can have only one microscope, what outfit would you select? How would you use it in instruction? Give reasons.

3. To what extent could the making of biological equipment be provided for by projects, either in biology or manual arts?

4. What essential parts of the biological equipment could be contributed by the pupils from their homes?

5. Draw up a plan for gradually acquiring a good series of homemade wall charts. What other departments of the school could help in this scheme?

6. Draw up a plan for acquiring, housing, and cataloging a library of state and governmental biological bulletins.

7. Draw up a plan for selection and use in teaching, of materials from the library of bulletins.

8. Assuming that the class is a committee of the school board, make an appeal for an appropriation for needed biological equipment.

REFERENCES

A list of firms that deal in apparatus and supplies will be found at the end of Chapter X.

The books referred to in this chapter, and others containing hints on equipment, are listed at the end of Chapter XII.

CHAPTER XIV

The new geography. — The publication of the report of the geographical conference of the Committee of Ten, together with the appearance in rapid succession of textbooks by Tarr, Davis, Gilbert and Brigham, Dryer, and others, and the founding of the *Journal of Geography* by Dodge at Teachers College started a movement for "The New Geography" that swept the country like a prairie fire. In this period from 1894 to 1904, there was brought about an over-emphasis on the study of the origin, development, distribution, technical description, and classification of land forms. Laboratory work was introduced which turned mainly on finding examples of various land forms on topographic maps, and on making profiles of such forms from the maps. The result was neglect of the biological and human relations in geography, which was far from the intentions and practice of the new school of geographers, and which probably had not been foreseen by them.

Accordingly in 1904 Professor William Morris Davis in his vice-presidential address [1] before the geographical division of the American Association for the Advancement of Science, inaugurated a new movement which looks toward greater emphasis on the relations of plants, animals, and man to their environment, and in which the human, economic, and political

[1] Elaborated in the *Geographical Journal*, Vol. XX, page 413, and also in the *First Year Book of the National Society for the Study of Education*, Part II.

phases of life that are subject to geographic conditions are to receive the greatest amount of attention.

Changes in subject matter and method. — This movement tends toward the restriction of the study of land forms, of meteorology and oceanography, to what is necessary to the formation of clear ideas of these biological and human relations to environment. It looks toward the omission of many details about scientific curiosities. It calls for increasing emphasis on the geography of the United States and the other modern nations that dominate the earth to-day, viewed from the causal standpoint. It seeks to give an understanding of these countries and their peoples and the activities of those peoples as influenced not only by topography, climate, vegetation, and animal life — by physical and biological conditions and interactions, — but also as influenced by economic, social, and political reactions among themselves.

Professor R. H. Whitbeck [1] puts this phase of the movement thus :

> "First, it must give the pupil a fund of useful geographical knowledge, the kind that will serve him in the various activities of citizenship. We shall find it difficult to defend the teaching of the causes of the Peloponnesian War, the details of the Amphictyonic Council, and scores of similar matters of ancient and medieval history, which we drill into school children, and then excuse a school which makes no serious effort to give its pupils an understanding of modern Germany, Japan, or Argentina. The life and industries of the people of Babylon and Thebes is a proper subject for study ; but it is not a substitute for a knowledge of modern Mexico, Canada, or Russia. Fossil facts are not worth more, they are as a rule worth less, than living facts. . . . The geography which is going to be demanded to-morrow is the geography that makes people reasonably intelligent about the cities and countries and peoples of their own day. This is politico-economic geography. It is a social science ; but it will, I hope, be built upon a knowledge of the principles of physical geography."

[1] Proc. N. E. A. Ann Arbor, Mich., 1914, page 733, Address before the Department of Science Instruction.

What geographical knowledge is of most worth? — It seems fairly obvious that the most valuable geographical knowledge is first that of the home locality, next that of our own country, and last that of those foreign countries that are most intimately related to our own.   Such knowledge implies the ability to locate on a map the cities, states, rivers, ports, plains, and mountain ranges that are of greatest interest and significance, to trace the routes of travel by means of which they may be reached, and to understand in a general way how they are related to one another as to size, direction, and distance. It appears also that these facts can be thoroughly understood only through a knowledge of the physiographic and physical forces that underlie topography, climate, and the other conditions that control vegetation and animal life; so that knowledge of these conditions and causal relations is of fundamental worth also.

Further, one needs to know in a broad way how the peoples of foreign countries are related to his own people socially, economically, and politically.

Finally, it appears that the ability to find and use maps, charts, gazetteers, and government reports is an essential part of the ability to get and organize needed geographical information at any time; so this kind of geographic knowledge is worth most of all.

Length of the course, and its place in the curriculum. — It would seem to be quite clear that if such an ambitious program as is suggested by the preceding inventory of needed geographical knowledge is to be carried out, it cannot be accomplished in a half year, even though with the advent of better prepared teachers, better equipment, and better methods of instruction we may hope for the accomplishment of much more effective work in the elementary grades, and expect to build on that in high school.   If a half year only is to be spent on this important subject, it may perhaps be better to place it in the first year of the high school, and limit it mainly to physical geography, starting always with local problems, and radiating out to other countries only in a very broad and impressionistic way. In this case the facts and relations given should be accurate and carefully proportioned so far as they go; but all attempts at detailed knowledge of economic and political geography would have to be given up. If a larger program is to be attempted, the course should be placed in the second year, and preceded in the first year by a course in biological study.

The teacher's point of view. — In the preceding chapters an attempt has been made to give the teacher the right point of view and a proper sense of the relative proportion of things from the psychological and social standpoint, together with some knowledge of the meaning of science as related to human progress. The teacher of geography must add to this the right point of view with special reference to geographical facts and particularly with reference to their relative importance and their relations to one another. There are, therefore, a number of underlying geographical principles with which he should make himself so well acquainted that he has thorough command of them, and can use them for ordering and connecting the geographical facts that he teaches; for it is only through the use of such principles that his students can acquire the power to use the geographical facts that they know in order to gain a working comprehension of geographical conditions and facts that lie beyond their immediate and intimate experience. These principles are briefly described in the paragraphs that follow.

Relations between peoples and their environment. — The activities of man in carrying out his life purposes are controlled by the distribution of heat and moisture. These in turn are controlled by the movements of the atmosphere, and these again by the form and movements of the earth and its relations to the sun. Streams, lakes, and oceans, mountains, plains, plateaus, valleys, and shore lines, all combine in various ways to affect his activities both directly and through their effects on the distribution of plants and animals, of soils and other mineral resources, as well as through their control of transportation routes and means of intercommunication. All these interdependent forms and agencies constitute the environment to which man must adjust himself, or which, when he can do so, and with advantage, he adjusts to himself. To affect this adjustment to his environment he must understand it, — he must comprehend it; and herein lies the central motive for the study of geography. The process of adjustment, which is life itself, gives rise to multitudes of problems to be solved. Problems of vital utility and problems of absorbing intellectual interest grow directly out of the pupil's daily life, and reach out to the distant parts of the earth and off through millions of miles of space to the sun. But man's environment is not physical and biological alone; it is social, political, and economic as well; and his adjustments in this field involve actions and reactions among organized bodies of men, which reach out to the uttermost parts of the inhabited earth.

Physiographic processes and their results. — The processes which combine to produce the different land forms are of three general kinds:

1. Large areas of the earth's crust slowly sink down in some parts of the earth and other areas are slowly elevated bodily, or are arched or folded upward.

2. The crust of the earth in some places becomes fractured; and lava is thrust up from the heated interior, either locally as in volcanoes, or over large areas as in the case of the Columbia River lava plateau.

3. The elevated lands are weathered by the action of the atmospheric gases and moisture combined with changes of temperature; by the action of gravity the waste materials fall or slide or creep down the slopes; and the water that falls on the lands as rain or snow moves downward as streams

or glaciers, carrying the wasted rock seaward and grinding down the land.

The erosion by streams cannot wear down the land below the level of the waters into which it flows. This level is called its *base-level;* and when the stream has worn down its bed till the slope is such that the water, with the speed that it has in consequence of this slope, is just able to carry the rock-waste that comes to it, the stream bed is said to be graded to its base-level. It then has a very gentle slope to base-level near its mouth and a steeper slope in the uplands near its sources. It approaches this graded condition by cutting down or degrading its bed where the bed is above grade and building it up or aggrading by depositing sediments where it is below grade. The deposition of sediments is caused by the checking of the speed of the water when it reaches a slope that is too gentle to give it a sufficient fall. In a somewhat analogous manner, the shore lines become graded and adjusted to the movements of the waters of the lakes and oceans.

The condition of the lands and the forms into which they are molded and carved is the resultant of these three kinds of processes (called respectively diastrophism, vulcanism, and gradation), just as each of these processes is itself the resultant of physical and chemical forces and conditions that are coöperating in various combinations everywhere and have been coöperating through all time, since the first land appeared above sea level.

The physiographic cycle. — Because these physiographic processes follow in sequences of cause and effect there results in the case of a plain, plateau, or mountain system a sequence of changes whereby valleys are carved into the uplifted lands and are gradually deepened and widened until ultimately the uplands between are worn away to a very even and gently sloping plain diversified and interrupted only by occasional portions of the more resistant uplands and highlands. Such a worn-down region is called a *peneplain;* and the upstanding portions of the more resistant highlands that remain above the even sky-line of the peneplain are called *monadnocks*. After a region has been worn down to a peneplain it may have been again uplifted, and the process of grading may have been begun over again, and carried to the stage of maturity or of old age, or it may be still in the youthful stage of this new cycle. Southern New England is such a peneplain, uplifted and tilted toward the southeast, and redissected to the stage of maturity. It has been further modified by glaciation.

Thus the streams themselves and the lands through which they flow go through sequences of changes which can be predicted when the conditions are known, and which are somewhat analogous to the larger changes that go on in the life history of a plant or animal. This notion of a physiographic cycle including the life-history periods of youth, maturity, and old age, when applied to river systems, lakes, plains, plateaus, mountains, and shore lines is very useful as a means of organizing geographical facts and phenomena into condensed and meaningful concepts that are easy to remember because of their obvious causal relations. These concepts in turn are useful in connection with understanding the controls that these physiographic features, when combined with physiographic, economic, and political tendencies, exert on the life and activities of the people who live near them.

Geographic influences. — Thus we have (1) the physiographic influences of temperature and moisture, of the atmosphere and its movements, of soils and rocks, and of topographic features, barriers, and outlets; (2) the organic or biological influences of the mutual interactions of living things; and (3) the human or social influences of the tendencies and motives that direct human conduct. So also we have the *responses* of individuals and social groups to these influences or controls. For example, the activities of peoples who inhabit rich and level plains are predominantly pastoral or agricultural until the pressure of increasing population forces the development of manufacturing. Again, peoples living on narrow strips of coast separated from the hinterland by mountain barriers, but furnished with abundant harbors, are forced to become fishermen and marine traders.[1]

There are many important responses also by which man seeks with success to control natural conditions for his own benefit. Some of the most interesting are those wherein organized groups of men, such as private corporations, and municipal, state, or national governments through their agents and engineers, build roads, railroads, levees, canals, and reservoirs, irrigate deserts, dig a Panama Canal, dredge harbors, dam and bridge streams, create and regulate forest reserves, build fires in orchards on frosty nights, and do many other things that control nature herself for human needs. All such actions and reactions constitute the processes of geographic adjustment whereby men get on with nature and with one another. The study of these controls and adjustments, their causes and consequences, involves the consideration of causes and effects. Not merely What is this like? and Where is it located? but How came it to be? and What will be the consequences? are the questions for which the inquiring mind seeks answers; and the boys and girls have a right to these answers so far as they want them, can understand them, and can get them mostly through their own efforts.

The type concept and the comparative method in geography. — Because the forces that operate on them are alike everywhere, and the conditions under which these forces operate are

[1] The potent influences of natural surroundings, and of other peoples, on the development and activities of the American people, are described clearly and most interestingly in the following volumes, which should be read by every teacher of geography or American history. Semple, Ellen C., *American History and its Geographical Conditions*, Houghton, Mifflin & Co., Boston, 1903; Brigham, A. P., *Geographic Influences in American History*, Ginn, Boston, 1903; Shaler, N. S., *Nature and Man in America*, Scribner, N. Y., 1915. Professor James H. Breasted in his *Ancient Times, a History of the Ancient World* (Ginn, Boston, 1916) describes in a fascinating way the influences of geographical environment on the development and mutual relations of the ancient peoples.

R

similarly combined in various places, it happens that similar land forms are produced. Thus, there is a narrow coastal plain lying between the mountain highlands of Mexico and the waters of the Mexican Gulf, extending to the northwest and southeast of Vera Cruz, and another that resembles it lying between the plateau of Dekkan and the Bay of Bengal. These two plains are very similar in their origin, are about equally distant north from the equator, and resemble each other in many other ways; so that if one of them has been studied and is well known much is also known about the other. There are narrow coastal plains in other parts of the earth which resemble these in most ways, but each has its individual characteristics. If one were to study each of these without comparing it with the others he would have to burden his memory with many details about each of them; and no one of them would have much of meaning or interest to him; but if he acquainted himself thoroughly with one of these plains, and used it as a type for all others that were like it in most ways, he would have only to compare each with the type, and learn in what important ways it differs from the type and why. Thus he would be able to know the characteristics of all of them by studying one carefully and learning its origin and characteristics, and then adding to this knowledge only a few additional facts about each of the others. Thus rivers, lakes, and shore-lines, mountain chains, plateaus, coastal plains, lake plains, and river plains fall into classes, that may be represented by typical specimens, and briefly described by comparing them with these types. The immense economy of thought that is brought about by the use of this type notion in geography should be obvious to the thoughtful teacher, and he should be prepared to use it in his teaching on every occasion, in order to assist his pupils in the comprehension and organization of geographical facts and relations.

Not only physiographic features, but also large areas or regions exist, all parts of which have the same general character and origin and are characterized by similar conditions of elevation, topographic form, climate, and organic life. Such regions, for example, are the Atlantic coastal plain, the Piedmont plateau, the Appalachian mountain system, the basin of the Great Lakes, the Mississippi valley, the Rocky mountain system, the Great Basin, the broken Colorado plateaus, and so on. These regions may be described broadly, and one may know that the general conditions of the description apply to any locality that lies within them or forms a part of them; so again the general study and description by physiographic regions is of great convenience and utility in the economy of thought, in the formation of clear mental pictures, in the organization of geographical information for ready recall when needed, and in the interpretation of the relations of plants, animals, and people to their physiographic environments.

The use of the causal notion. — The habit of tracing sequences, and looking for relations of cause and effect between geographical facts, is of prime importance, because causal relations form the natural and logical basis for the organization of those facts. The reference of facts and processes to their causes, the explanation and grouping of facts according to their origins, enables us to classify them and refer them to types which stand for them, and to infer the past and future from the present. Such rational treatment appeals to the instinctive desire of every normal child to know the why of things. It keeps interest alive and assists immensely in memorizing facts for future use. The habit of tracing causes and inferring consequences is the most practical and useful mental habit that we can inculcate, because inferences as to causes and consequences are needed as the basis for every judgment or decision for the determination of conduct. Concerning a geographical fact, therefore, the teacher should ask not merely What is it? and Where is it? but also How came it to be? What will become of it? and What effects does it produce on our lives or on the lives of those who are related socially or politically to us ?   The causal relations of a fact furnish a good criterion of its worth as knowledge ; for if its causes and consequences are not important to us, the fact itself is practically not worth learning.[1]

Mental functions in geographical study. — In solving geographic problems and in getting and organizing geographic information there are certain things that the student must learn to do.

1. He must observe the facts and phenomena that are related to the problem and may throw light on its solution, and neglect those that have no bearing on it.   That is, he must *observe selectively* in order to be successful.   This process is carried on in the field and laboratory work on the problem.

2. He must learn to *represent* what he observes so that it may be preserved for reference, thought, and discussion.   This means the making of sketches, models, or sketch maps that present the essential features so that they may be used to assist recall in the process of reflection or to make matters clear in the discussion of these features in the class conference. This practice of representation also assists him in learning to read maps and interpret pictures and descriptions.   This ability to read maps and interpret pictures and descriptions, made by others, of places that he has not seen is of the very greatest importance to any one needing geographical information.   Incidental to this is the knowledge of where to get the maps and descriptions that are available, and this the student of geography ought to be taught by being sent to card catalogues and bibliographies and by being told where and by what procedure maps, reports, and monographs can be obtained.

3. The student should learn to single out and *describe* accurately and concisely the essential geographical features of the forms that he observes in the field ; and he should be

[1] Cf. Spencer, Herbert, *Education*, Appleton, N. Y., 1883, p. 64 ff.

trained in the laboratory and class conference to make similar descriptions of physiographic features as he infers them in reading maps and pictures.   This process involves analysis, classification, and generalization.

4. He should be guided in the *rational* mode of geographical study, so that he may learn to analyze out and consider the features of a situation that bear on the problem in hand.   He should be guided in handling mentally the features which he has analyzed out and described, so that he can learn by practice to reason inductively from effects back to origins, causes, and general geographic principles, and to reason forward deductively to consequences of these principles under varying conditions.

5. His attention and thought should be directed not only to the origin and development of land forms as consequences of combinations of physical forces but also to the movements of populations and the activities of men as the results of physiographic conditions and processes combined with social conditions and processes.   In other words, he should learn to use the *causal notion* in its application to both physical and social relations.

The mental processes here described are not to be thought of as going on successively or separately.   In problem solving — that is, in thinking — they never do.   They must be thought of separately by the teacher in order that he may know how to study them and guide the pupils in using them. They are *not* " mental powers to be exercised and developed "[1] like the muscles of an athlete.   They are specific mental activities that enter into the processes of solving specific problems;   and the complex ability to deal with geographical questions and master geographical concepts is acquired if at all, not by training mythical powers of memory, imagination, and concentration, but just by practice in solving such problems.

[1] Report of the Committee of Ten, p. 214.

QUESTIONS FOR FURTHER STUDY

1. Sketch briefly the recent changes in point of view with reference to the teaching of geography.

2. Why are the most intrinsically useful phases of geography also the most cultural, if rightly taught?

3. Briefly summarize the kinds of geographical knowledge that are of most worth. Would you, in this connection, differentiate between rural and urban people? Give reasons.

4. What is the individual and social basis for a central motive in the study of geography?

5. How is geography related to history and civics as regards this central motive?

6. Can the three basic physiographic processes be made clear to ninth and tenth grade children? In attempting to do this should the teacher try to discuss geological theories of diastrophism and vulcanism? What is the proper procedure?

7. Would you bring out the idea of geographic cycle, and of physiographic controls inductively and gradually, or would you present them early in the course and use them in later work to "explain the facts"? Why?

8. What advantages to you as a teacher can be obtained through reading a book like Ellen C. Semple's?

9. Explain with an example, not used in this book, how you would use the type concept and comparative method in teaching geography.

10. How would you relate your home or school locality to the physiographic region of which it is a part?

11. Why is the use of the causal notion in geography so useful as a factor in general cultural and disciplinary education?

12. How would you, in teaching, provide for forming the habit of tracing causes and effects?

13. How would you provide for practice in the different mental processes enumerated as factors of geographical thinking?

14. What are the advantages, in teaching geography, of beginning with a problem of immediate local interest?

15. Illustrate, by an example of the draft of a lesson plan, the correct use of the textbook.

REFERENCES

Consult the list at the end of Chapter XV.

CHAPTER XV

METHODS IN GEOGRAPHY

Begin with local problems. — To the teacher who has the point of view that has been set forth, it will be obvious that the study of physical, of politico-social, or of economic geography should begin with intimate home problems. Perhaps no better one to begin with could be found than that suggested by the question, How do we get our drinking and wash water? In the country this would lead at once to wells and cisterns and the conditions that maintain them, and thence to the sources and movements of ground water. This would lead to problems of farm and village drainage, the effect on crops, and to other related facts and conditions affecting or controlling farm and village life. Directly connected with drainage problems are the problems of soil. What kinds of soils are found in this locality? What crops grow best in each kind? Why do these soils differ? From what were they made? These questions lead to field studies of the processes of weathering and stream erosion as related to rainfall and to the production and transportation of rock-waste, and involve a brief laboratory and field study of rocks and rock-forming minerals. The study of neighboring streams, which the solution of these problems necessitates, raises other questions as to where the stream begins (springs and lakes) and where it goes (river system, river basin, life history of rivers, and the kinds of controls they exert on populations at their various stages of development). The study of the drainage basin to which the locality belongs also leads, either immediately or later as the teacher may decide, to the study of the larger physiographic region of which it is a part, and to the life relations that exist between this part and the whole. The study of the local rainfall and run-off in relation to water supply for man, beast, and vegetation leads back to the conditions that produce the precipitation and distribution of atmospheric moisture; and this in turn to atmospheric movements, weather, climate, and the relation of climate to topographic features.   Thus each problem suggests others which are more or less closely related to it, or grow directly out of it. As these problems are solved, the information accumulated should be organized and built up into small systems,[1] which in turn are incorporated into larger outlines as the knowledge of the pupils grows.

In the city the question of water supply leads to a study of the city water plant, this to the sources of supply, and this in turn to the study of streams and their work.   The problem of city sewage disposal leads also to the streams, and suggests a question of grave import to every city.   Is our water supply polluted by sewage from our own city or from elsewhere?

Again, by what roads, railways, and waterways are our food and raw materials brought in and our manufactured products carried out?   Why were these routes chosen? (Valleys, ancient lake beaches, mountain barriers and passes, road-making materials, etc.)   There should be no difficulty in starting such problems when approaching any new topic whatever.   If the teacher is not inhibited by medieval traditions of " logical order," they will bristle up in such abundance that one will be ready for every lesson.   For the child, the personal relation is the natural, psychological starting point of interest in every one of them [2]; and next to this comes the social relation.[3]   The question, Where does our

---

[1] Cf. pp. 76–79, *ante.*
[2] Cf. Dewey, John, *Interest and Effort,* Houghton Mifflin Co., 1913, p. 23 ff.
[3] *Ibid.*, p. 84 ff.

coal come from? leads not only, say, to the dissected Allegheny plateau and its origin and history as a physiographic feature, but also to the questions, What kinds of people are the miners who get this coal out of the ground for us? How do they live? How do they work? Where do they come from? (Poland, Hungary, Sicily, etc.) Why did they emigrate? So the same problem, according to the turn the teacher gives it, leads through personal and social relations to the study of a distant part of our own country or even to the countries beyond the seas.

Textbooks. — There are half a dozen excellent and (at least to an adult) attractive textbooks on physical geography which differ but little one from another either in the amount or the choice of subject matter that they present. It matters little which one the teacher uses. What really matters is the way in which he uses it. *The wrong way* is to assign a lesson to be studied and recited from the book. *The right way* is to start a problem and send the pupils to the book for information which, combined with their own observations and reflections, and the assistance given by the teacher, will help them to solve it. Textbook study, field and laboratory study, class conferences, all then become means instead of ends. For the pupil the end is no longer to make a perfunctory recitation from artificial academic motives, but to find out something that he wants to know, because he can see its meaning and value in connection with the realization of his own life purposes and activities and with the purposes and activities of people who he finds are in some way related to him. *The textbook, then, finds its proper place as a mine of information and a guide for organization and review.* " Pupils, from the start, must be impressed with the fact that geography is a study of the earth and not of the book." [1]

---

[1] Sutherland, William J., *The Teaching of Geography*, Scott, Foresman & Co., Chicago, 1909, p. 43.

In connection with the use of a textbook it is important for the teachers to recognize three facts: (1) Every one of the textbooks has more matter in it than any high school pupil can assimilate in a year; hence selection is absolutely necessary. (2) The teacher should make the selection, using only the materials that can be made significant and comprehensible to the pupils of his own locality. There is more danger in attempting to cover too much ground than there is of covering too little. (3) There will always be differences in the significance of topics due to differences between localities; and therefore for any locality the treatment of the text on some topics may not be full enough to suit the case. Here the teacher must supplement the text from other sources, such as special monographs and government reports. On this principle, pupils in Colorado would study mountains in more detail and pay less attention to the oceans and shore lines than would pupils living near the sea. The latter would study mountains less in detail because mountains and mountainous conditions are farther removed from their actual experience, and are therefore less significant to them.

This principle, however, should not be carried to an extreme, for often it will be found that children are much more keen to learn of that which is novel and far removed than of that which lies close at hand; and in this their instincts are correct in large measure. Even people situated among the mountains or in the midst of the great plains of the interior states cannot understand their New England countrymen politically unless they have some comprehension of the shore lines of New England, and the controls which they exert.

Field work. — The general method for conducting field lessons has been outlined in a previous chapter.[1] As to what to study in the home locality, the teacher will find at the end of each chapter of Tarr's "New Physical Geography"[2] an

[1] Pp. 143–149, *ante.*
[2] The Macmillan Co., N. Y., 1904.

abundance of suggestions. "The Teacher's Guide "[1] to accompany Gilbert and Brigham's "Introduction to Physical Geography "[2] is also replete with helpful hints and directions for field work. Specific directions which will suggest general procedure, what to study, and how to attack local field problems in detail are given by Whitbeck and Martin in their bulletin on the High School Course in Geography.[3] The teacher should also read Sutherland's "Teaching of Geography "[4] for light on this important subject. Dryer's "Studies in Indiana Geography "[5] is very suggestive, especially Chapter IX.

As far as possible the order of topics and the times of excursions should be correlated so that the field observations represent definite steps in obtaining facts needed for the solution of problems raised in the classroom; and manifestly the search for these facts should be made at the time when the problem is under consideration, rather than at some time before or after. This is not always possible, however; and therefore when facts are learned in the field which are to be used in the classroom on a problem that must come up later, the pupils should be urged to note and remember these facts because they will help to answer a question that will be raised later in the course, and the question should then be stated. So also when a problem is taken up in the classroom, and the field data cannot be obtained until some time afterwards, the teacher should state the facts to be noted in the field, and urge the pupils to remember their connection with the problem, so that they may verify it when the excursion can be made. The observance of this precaution will help

[1] Appleton's, N. Y., 1907.

[2] *Ibid.*, 1902.

[3] Whitbeck, R. H., and Martin, L., University of Wisconsin, Bulletin No. 382, High School Series, No. 10. Secretary of the Committee on Accredited Schools, R. 119, University Hall, Madison, Wis.

[4] Scott, Foresman & Co., Chicago, 1909, pp. 209–216.

[5] Inland Publishing Co., Terre Haute, 1905 (out of print, 1917).

greatly in establishing the memory bonds desired, as well as in motivating both parts of the work.

Field projects and problems. — It will be sufficient here to present as examples only a few of the many field projects that may be easily carried out in most localities.

1. Find the local depth of the level of permanent ground water by measuring the depths of several wells. Use string, large block, and yardstick.

2. Is the soil local, river borne, or glacial? Account for the differences in soils in different localities. What kinds of crops grow best in each kind, and why? Examine new cellars and wells. If the soil is glacial, determine whether it is till, or washed gravel, or loess, and account for its presence. Account for striations, large boulders, and sheepbacks. If there are artesian wells or oil wells in the vicinity, get the driller's records and learn kinds and depths of soils and strata from them.

3. If there is a brook or river near, make a careful study of its valley. Determine depth of valley and slope of sides. In what parts is the stream cutting down? Where building up? Sketch and map terraces and meanders. If there is a gorge make cross-sections and profiles in different parts, compare width and slopes with resistant qualities of the rocks and soils.

4. Compare the local stream with other streams, with the aid of topographic maps and pictures, so that the first-hand knowledge of the stream may be used in building mental pictures of streams that have not been seen.

The teacher should obtain all the topographic contour map-sheets for his vicinity, if any such have been made. This he can find out by addressing a letter of inquiry to the Director of the United States Geological Survey, Washington, D. C. Whenever an excursion is made the map, if there is one, should be taken along, and the route and all the topographic features seen on the way should be identified on the map. At times the procedure should be reversed, and topographic features represented on the map should be found with its aid and identified in the field. In this way the pupils of a school that is fortunate enough to be located within an area that has been mapped by the Survey will soon learn to read a topographic map with intelligent appreciation, and will know how to use one for pleasure and convenience when spending a vacation or traveling in localities that have been mapped.

The pupil's attitude in field work. — As far as it is possible to make it so, the attitude of the pupils on the excursion should be that of getting facts for the working out of a definite project or for the solution of a specific problem, rather than the more indefinite attitude of getting as much information as possible about the locality that is being studied. In visiting a stream, for example, one might state the purpose as " Study of a Stream and Its Valley," or " To Study Weathering and Erosion." In this case the pupil's attitude is likely to be passive, his observations casual, and his ideas and conclusions very vague; but if the teacher states the purpose as a specific question or project, reflection and selective observations will probably begin at once. Thus, " Study Rapid Creek below the point where Jones's Brook flows into it, and find out (*a*) why there is an island there; (*b*) why there is a steep bluff on the west side and a gently sloping, gravelly bank on the opposite side; and (*c*) why just below this point there is a bluff on the east side and a gravel slope on the west bank; (*d*) write a statement telling the conditions that determine the meandering habit of this part of the stream, the formation of bluffs and alluvial deposits, and the special effects produced by floods." It takes more time and care to state the purpose in some such way as this; but if any one doubts that the specific and problematic form of statement is better, let him try it and note the difference in the attitude of the pupils toward the work.

Laboratory work. — As in the field work, so in the laboratory work the assignment should be a project or a problem, or a part of one, to the full extent that this is practicable, and for the same psychological reasons. It should never be conceived as a merely disciplinary exercise or task. Because geography goes far afield, and involves information about features and places that the students have never seen, there should be an abundance of illustrative materials of all kinds, such as wall maps, physical and political, blackboard outline maps, seat maps, globes, geographic models, pictures, lantern slides, minerals and rocks. These should be used freely and generously both in classroom and laboratory, whenever they will assist in any way in forming clear and meaningful concepts. Wall maps and lantern slides are especially appropriate in the class conference, but pictures, specimens of rocks and minerals, and topographic maps also should often be displayed or handed around during the conferences. Some simple physical and chemical experiments, furthermore, are very necessary at times; and these may often be made at the lecture table instead of being used as individual laboratory exercises.

Some laboratory projects and problems. — A few simple laboratory problems and projects are given in order to indicate what kinds of work are likely to be most vital.

1. In connection with the study of ground water, stand several student-lamp chimneys of the same size in deep saucers. Half fill one with humus, another with sand, another with clay, another with coarse gravel, and another with half sand and half clay surmounted by a layer of humus. Pour equal amounts of water into each, and let each stand for the same length of time. Measure or weigh the water that seeps through each one, and calculate for each the per cent that seeps through and the per cent that is absorbed. Tabulate the percentages in the notebook, and indicate them graphically on cross-ruled paper, by a series of vertical bars arranged in the order of the permeabilities of the specimens. For example, if in the case of one sample 75 per cent of the water seeps through and 25 per cent is absorbed, let the bar be, say, 4 inches high, and represent 100 per cent; and color the lower 3 inches blue, to represent the per cent of seepage, and the upper inch red to represent the per cent of absorption. Weigh samples of various kinds of rock that have been soaked in water for a given time; then bake them, and weigh them again, to determine the ratio between the weight of each sample and the weight of water that it has absorbed. Express the ratios as percentages, tabulate, and represent graphically as before.

2. In the cities or in other localities where it is difficult to get field examples of the various types of land forms due to weathering and erosion, the teacher may have a load of sand and a load of

clay hauled into a corner of the school yard, and with the aid of the boys make an experimental erosion tank, by banking up an area of a few square feet with dikes of clay. At one end of this area land forms of various sorts may be built up of layers of sand and clay, representing weak and stronger layers of rock. These land models may be made to represent plains, plateaus, or mountains. With a fine spray from a garden hose, a tree-spraying apparatus, or even a sprinkling-pot, heavy or light showers may be allowed to fall on the land model. The water will run down the slopes and form a lake at the foot of the tank. The water will carve out valleys and deposit sediments in the lake. Since the materials are soft, valley development and deposition will go on very rapidly. Let the students sketch, map, or photograph the different forms and explain in their notes the way in which they are wrought out. Let them compare these forms with similar ones on a larger scale that are represented on the topographic map sheets of the distant regions to be studied. Care should be taken to aid the pupils in imagining the actual sizes of the real land forms represented on the map sheets.[1] With such a simple contrivance miniature examples of gorges, terraces, waterfalls, rapids and reaches, meanders, flood plains, alluvial fans, talus slopes, deltas, and marine plains may be formed, and even miniature cliffs, beaches, and sand spits may be worked out by making artificial waves and currents in the water. Such projects are almost sure to interest the students if the teacher gets them started to working these out themselves instead of having them look on passively while he does all the working and thinking for them. These are not as good, of course, as real examples seen and studied in the field, but when used in connection with careful teaching they may be made immensely helpful to students in understanding the nature of processes and forms which otherwise might often be obscure. The teacher must constantly impress upon the pupils that the real land forms are immensely larger and the processes almost inconceivably slower.

It is very difficult for a class living in a hill country, like that of southeastern Ohio, to imagine a coastal or lacustrine plain, or for a lot of children who have never been away from a glacial lake plain to imagine a mountain. The teacher's resourcefulness will

[1] Detailed directions for experimental studies of this kind are given in Tarr and Von Engeln's *Laboratory Manual of Physical and Commercial Geography* and in Von Engeln's *Guide for Laboratory Geography Teaching*. The Macmillan Co., N. Y., 1913.

be taxed to the utmost in order to give them adequate ideas of things for which they have in their experience no real basis for comparison. Mere figures of heights and areas will not do it. Concrete comparisons must be made. For example, to give a class living on a glacial plain some idea of the extent of the Great Plains, let them consider a ten-mile stretch of the home plain, look up the railway time-tables and see how long an express train takes to traverse it. Then let them look up, on the Missouri Pacific time-table, the length of time required to travel from Kansas City to Pueblo, using a train that travels at about the same rate; and give the idea time to sink in by talking it over and comparing the distances in terms of the relative times required for traversing them.

To give children of a hill country an idea of a plain, they should be conducted to a hilltop and asked to imagine the valleys to be refilled to the level of the hilltops by the sediments that the streams have carried away. It is not difficult for these children with the aid of comparisons to get some idea of the size of a mountain; but for the children of the plains it is very difficult. Something may be done, however, by measuring river bluffs or such small elevations as there are in the neighborhood and making a comparison between the time required to ascend the bluff and that required to ascend a similar one that would be as high as a real mountain. Additional help may be obtained from profiles of the bluff and of the mountain drawn to the same scale, and from photographs of mountains with trees and large buildings in the foreground by means of which comparisons can be made.

3. Two or three laboratory periods may well be spent in a study of rocks and rock-making minerals. Show the pupils typical specimens of these, let their characteristics be observed and the simplest tests be made. Let the students tabulate their observations. Then give them fragments of the different minerals and rocks to describe and identify. Be sure to make careful studies of the brick clays, coals, building stones, or other mineral products of the locality, and of others from outside which are used in the locality. Always have the pupils locate on maps the places from which these outside products come; and find out as much as they can about the rockbeds and quarries from which they were taken.

4. When any type of land form or region is being considered, let the pupils study several topographic maps on which such types are represented. Have them record the latitude and longitude of the chief feature to be studied from the map sheet, and locate the sheet on the United States contour map. Find what general

physiographic region it belongs in. Over what railroads or roads would one have to travel to reach it? Trace the route on a railroad folder and a wall map. Look up the through trains and find out how long it would take to reach it. From the railroad agent, find out the railroad and sleeping car rates for the round trip. Find on the map and describe the features of topography and drainage that are mentioned in the books as being characteristic of that type of land form or physiographic region. Are the slopes steep or gentle? Why? Where are the roads and railroads and the towns located? What are their relations to the topography? What is the nature of the climate? With reference to weathering and denudation are the features under consideration young, mature, or old? How do you infer this? What are the typical conditions of animal, vegetable, and human life in this region? How are they affected by the type of topography? These are only a few of the problems that may be worked out from topographic maps. Only general hints may be given here; but the teacher should determine definitely what he wants the students to learn from each map, and should define the problems for them by specific questions, directions, or suggestions, indicating what information they are to get from the maps, what they are to do with it when they get it, and what kinds of notes, measurements, drawings, and records they are to enter in their notebooks. Everything required of them should have a definite bearing on the problem that they are set to solve. The teacher who is not able to do this for himself should place in the hands of the students one of the well-known laboratory manuals, such as that of Tarr and Von Engeln, selecting from the large number of exercises those best adapted to the use of the class. These manuals will suggest other kinds of laboratory work, all of value if there is time for them. But it is better to do a few things well and thoroughly, giving the pupils time to get clear ideas and to work intelligently, than to do many things in a hurried way and have them come through it in a state of confusion and mystification.

5. Another excellent type of laboratory work consists in having good pictures described and interpreted by the pupils. Here the pictures may serve as substitutes for field study in distant localities. Let the pupils make out routes and daily itineraries for trips to such regions as the Grand Canyon and the surrounding plateaus, to the Columbia Lava Plateau, to Shasta and Lassen peaks, to the coastal plains of New Jersey, to the lake cities, or to New York or San Francisco. Plan routes and estimate cost of trips. Have

S

imaginary stories or reports written about objects supposed to be seen and studied. Send to the general passenger agents of the railroads for folders and illustrated literature, telling them what use is to be made of these. Use railroad maps, automobile road guides, wall maps, topographic maps, government reports, such as Dutton's monograph on "The Tertiary History of the Grand Canyon," the United States Geological Survey Bulletin on the Yellowstone National Park, and the like, when they are accessible. Get the assistance of the librarian in looking up such sources of information. Such work may be made full of realistic and vital interest, and the interest is likely to be lasting. Many of the pupils of city schools spend their summer vacations in localities replete with features of geographic interest. Find out where such pupils expect to go next summer, and get the whole class into the work of studying out their trips and what may be seen there. If the localities have been mapped by the Survey, send for the topographic sheets and work out the topography. Encourage the pupils to buy the maps and take them along. If they have cameras ask them to bring back pictures for the next year's class, or if they have no cameras, to write up the principal geographic features for an article to be published in the school magazine when they return in the fall. A few localities studied in the ways suggested will give the pupils more real, practical geographical knowledge then the formal recitations of many pages of the textbook.

The use of the library. — The suggestion that part of the laboratory work should consist in the actual planning of trips to study features of geographic interest and value leads naturally to the consideration of the use to be made of the geographical material in the school or city or county library. It should be evident that assigned readings are of little value unless the pupils have a specific purpose for the reading, one that appeals to them as worth while. If they are led to hope that sometime they may personally visit the locality that is being studied, they will probably enter with enthusiasm into the game of planning out the trip, estimating the necessary expense for railway and steamboat and hotel accommodations, and fitting the arrangements to the time allowed. When they know something of the time and expense involved they will probably be interested in finding out how much they can see and learn each day of the trip, and will be strongly motivated to read books and reports and look up data that will help them to understand and appreciate that which may be seen. When references are given, these should be made very definite, and limited to that which bears directly on the problem of the day. In every case the pages and paragraphs should be given specifically, and usually in connection with a definite question on which the reading matter indicated has a direct bearing, so the student will know that when he has consulted these passages, obtained the definite information called for, and prepared a written or oral report he has completed his assignment.

A mature and trained reader knows how to leaf over a book or consult an index and locate the information that he wants, as well as how to select from the card catalogue the books that will be of service, but it is not to be presumed that students can do this. They must first be trained by practice with the aid of definite directions. The teacher should rarely, if ever, give a reference to students that he is not himself pretty thoroughly familiar with. Indefinite or careless reading assignments are likely to bore the pupils and give them a distaste for library work instead of a liking for it. Even if such assignments do not do this they will almost surely fail to train the students to read selectively, which is an art that everyone must learn if he is to become a wide and efficient reader, either for pleasure or mental profit. The teacher should by all means take time to teach the pupils how to use a card catalogue, how to consult the cumulative magazine indices, how to make up brief selected bibliographies, and how to get facts from such sources of information as atlases, gazetteers, *The Statesman's Year Book, The Times Almanac,* the United States Consular Reports, and the like. If he does not himself know how to do this, and to catalogue his own department library, he should take a course in a summer school where he can learn how. If he lives in a town where a trained librarian is employed, the librarian will be glad to teach him, and will take great interest in assisting the pupils about reference work.

Do not neglect the library work entirely, but do not require too much of it.

Card abstracts. — In connection with library work in cases where the information obtained is likely to be of permanent value, such as abstracts from authoritative articles describing geographic features or conditions of importance, it is an excellent plan to have the students place their abstracts on filing cards of one of the regular sizes.[1] The teacher may provide a drawer or box of the proper size for the cards, and file them by subjects as they come in. The source of the abstract, giving title, author, publishers, place and date of publication, and pages, should always be placed on the card, and cross-references to other cards or to the textbook should be made wherever they are likely to be helpful.

Principles and methods. — Bearing in mind the point of view and the considerations that have been brought out in the preceding pages, we may formulate briefly the principles which should control the selection of subject matter and the working out of special methods for geography:

1. Wherever practicable begin with problems and begin at home.

2. Connect the far with the near and the unknown with the known by human relationships.

3. Use the textbook as a help in the accumulation and organization of facts.

4. Use the causal relation as a link for organization in the ordering of concepts.

5. Trace physiographic features back to physiographic processes, and these back to physical causes.

---

[1] 3 × 5 inches, 4½ × 6 inches, or 5 × 8 inches.

6. Trace conditions forward to their consequences.

7. Use the cycle concept and the concept of adjustment as unifying principles.

8. It cannot be presumed that the casual observation of outdoor facts by the pupils will be sufficient to make the laboratory work and the textbook study always meaningful. The textbook has been referred to as a mine of information, but much of the information will be unintelligible to the students if, as is so common with this subject, the teacher relies on the textbook as the only source. The pupils must have opportunities for selective observation under guidance in the field and laboratory. Both field and laboratory work are necessary; and the former more so than the latter.

Order of topics. — The general order of topics favored by the writer is as follows: 1. Underground water. 2. Streams and lakes. 3. Rocks and soils. 4. The lands. 5. The atmosphere. 6. The earth as a whole. 7. Review of physical geography on a regional basis. 8. Review on the basis of distribution of vegetation and animal life. 9. Review on the basis of human relationships, economic, industrial, and social. 10. Review on the basis of locational geography.[1] Let the pupils list the significant places mentioned in current numbers of the daily newspaper and the *Review of Reviews, Literary Digest,* or *Current Opinion.* Locate them accurately on the wall maps and drill by locating them on outline seat maps in the manner that will be described farther on. This kind of work should not be confined to the final review, but should be carried on in connection with other phases of the subject. All places, rivers, glaciers, plains, mountains, and the like whose locations are important should be located when studied as types and examples. For instance, if the " fall line " that marks the boundary between the Piedmont plateau and the

[1] Cf. Whitbeck and Martin, *op. cit.*, p. 27 ff.

Atlantic coastal plain is being studied, the principal manufacturing cities that mark the line should be located in the
manner described.

The order recommended is not necessarily the best for all
schools. Other orders may be as good; but the author is
convinced that it is a pedagogical mistake to begin with a
textbook treatment of the facts of mathematical geography.
It is likely to kill interest, and give both teacher and pupils
a didactic, textbook attitude at the very beginning. As geography is the study of the earth and not a book, it should
begin with parts of the earth that the pupils can see for themselves, and not with things that they must learn mostly from
books.

QUESTIONS FOR FURTHER STUDY

1. Briefly review the psychological arguments for beginning geography in the high school with home problems.

2. Bearing in mind the right and the wrong way to use a textbook,
make a comparison of several standard textbooks and submit written
recommendations, as to your superintendent, selecting the textbook
that you would prefer to use, and giving the reasons why you prefer it.

3. Make a list of the field excursions that can be made in your home
locality, and with each enumerate the things that you would teach in
connection with it.

4. How much importance do you attach to the contention that the
statement of the aim in a field lesson should be problematic rather than
formal? Make a brief critical review of the arguments.

5. What is your estimate of the value of geographical study without
an abundance of illustrative material?

6. Make a brief critical analysis of the discussion of this chapter on
laboratory work.

7. What is your judgment as to the importance of specific purposes
and assignments in connection with library work? Are the suggestions
on library work sound? Give reasons for your opinion.

8. Have you formed the "card file habit"? If not, do you intend
to begin? Why?

9. State the eight items under "Principles and Methods" and give a
brief defense of each. If the need or advantage of any one of them has
been realized in your own experience, recount and comment on the circumstances.

10. What do you think of the order of topics favored by the author? Suggest other possible orders, and if you think one or more of them is better, argue for it.

11. Do you think that a review of locational geography is desirable? Do you think it would be interesting after such a course as is suggested in general geography?

REFERENCES

On Methods

BROWN, ROBERT M. Map Reading. Jour. of Geog., 4: 273–288, September, 1905. (With 10 sketch maps.)

CARPENTER, FRANK O. Commercial Geography: The New Science. Proc. N. E. A., 1903, pp. 732–737. Discusses method and scope of subject. Demands laboratory studies.

CHAMBERLAIN, JAMES F. Report of the N. E. A. Committee of 1909 on Secondary School Geography. Proc. N. E. A., D. W. Springer, Sec'y, Ann Arbor, Mich., 1909, pp. 820–828. Also Jour. of Geog., Madison, Wis., September, 1909, 8: 1–9.

DAVIS, KING and COLLIE. Governmental Maps for Use in Schools. Holt, N. Y. 1894. 65 pp. 30 ¢.

DAVIS, WILLIAM MORRIS. Geographical Essays. Ginn, Boston. 1909. 777 pp. $2.75. Covers nearly every phase of good practice in the teaching of geography.

DAVIS, WILLIAM MORRIS. Teacher's Guide to accompany Davis's Elementary Physical Geography. Ginn, Boston. 1903. 30 ¢.

DODGE, RICHARD E. Geography for the Secondary Schools. Jour. of Geog., 7: 121–125. Round table discussions, Asso. Am. Geographers, on humanized geography.

DODGE, RICHARD E., and KIRCHWEY, C. B. The Teaching of Geography in Elementary Schools. Rand, McNally & Co., N. Y. 1913. 7 + 248 pp. $1.00. Written for elementary teachers, but very useful to high school teachers, especially the sections on equipment and bibliography.

DRYER, CHARLES R. What is Geography? Jour. of Geog., 4: 348–360. Definitions and quotations from European and American authorities.

GENTHE, M. K. Geographical Textbooks and Geographical Teaching. Jour. of Geog., 2: 227–243, 360–368, May and September, 1903.

GEIKIE, ARCHIBALD. The Teaching of Geography. Macmillan, N. Y. 1906. 205 pp. 60 ¢.

GIBBS, DAVID. The Pedagogy of Geography. Pedagogical Seminary, 14: 39–100, March, 1907. A very complete general discussion.

GOODE, J. PAUL. The Human Response to Physical Environment. Jour. of Geog., 3 : 333–343, September, 1904.

JEFFERSON, M. S. W. Commercial Geography in Secondary Schools. Jour. of Geog., 4 : 425–432, December, 1905.

JEFFERSON, M. S. W. Out Door Work in Geography. Proc. N. E. A., 1904, pp. 583–588.

JONES, EDWARD D. Sources of Literature for Commercial Geography. Jour. of Geog., 1 : 151–155, April, 1902. Very useful on the commercial side.

KELTIE, J. SCOTT. Applied Geography. Philip & Son, London. 2s. 6d.

KELTIE, J. SCOTT. Function and Field of Geography. Smithsonian Report. 1897. Washington, D. C.

MERRILL, J. A. Physiography in the Secondary School. Proc. N. E. A., 1902, pp. 784–789. Stresses field work.

MILL, HUGH ROBERT. Guide to Geographical Books and Appliances. Philip & Son, London. 1910. 207 pp. 5s. "Most complete bibliography of the kind in English."

MORRISON, G. J. Maps, Their Uses and Construction. Stanford, London, Eng. 1902.

SUTHERLAND, WILLIAM J. The Teaching of Geography. Scott, Foresman & Co., Chicago. 1909. 292 pp. $1.25. Treats of general and special method, equipment, etc. Is psychologically sound. Contains extensive and carefully selected bibliographies.

TROTTER, SPENCER. The Social Function of Geography. 4th Annual Year Book Herbart Society. Univ. of Chicago Press. 56 pp. 28 ¢.

TROTTER, SPENCER. Lessons in the New Geography. Heath, Boston. $1.00.

WHITBECK, RAY H. Geography in the Large High School. Proc. N. E. A., 1914, pp. 732–737.

WHITBECK, RAY H., and MARTIN, LAWRENCE. The High School Course in Geography. Bull. Univ. of Wisconsin, Madison. 1910. Exceedingly valuable to the teacher. Excellent on methods and equipment.

ATLASES AND STANDARD REFERENCE BOOKS

BARTHOLOMEW, J. G. Atlas of the World's Commerce. Newnes, London. 1907. $2.70.

BARTHOLOMEW, J. G. School Economic Atlas. Frowde, London. Clarendon Press. 1914. 2s. 6d.

BEDDARD, F. E. Zoögeography. University Press, Cambridge, Eng. 1895. 246 pp. Putnam, N. Y. $1.50.

BRIGHAM, ALBERT P. A Textbook of Geology. Appleton, N. Y. 1901. 10 + 477 pp. $1.40. Elementary textbook, and accompanying Suggestions to Teachers. The latter has specific suggestions for field work in the vicinity of 19 large cities.

CHAMBERLAIN, T. C., and SALISBURY, R. D. College Text Book of Geology. Holt, N. Y. 1909. 978 pp. $3.50.

CHISHOLM, G. C. Handbook of Commercial Geography. Longmans, N. Y. 1890. 515 pp. $4.80.

DANA, JAMES D. Manual of Geology. American Book Co., N. Y. 1895. 1088 pp. $5.00. The standard American reference book on geology.

DANA, JAMES D. Textbook of Geology. Revised by Rice. American Book Co. $1.40.

DAVIS, W. M. Elementary Meteorology. Ginn, Boston. 1894. 355 pp. $2.50. The standard American text.

DIERCKE, C., and GAEBLER, E. (Editors). Schul-atlas. Westermann. 1914. 156 pp. Maps. $2.70. "An excellent physical and cultural atlas."

DUTTON, C. E. The Physical Geology of the Grand Canyon District. 2d Annual Report U. S. Geological Survey, 1880–1881, pp. 49–166. $2.00. Also, The Tertiary History of the Grand Canyon District. Monograph II, U. S. Geological Survey. 260 pp. With atlas and Holmes's drawings. $10.00.

FREEMAN, W. G., and CHANDLER, S. E. The World's Commercial Products. Ginn, Boston. 1907. $3.50.

GANNETT, HENRY. Manual of Topographic Methods. U. S. Geological Survey, Washington, D. C. $1.00.

GEIKIE, A. The Teaching of Geography. Macmillan, N. Y. 1906. 205 pp. 60 ¢.

GILBERT, G. C. History Lake Bonneville. Monograph I, U. S. Geological Survey. 429 pp. Also in 2d Annual Report, U. S. Geological Survey, 1881, pp. 169–200. $2.00.

GREGORY, H. E., KELLER, A. G., and BISHOP, A. L. Physical and Commercial Geography. Ginn, Boston. 1910. 469 pp. $3.00. College text, correlating the two phases of geography from the humanistic standpoint.

KELTIE, J. S. Statesman's Year Book. Macmillan, N. Y. 1911. $3.00. Very useful for reference.

MILL, H. R. (Editor). The International Geography. Appleton, New York. 1900. 1088 pp. 70 authors. $3.50. Valuable regional treatment of the continents by high authorities. Interesting, not difficult, should be in every school library.

RUSSELL, I. C. Lake Lahonton. Monograph XI, U. S. Geological Survey. 283 pp. Also in 3d Annual Report, U. S. Geological Survey, 1882, pp. 195–235.

SALISBURY, R. D. Physiography. Holt, N. Y. 1907. 770 pp. $3.50. Standard college text. Comprehensive and very suggestive.

STANFORD'S Compendium of Geography. Edward Stanford, London. 1904. 12 vols. Volume on the United States, by Gannett. 1904. Lippincott, N. Y. $5.50.

SUTHERLAND, WILLIAM J. Geography in Village and Rural Schools. Proc. N. E. A., 1914, pp. 738–742.

Times Almanac. New York Times, N. Y.

Tribune Almanac. New York Tribune, N. Y.

TROTTER, SPENCER. The Geography of Commerce. Macmillan, N. Y. 1904. 388 pp. $1.10.

UPHAM, WARREN. The Glacial Lake Agassiz. U. S. Geological Survey. Monograph XXV. 658 pp. 38 pl.

For other special and general books on the subject matter of geography consult the list of library books, Appendix A.

CHAPTER XVI

GEOGRAPHICAL EQUIPMENT

Building up the equipment. — The kinds of apparatus needed for the equipment of a geographical classroom and laboratory have already been indicated in a general way. As compared with apparatus and supplies for physics, chemistry, and biology, geographical equipment is not excessively expensive. If purchased in yearly installments a good equipment can be accumulated in a few years; and if properly cared for it will last many years.

Wall maps. — Among the most essential items of geographical equipment are sets of wall maps. These fall into two general classes, (1) physical and (2) political, commercial, or economic. Those of the first class are designed to show physical features, such as mountains, plateaus, plains, lakes, and rivers. Some physical maps show also isotherms, isobars, rainfall areas, vegetation areas, ocean currents, and the like. Such maps omit most of the minor political boundaries, cities, and the like in order that the conditions to be represented may stand out clearly. Relief is represented by contour lines inclosing different colors for different elevations, or by hachures, or by different densities of light and shade. The maps of the second class show political boundaries, cities, roads, railroads, steamboat lines, and harbors. Maps of another type show the distribution of crops, mineral products, forests, and the like in order to make clear certain economic features of the areas that are represented. The political, economic, and commercial maps usually show differences in elevation, where they are especially prominent and significant as barriers, by means of hachures. The essential features of excellence in such maps are: (1) accuracy, which the teacher may best judge by the standing and reputation of the geographers whose names they bear; (2) the clearness and distinctness with which they show the things that they are intended to show; (3) "carrying power," which is determined by the distance from which the principal features that they represent can be clearly distinguished. Such maps as those of the Habenicht-Sidow physical series or the Kuhnert-Leipold relief-like maps are especially distinguished for their carrying power. This feature is very important.

All wall maps should be backed with stout cloth and should have a hanging-strip and a roller attached to them at top and bottom respectively. If desired, dealers will furnish each map with a spring roller, and also with a light, strong, nearly dust-proof cylindrical steel case. The spring rollers and the steel cases are of great advantage for convenience in using the maps and for protecting them from dust and wear; but they are relatively expensive, and not at all necessary. If funds are limited, it is far better to order the maps on common wooden rollers, and to apply the amount saved to the purchase of more maps or a better quality of maps. When mounted on common rollers or on spring rollers without a protecting case, each map should have attached to the bottom a strip of enameled cloth which will entirely cover it when it is rolled up, and will thus protect it from damage by dust and wear. The wooden cases and cabinets furnished by dealers for single maps and sets of maps respectively are not strongly recommended. A cabinet built into the room is usually better, because it has space in it for the storage of additional maps that may be purchased from year to year, and because the maps may be so arranged in it that any one that is wanted may be quickly and easily got at. In schools where maps must be transferred from one room to another, they can be much more easily removed and transferred if stored in such a built-in cabinet.[1]

What maps are necessary. — Every school where physical geography is taught should have a series of physical wall maps representing the world on Mercator's projection, the United States, and each of the continents. Polar projections of the northern and southern hemispheres are desirable also, but not so necessary. So also are maps of the Atlantic and Pacific oceans on the globular projection. If the suggestions of this chapter concerning locational geography and political, economic, and commercial studies are to be carried out, a series of political wall maps is also very necessary, and should include a map of the United States and one of each of the grand divisions.

Among the best physical maps are those of Habenicht and Sidow, Kuhnert and Leipold, Kiepert, the Oxford maps, by A. J. Herbertson, and the series by J. Paul Goode. The first three are published in Germany, the fourth in England, and the fifth in Chicago by the Rand, McNally Co. The Oxford maps are not yet well known among teachers in America. Professor Dryer [2] says of them, " Do you all know that, thanks to Dr. Herbertson, you can now buy a set of Oxford wall maps for the world and each continent showing physical features, structure and soils, thermal regions, pressure and winds, rainfall, vegetation, natural and economic regions, and political divisions? " The Goode maps have been highly commended by geographical experts for accuracy and clearness, but are criticized by some for being rather too small for use with large classes. The W. & A. K. Johnston maps are published in several series, physical, political, historical, etc., and in several grades, at prices that correspond

---

[1] Cf. pp. 175–6, Chapter X, *ante.*

[2] Dryer, C. R., *The New Departure in Geography*, Proc. High Sch. Conferences, 1912. Bull. Univ. of Ill., Vol. X, No. 19, February, 1913. A valuable paper tracing clearly the history and present tendencies of geography teaching in high schools.

with the sizes and qualities. The higher grades are of large size and are very good; but the cheaper grades are not strongly recommended.

Among the large and reliable dealers who sell maps, globes, and geographical models are the J. L. Hammett Co., Boston; A. J. Nystrom & Co., Chicago; and Rand, McNally & Co., Chicago. Schools are entitled to import foreign maps duty-free; and this can be done through these houses, or through L. E. Stechert (9 E. 16th Street, New York). School officers who are wise will order from the large and well-known firms, all of whom advertise in the standard school journals, and will avoid irresponsible agents who try to sell them cheap and out-of-date maps.

Care in the selection of maps. — No maps should be purchased without making a careful comparative examination of the catalogues of the best dealers, which will be sent free to prospective purchasers. The teacher who is not an expert would do well to make up his list and submit it for suggestions to the professor of geography in some college or normal school which is known to have a high-grade equipment. It would be better still to visit such an institution, examine the equipment there, and have a personal conference with the professor.

Methods of displaying maps. — For the display of maps there are three general methods. The first method is that in which all the maps of a set are furnished by the dealers mounted on spring rollers in a cabinet. The cabinet is fastened to the front or side wall of the room, and any map that is wanted is pulled down like a curtain. This method is not nearly so convenient in practice as it would seem to be; for if the case is placed high enough to display the maps well, the maps must be pulled down by means of a rod with a hook on the end of it, and it proves to be difficult to insert the hook quickly into the draw-ring attached to the map that is wanted. Furthermore, when the maps are mounted in this way, only one can be displayed at a time, so that simultaneous comparisons of two maps cannot be made. The second method is to suspend the maps from the molding at the top of the blackboard. This has the advantage of allowing a number of maps to be displayed all at the same time, and if the maps are in the steel cases with spring rollers they may be allowed to remain in position for several days or weeks. If they are to be used in other rooms hooks may be placed for them in the moldings of these rooms; and they can be quickly transferred at any time. The objection to this method is that the molding is too low to permit the maps to be seen by those who are not near them. If a special molding is placed higher up for this particular purpose, the objection that has been mentioned does not apply. The third method, the best for maps mounted on plain rollers, and for charts of all sizes, consists in suspending the maps from racks that are swung from the ceiling by means of halyards, as described on page 176, Chapter X.

Local maps. — In addition to the sets of wall maps that have been mentioned the school should have a railroad map of the state, a geological map of the state, a large-scale map of the county, and a map of the city. In several states the two former are furnished free or at a nominal price by the state departments. Several state departments also supply large-scale topographic maps of their respective states. These should by all means be obtained if they are available.

Blackboard outline maps. — These are wall maps having a black surface on which the outlines of the continents, the meridians and parallels, and the principal rivers and lakes are drawn in white. They are very useful for representing and locating special regions or features that are being studied. Such features may be drawn in with crayons of various colors. The great advantage of this mode of representation is that the particular features to be studied may be drawn in as the problem is developed in the classroom, while other features having no relation to the problem under consideration are

not present to distract attention and cause confusion.   When
the occasion for their use has passed, these features can be
erased and the outline map will then be available for the study
of other features.   They may be photographed, and lantern
slides made of them before erasing, so that they will be available for reviews and drills at any time.   These maps may be
bought from any of the dealers in maps or school supplies,
and every school should have a set including the world on
Mercator's projection, the United States, and each of the
continents.[1]

Outline seat maps. — These are similar to the outline wall
maps, but are printed on white or buff paper with black lines.
They are sold by D. C. Heath & Co., Boston; the McKinley
Publishing Co., Philadelphia; and A. J. Nystrom & Co.,
Chicago.   They are to be used with colored pencils in the
same way that the former are used.   An excellent plan is to
have the features to be studied traced on the physical or
political wall map, then represented on the corresponding
blackboard map.   Then after study and discussion, let the
pupils represent the same features on their corresponding
seat maps, and add such notes and conclusions about them as
represent the solution of the problem that has been set up.
The outline maps may be used very effectively in review drills
on locations.   Let the teacher read in rapid succession lists
of names of places or features to be located, and let the pupils
quickly draw them in on the maps.   The maps can then be
exchanged and each pupil's performance scored by another
pupil, or the teacher may collect the maps and score them,
according to whether the exercise is to be used for drill merely,
or for a test.   The exercise may be reversed by letting the
teacher or a pupil point rapidly to locations on the outline
blackboard map or the wall map, while the pupils write down

---

[1] A. J. Nystrom & Co., Chicago, issue a little pamphlet gratis, which gives
many valuable suggestions as to the use of these maps in history and geography.

the names of the places indicated. If locational work of any kind is to be attempted, occasional brief rapid-fire memory drills of this sort are necessary in order to make it effective. If accuracy and speed are aimed at in conducting them, as in psychological memory experiments, the pupils are sure to enjoy them and profit by them.

Government maps. — It is surprising that so few teachers are acquainted with the wonderful variety of useful maps that may be obtained at nominal prices from various departments of the United States Government. Information about these maps has been repeatedly printed in the school and geographical journals, and in the texts and appendices of the standard physical geographies; yet, comparatively speaking, very few schools have any considerable stock of them. One who visits many schools is continually amazed to find that a large majority of teachers of geography and principals of schools know nothing of them. Adequate information about them and about other important maps may be obtained from a little book called " Governmental Maps for Use in Schools " by Davis, King and Collie.[1] The *Journal of School Geography* contains many articles concerning them. Articles giving help in their selection and use will be found in Vol. I, 1897, p. 200; II, 1898, pp. 340, 386, by Professor W. M. Davis, and in Vol. V, 1901, p. 128, by Blount.

The United States Geological Survey topographic maps. — These, printed on white paper, show rivers, lakes, swamps, and oceans in blue; roads, towns, buildings, and bridges in black; and sometimes forests in green. All elevations are shown by contour lines in brown. The horizontal scale is usually one inch, sometimes two inches, to the mile; and the vertical distance between any two contiguous contour lines is usually ten or twenty feet. The elevations above sea level are marked on the lines at various points. A generous selection of these maps is invaluable; first, for the purpose of copiously

---

[1] Published by Henry Holt & Co., N. Y., 1893. Price 30 ¢.

T

illustrating such land forms and regions as are studied in the
text, and second, for laboratory studies such as have been
briefly indicated.   The Survey furnishes " a set of 100 sheets
illustrating physiographic types " of all sorts of land forms and
regions, accompanied by an index sheet listing the maps
according to the features that they represent, such as sand
dunes, glacial moraines, folded mountains, etc., and according
to the names of the sheets, with a statement of what each
sheet shows.   Every school should have one of the 100 sheet
sets, and in addition copies, as many as there are pupils in the
class, of the sheets of the home locality, if these have been
published.   When certain kinds of features have been selected
for laboratory work, and such features are shown on sheets
representing several different localities, a sufficient number of
each of these different sheets should be ordered so that there
shall be a copy of one or another of them for each student in
the class.   This is a better plan than to have the features
that are being studied represented by maps all of which are
of one locality.   Several states have been covered entire and
others partly, by the topographic survey.   The price per sheet
is small, 10 cents for each single sheet or 6 cents where 50
or more are ordered.   Certain sheets, as *Niagara River and
Vicinity*, are special, and must be ordered singly at higher
prices ranging from 20 to 50 cents.   The topographic
sheets must be ordered by name from the Director of the
United States Geological Survey, Washington, D. C.; and
the request must be accompanied by a United States postal
money order for the amount of the purchase.   Complete price
lists of the topographic map sheets and other maps and publications of the Geological Survey may be had free by applying
to the Director.

Mounting and storage of topographic sheets. — The sheets
are liable to be torn, even with careful handling, unless they
are mounted on thin bleached white cotton cloth of the ordinary width.   As bookbinders charge rather heavily for special

work of this kind, the teacher and pupils should learn to do it. Stretch the cloth smoothly over the top of a large pine table, fastening it with thumb tacks, and thoroughly moisten it with a wet sponge. With a flat brush, apply paper-hanger's paste to the back of the map. Rub the paste in gently with the brush till the sheet is thoroughly limp and the excess of paste has been removed. If the paper has not softened, let it lie for a while, but not long enough for the paste to harden. Now press the map carefully down on the cloth in the proper position, beginning at the center and working cautiously outward toward the edges so as not to wrinkle the paper. Use a paper-hanger's brush, a photo-mounting roller, or a soft cloth, and leave the sheet for twenty-four hours to dry, pressing so that it will not curl. Trim it then with a pair of long shears, and it will be ready for use.

The maps are best kept classified in labeled manila folders. The folders when the maps are not in use should be stored in a suitable cabinet either in flat drawers with hinged drop-front or on shelves that may be pulled out like drawers. The shelves or drawers, as well as the manila folders, should be labeled. The most convenient method of classification is by types represented; but there should be a card index with the name of each map, the names of features represented on it, and the number of copies of each map in stock. For obvious reasons, the teacher should by all means have the pupils do the greater part of the work of preparing the index cards and the labels.

Mounting grouped sheets. — Some features can be shown to best advantage only by assembling groups of sheets for use as a wall map. Among these are all the sheets representing the vicinity of the school, if they have been published. Trim the sheets with paper-hanger's shears or with a sharp knife and a metal straightedge, leaving on each alternate edge a quarter-inch margin for overlapping. Mount the sheets on double-width cloth in the manner described for the single sheets. When the map has been completed and trimmed, tack it at the top to a strip of molding or a spring shade-roller, and at the bottom to a slender wooden curtain pole.

In Tarr's "New Physical Geography," p. 435, will be found a list of thirty-five such groups, from which a selection may be made.

The United States contour map. — This is a three-sheet map intended to be mounted as a wall map. Besides being very useful for regional studies it is of importance as a means of finding the exact locations of the single sheets when they are studied. When mounted, its size is about $4\frac{1}{2}$ by $6\frac{1}{3}$ feet.

Physiographic and geologic folios. — The United States Geological Survey issues two sets of paper-bound folios which are very valuable for school studies. There are three Physiographic Folios consisting of maps, pictures, and descriptions of physiographic types, and more than eighty numbers of the folios of the Geological Atlas of the United States. The first two at least of the former and several of the latter should be in every geographical laboratory. They are described in the free price list issued by the Survey.

Coast charts. — The Pilot Charts of the United States Coast and Geodetic Survey are very useful for the study of shore features. They give outlines of shores, depths of water, position of buoys and lighthouses, elevations by hachures, and other features of interest to the mariner and student of geography. Charts that are slightly out of date are sometimes sent free. Otherwise the charge is fifty cents each. Requests should be made by catalogue numbers and accompanied by money order. Address Director United States Coast and Geodetic Survey, Washington, D. C. The catalogue is free.[1]

River and lake maps. — The maps of the Mississippi River Commission and of the Missouri River Commission, both

---

[1] For a selection of these charts see Davis's *Elementary Physical Geography,* Ginn & Co., 1902, p. 388; Davis, King and Collie, *op. cit.;* and Tarr, *Elementary Physical Geography,* 1904, p. 436.

located at St. Louis, are unrivaled for the study of river features. The *Charts of the Great Lakes*, issued by the United States Engineer's Office, Detroit, Mich., illustrate lake and shore-line features of much interest.

Schools located near these rivers or lakes should by all means have a generous selection of these maps.[1]

Weather maps. — These will be sent free daily on application to the Director, United States Weather Bureau, Washington, D.C., or to the Observer at the nearest Weather Bureau Station. The various laboratory manuals in geography give full directions for their use. Every school should have them; and the pupils should learn how to read them, to trace the storm tracks on them, and to make weather predictions.

In connection with the study of weather maps [2] a supply of blank weather maps will be of great advantage. These may be obtained in quantity from the Director of the United States Weather Bureau, Washington, D. C., or from the nearest Weather Bureau Station, at a nominal price.

Globes. — Since in all flat maps all but the central areas are more or less out of proportion in size and shape, a globe is necessary in order to correct the wrong impressions that they give. The Johnston 18-inch suspension globe with " moon-ball " counterweight is listed at $22.50 in the Nystrom Company's catalogue. Suspension globes of this size can be bought for slightly lower prices, but in general it is cheaper in the end to buy the best.

A 12 or 18-inch slated globe is very useful for teaching many of the facts of mathematical geography that every intelligent person should clearly comprehend. On such a globe the meridians and parallels can be clearly outlined in crayon, and it is easy to show how the tropics, the polar circles, and the circle

---

[1] Write for the price lists; and consult Davis, King and Collie, *op. cit.*, and Tarr, *op. cit.*, p. 437, for help in selection.

[2] Cf. Ward, R. De C., *Practical Exercises in Meteorology*, Ginn, Boston, 1896, $1.12.

of illumination are outlined on the earth by the rays of the sun.   Such a globe can be mounted on a counterpoised hanger like that for the globe mentioned above.

If the globes must be used in more than one room, extra hangers, one for each additional room, can be purchased for $1.50 each.

Besides the large globes, all school supply dealers furnish small individual globes to be used by the pupils at their seats. These can be bought at a very low price and are well worth the money they cost.

Models and relief maps. — Only a few makers produce models and relief maps that are really worth their cost to a school.   They are usually on too small a scale to give an adequate idea of the real character and detail of relief.   Yet in the hands of a teacher who is an expert and knows how to use them, good models and relief maps may be made highly serviceable.   The following are some of the most valuable, and they should be added to the equipment if funds are available without the sacrifice of other necessary aids.

The Harvard Geographical Models by W. M. Davis and G. C. Curtis, are sold by Ginn & Co., Boston.   The price for the set of three models is $20.   These models illustrate clearly the origin and development of a large number of typical physiographic features.   These are superior to most others in that the vertical scale is not exaggerated, and in that since they represent small areas, much of the natural detail of relief is shown.   They may be used very profitably in a number of laboratory studies, and are invaluable on numerous occasions for clarifying the pupils' ideas in the classroom.   A pamphlet telling how to use these models is sold by the Boston Society of Natural History, Berkeley Street, Boston, for 25 cents.

G. C. Curtis [1] also sells a set of three similar models showing glaciers, volcanoes, and seacoast, which supplement the Harvard models.

[1] Address at 64 Crawford St., Boston.

The Jones Model of the Earth [1] is authentic and very valuable, but rather expensive.

The relief maps and models made by E. E. Howell [2] are standard. They are found in the best college laboratories, and in school laboratories of some of the larger cities. They are very interesting and instructive, but expensive, and require a considerable amount of floor or wall space.

A set of five of these models representing each of the continents with the adjacent ocean bottoms may be bought of Mr. Howell or of A. J. Nystrom & Co., Chicago, for $150. A grand model of the United States, on a section of a globe 16 feet in diameter, size 96 by 50 inches, with a horizontal scale of 50 miles to the inch, and with a vertical exaggeration of only 5 times, is sold for $125. A smaller one, 34 by 18 inches, is sold for $25.

A. J. Nystrom & Co. offer a large number of other models by Howell and other accurate makers at prices from $12 upward. It is much better to have one or two of these standard models than to have any number of the cheap and unreliable relief maps that are so widely sold to school boards.

Meteorological instruments. — A good mercurial barometer can be bought from any of the reliable dealers in physical apparatus for about $15. A standard United States Weather Bureau Station barometer [3] costs a little over twice that amount. Every geographic outfit should include a good barometer, standard Weather Bureau thermometer, a wet and dry bulb hygrometer or sling psychrometer, and a homemade wind vane. Among the other instruments that are very desirable are a rain gauge, a pocket aneroid barometer graduated to read both pressure and elevation above sea level, and a maximum and a minimum thermometer. If

[1] Sold by A. H. Andrews & Co., Chicago, at $50.00.

[2] Address at 612 17th St., N. W., Washington, D. C.

[3] The best is made by Henry J. Green, Brooklyn, N. Y., who sells standard meteorological instruments of all kinds. The teacher should send for his catalogue.

luxuries can be indulged in, an anemometer, a thermograph, and a barograph would not be out of place, but they should not take the place of less expensive items of equipment that are really essential.

Directions for the mounting and use of all these instruments will be found in standard textbooks on meteorology,[1] and in the pamphlet of the Weather Bureau called "Instructions for Voluntary Observers."[2]

Minerals and rocks. — The laboratory should contain a case of labeled specimens of the most important and typical rocks and rock-making minerals, especially those obtainable in the vicinity. E. E. Howell furnishes a good collection of such specimens at a very reasonable price, and also a supply of small fragments of each for use in laboratory study. Larger and better specimens, and sample fragments of more generous size can be bought from Howell and several other dealers.[3] Every school should have such minerals, rocks, clays, building stones, and other mineral products as are typical of the state in which it is situated. A good collection of this sort can be built up by barter between schools in different localities, — a good " socializing " project.

Pictures. — Good photographs, photo-engravings, and three-color-process prints are indispensable in the study of geography. It is easy to make a collection of such pictures from magazines and advertising matter. All the great railway lines give away or sell at a nominal price descriptive folders and booklets containing pictures of high merit both from a geographical and an artistic point of view. Write to the general passenger agents of these roads, and see what an avalanche of valuable material you will get. Many land and irrigation companies also issue booklets giving typical scenes of interest-

---

[1] See References, Chapter XV.

[2] See also, Tarr, *op. cit.*, pp. 420–425.

[3] Ward's Natural Science Establishment, Rochester, N. Y.; E. A. Foote, Philadelphia; and Eimer and Amend, N. Y.

ing regions and their industries. Such companies advertise in the standard magazines. Mounted and unmounted photographs and half-tones of all sizes are sold by the Detroit Photographic Co., Detroit, Mich.; The Perry Pictures Co. of Malden, Mass.; and The Keystone View Co. of Meadville, Pa. Consult the advertising section of the *Journal of Geography* for the names of others. A few good pictures should be framed and hung on the walls. Others should be mounted on cards, and kept in manila folders in a vertical filing drawer. They should be labeled, classified, and indexed, like the topographic maps. The cards for mounting, cut to any size, can be bought at wholesale prices from a paper-jobbing house; and the mounting can be done by teacher and pupils. A typewritten list of questions may be attached to each picture, or placed loose in the folder with it. All pictures should be carefully selected for the purpose of teaching some definite things; and pictures which do not have some clear meaning in connection with the subject matter to be taught should be excluded from the collection. In selecting material of this sort the teacher should always ask himself first, " What am I to teach? " second, " For what reasons is it worth teaching? " third, " What illustrative material is best to use? " and fourth, " How shall the material best be used to accomplish the result sought? "

The Hölzel Charakter-Bilder are very useful large-size pictures mounted on cloth illustrating beautifully many phases of geography. They may be imported through the Kny, Scheerer Co., New York; E. Steiger & Co., New York, or Nystrom of Chicago.

A very beautiful form of geographical illustration is the picture postal card. These are cheap and easily obtainable through friends who are touring either in America or Europe. Most of them are good enough so that they may be well shown by a " reflectoscope," or projecting lantern for opaque objects.

Lantern slides. — For class work, lantern slides have many advantages over pictures. The projection pictures are large and brilliant, and show detail with little eyestrain; and furthermore, all can see the same thing at the same time. With a good electric lantern, when slides are being shown, the room need be only half darkened; so the teacher can see each member of the class, and occasional notes can be taken. It is better to show a few slides each day, at just the moments when they are needed, than to have a " lantern show " only once or twice a term and show a lot of slides at one time. Still better is a combination of both plans, using the former for advance work and the latter for reviews and drills.

Several apparatus houses supply extensive collections of geographical views, and issue classified price lists of slides. The best single collection known to the writer is the " Davis Collection," sold by E. E. Howell. Every one of these slides is of value, and most of them are of excellent quality. The American Bureau of Geography has prepared a large number of selected slides illustrating definite features of geographical interest.[1] When there are interesting geographic features near the school, good negatives should be made of them, and if several slides are made from each negative these slides may be used in obtaining others cheaply by bartering with classes in other schools.

Use of the blackboard and the modeling table. — Many teachers think that the modeling table is appropriate only to the kindergarten or the lowest elementary grades, and has no place in the high school. The author believes otherwise. It is quite difficult for pupils, even at the high school age, to

[1] Address E. R. Shepard, Minneapolis, Minn. Other dealers are as follows: T. H. McAllister, 49 Nassau St., N. Y.; Williams, Brown & Earle, Chestnut St., Philadelphia; The Keystone View Co., Meadville, Pa.; The Badger Stereopticon Co., LaCrosse, Wis.; McIntosh Stereopticon Co., Randolph St., Chicago; Detroit Photographic Co., Detroit, Mich.; copies of excellent slides in the collections of the University of California, and Cornell University, respectively, can be obtained from Professor H. W. Fairbanks, Berkeley, Cal., and John Troy, Ithaca, N. Y.

get new ideas from verbal descriptions only. Most teachers
are far too sparing even in their use of the blackboard and of
white and colored crayons. A teacher who can draw good
sectional and block diagrams on the board and talk at the
same time is immensely more interesting and lucid than one
who cannot command this means of expression. It is not
difficult to learn; and any one can acquire considerable skill
in it by industrious practice in copying on the board the
splendid block diagrams in the textbooks of Davis and Tarr.
Professor Davis had a clever trick of drawing his diagrams
on the board before the class came in, and partially erasing
them, so as to leave only a faint trace, which was easily visible
to him but not distinguishable to the class. Then while
lecturing, he would rapidly line in this " pony," as he called
it, so that the picture was quickly built up step by step, with
clearness and certainty, as he talked. The effect was to make
a very forcible and clear impression on his hearers of one
point at a time.

The practice in making such diagrams is highly conducive
to clarifying the concepts of the teacher himself, and if he
sets the example to the pupils, inciting them to try their hands
at it, they will derive similar benefits.

Sand modeling is another means of expression which appeals to the eye at the same time that the teacher's voice
is appealing to the ear. It is very difficult for most people
to translate a flat diagram into a picture of three dimensions,
and the teacher who can, as he talks, rapidly model a heap of
sand into a representation of the essential features of the thing
he is trying to describe in words, will find that many otherwise difficult ideas may be readily grasped by the pupils. It
is often hard for the teacher to realize that many concepts
that seem clear and almost obvious to him are so only because
on many forgotten occasions he has observed and reflected
on their essential features, and has worked them over and
mentally readjusted them repeatedly. They have grown up in

his own mind by gradual accretions and modifying readjust-
ments.   Yet he expects his students, with perhaps no experience of them, to get these same ideas from a single statement.
Many of the pupils, of course, cannot do this, even though the
statement be quite correct and clear.   They have not had the
previous experiences that the teacher himself has had; and
they have not by reflection and reasoning made the mental
connections or association bonds that are prerequisite to the
birth of the idea within their minds.   Hence the necessity of
incessantly placing before them in concrete form as many of
the essential prerequisite ideas as is possible.

For this reason a modeling table, with a supply of moist
sand and clay, a few modeling tools, and some skill in
using them, are of very great service, and should be always at hand, for immediate and often unpremeditated
use.   The pupils will not think a sand and clay model
childish if it helps them to understand something that
is puzzling their minds.   A table two by four feet in
area, with a rail two and a half inches high around the top,
and with bins underneath in which pails of extra sand and
clay may be kept, can easily be made by a local carpenter,
or by the boys in the manual training shop.   In order that
the class may easily see the models when made it would be
better to have the top rail that is toward them made so as to
slide out like the end-gate of a farm wagon.   No attempt
should be made to model specific objects or large areas.   It
should be continually remembered by the teachers and impressed by them upon the pupils that models, unless made on
a very large scale by highly skilled experts, are capable of
representing only generalized ideas.   It is the failure to recognize this fact that has brought models into disrepute among
many good teachers and school men.   For this reason, whenever a generalized model is used for illustration, it is well to
show in connection with it pictures and topographic maps of
examples of the real thing, and to point out the important

kinds of details that are entirely omitted in the model. If
the teacher wants an impressive lesson on avoiding the
dangers of giving the pupils wrong ideas, let him examine
the representation of the region of the Grand Canyon
of the Colorado River on the " politico-relief map " of the
United States, of a series that has been widely sold over the
country, and compare it with the United States topographic
map sheets of the same region, and with actual photographic
reproductions. If he will just *do* this instead of reading this paragraph and forgetting it, he will in all probability add something
at once to his power as a teacher. Seeing is sometimes more
and sometimes less than believing. In this case it is more.

Season apparatus. — One of the simplest and most effective
devices for illustrating the change of seasons is that of placing
a projecting lantern on a table in the center of the room, to
represent the sun, and to carry around it a slated globe on
which meridians and parallels are heavily marked with white
crayon. If the projecting lens and front condenser are removed from the lantern it will send out a beam of parallel
rays which may represent a parallel beam from the sun. If
the beam does not cover the circumference of the globe, move
the light a little nearer to the condenser. Now, if the globe is
moved around the lantern from point to point, keeping its axis
always inclined toward the position of the celestial north pole
(*i.e.* a point near the North Star), and if the lantern is simultaneously rotated so as to keep the parallel beams on the globe,
the great circle of illumination will be outlined on it. This
circle marks the division between day and night and also the
positions of the arctic and antarctic circles. The room should
be darkened just enough to render the circle of illumination
plainly visible to the pupils. These polar circles may then be
drawn on the globe by placing a piece of crayon successively
at the two extreme points reached by the rays, and slowly and
steadily rotating the globe on its axis. The tropics may be
similarly drawn by placing the crayon at the positions occu-

pied by a small beam from the center of the lantern condenser
when the northern and southern ends of the globe's axis
respectively are nearest to and farthest from the " sun "
as the " earth " is carried around on its " orbit." To get
the small central beam place in front of the condenser a card
screen perforated at the center of the condenser with a hole
the size of a quarter dollar.

Another good device is to represent the sun by a small
battery incandescent lamp placed at the center of a large pan
of water, and represent the earth by a floating apple with a
knitting needle stuck through it to show the position of the
axis.[1] The best mechanical device sold for this purpose of
illustrating the relations of the earth to the sun and moon is
the Gardner Season Apparatus, sold by Geo. S. Gardner, 141
Clifton Street, Rochester, N. Y., or by the apparatus dealers.
It is accompanied by directions for its use.

Helior. — Directions for making and using a " helior, or
sun board " may be found in Sutherland's " Teaching of
Geography," Chapter XIX, p. 219. This chapter contains
also many useful hints for teachers concerning laboratory and
observation work on the weather.

Clinometer. — A simple clinometer, which may also be used
as a level, may be made by attaching a protractor to the side
of a carefully squared rectangular block, so that the straight
edge of the protractor is parallel to one edge of the block.
Pivot to the point at the center of curvature of the graduated
semicircle of the protractor a small pendulum, made of sheet
metal and having a pointer just below the center of gravity of
the bob. The length of the pendulum should be such that
this pointer just reaches the edge of the scale on the divided
semicircle.

' To use this device as a clinometer place the block on the
inclined surface, so that its lower surface follows the inclina-
tion, and swing it around till the pendulum which hangs on

[1] Cf. Tarr's *Elementary Physical Geography*, p. 398.

the vertical side-face swings easily just clear of the scale. Then read off the angle in degrees between the position of the pointer and the middle point of the semicircle. This angle is equal to the angle of dip which the inclined surface makes with the horizontal. The direction of the dip is the direction of either of the upper edges of the block. It may be determined roughly with a pocket compass. The " strike " is the horizontal direction that is at right angles with the vertical plane of the angle of dip. To use the clinometer as a level, stand erect, and holding it at the level of the eye sight along the upper edge at some easily identified point on the slope whose elevation is to be measured. Let another person assist by adjusting the block to the horizontal position. When the block is horizontal, this will be known by the fact that the pendulum hangs so that its pointer is just at the middle division of the graduated semicircle.

Since the horizontal line through the edge of the block now strikes the side of a slope at the height of the observer's eye, he can fix on a point on this slope at that height, and taking a position there repeat the operation until he has measured from the bottom to the summit. Then the distance from the ground to his eye multiplied by the number of stations taken, will give approximately the vertical height of the slope. Allowance, of course, must be made on the last measurement for any fractional part of the observer's height.

QUESTIONS FOR FURTHER STUDY

1. Make out an order list of wall maps for your school.

2. Write a letter to the superintendent giving the main points for an argument before the board of education for an appropriation to purchase these maps.

3. Plan a lesson in which a wall map and the corresponding blackboard outline and seat maps are to be used, indicating the manner of use.

4. Make out a list for a first purchase of topographical maps, physiographic and geologic folios, and coast charts for your school.

5. For these (Question 4) write a letter similar in purpose to that of Question 2.

6. Select a list of laboratory problems and projects in which the weather maps are to be used.

7. Do the same for minerals and rocks, for pictures, and for lantern slides.

8. List the remaining kinds of apparatus mentioned in the order in which you would recommend their purchase. Give reasons for the order of your judgment.

REFERENCES

Consult the list at the end of Chapter XV, and for additional names and addresses of dealers in supplies and apparatus, see list at end of Chapter X.

CHAPTER XVII

PHYSICS. FUNDAMENTAL PRINCIPLES

Common sense notions, and physical principles. — In his
" Science of Mechanics " [1] Mach has shown that the early discoveries of mechanical laws and principles grew out of thinking that was aroused by problematic situations in which there
seemed to be some incongruity between observed physical
facts and the intuitive or common sense notions about them
which crystallize, so to speak, out of the manifold experiences
of the individual and the race in dealing with the materials
and tools of the industries. Physical principles, such as that
of the lever and that of flotation in mechanics, that of the distribution of heat by convection currents, that of the equality
of the angles of incidence and reflection for light, or Ohm's
law of flow for electric currents, are merely concise and convenient ways of describing events that persistently recur
under certain circumstances. As Mach points out,[2] such a
" law " or " principle " is an economical device of thought,
which enables us to keep in mind by means of a single statement or formula a multitude of single occurrences that are
alike in certain essential qualities or relations, although
widely separated perhaps in both time and space. The prin-

[1] Open Court Publishing Co., Chicago, 1907, *loc. cit.*, pp. 1–7, also 77–85.
(The word " intuitive " is preferable to the word " instinctive " used in the
English translation of Mach's book. Instinctive is probably intended only in
a figurative sense; but it is psychologically misleading in the connection used.
An instinctive reaction is one that is *unlearned:* an intuitive one is *learned,
but untaught.* This evidently is what Mach meant.)

[2] *Op. cit.*, p. 481 ff.

ciple states the relation that these single occurrences have in common. Those who have discovered such generalizations, as Mach shows,[1] have often used their intuitive notions, derived from familiar experiences, as guides in their thinking. So it is with us all, with children no less than with adults. New experiences which do not conflict with our intuitive knowledge, or common sense as we are wont to call it, are taken as matters of course, and do not arouse any feeling of doubt or incongruity. Understanding of principles grows by checking up new particular cases that are found to come under them, with the aid of these intuitions as guides. By this trying-out process both the principles and the guiding intuitions are clarified and made more precise and meaningful. One gets ultimately " a comprehensive, compact, consistent, and facile conception of the facts." [2]

Intuitions and the facts of everyday life as starting points. — It is very important that the teacher, at the outset, recognize this function of intuitions, and also that he keep in mind the close interplay of science and the industries, and so start his teaching of physical principles with problematic concrete situations in which the pupil senses a difficulty, or an incongruity with his intuitive experiential knowledge. Such a situation — one that involves a strange or novel element among the familiar occurrences of daily observation, and therefore piques the pupil's curiosity and arouses his interest — is the only kind of situation in which he will *think*. There is a vast difference, from the psychological and educational standpoint, between thinking and merely trying to recall dogmatic statements from the textbook. In the former case the pupil is acquiring meanings, learning to reflect, and learning to reason, while in the latter he is forming short-circuit memory bonds that cannot, excepting by mere chance,

---

[1] *Ibid.*, p. 26 ff. Every teacher of physics should read the entire chapter, especially Section V. The chapter, for the most part, is not easy reading, but it affords an outlook that is well worth the trouble required to gain it.

[2] Mach, *op. cit.*, p. 5.

function in real situations outside the schoolroom. Such short-circuit memory connections furnish one explanation for the condition so often described by teachers when they complain that pupils "know the principle, but cannot apply it."

In such cases it is obvious that they do not *know* the principle. The only association bond existing in their brain cells is the bond between the situation of being told (say), " State Pascal's law of fluid pressure " on the stimulus side, and recalling the sequence of words, " The pressure in a fluid in a closed vessel is transmitted . . . etc." on the response side. The necessary association bonds have not been formed between the *idea* of undiminished transmission of fluid pressure on the one hand, and a lot of concrete cases on the other hand. Such bonds can be formed in most cases only by a considerable number of concrete mental and motor *experiences* with fluids whose behavior under transmitted pressure has been intelligently and thoughtfully observed and measured in some way. Pupils cannot be railroaded into a knowledge of physical principles. *Real knowledge of a law or principle — that is, facility or skill in using it — can be gained only by practice in dealing with problematic situations in which it is involved.* Thus, if the pupil has gained such experience by measuring, with a pressure gauge, the pressure at several water taps which are located on the same floor of a building, and which come from pipes that have various diameters and that turn and twist in various directions, and if he has made similar measurements on one or two other floors, he will have little difficulty in grasping the idea, and connecting it in the class conferences with similar cases elsewhere.

How to associate symbols with things. — Let us pursue this important psychological principle further, so as to make sure that it is perfectly clear.

Suppose that the subject matter and organization with reference to the study of fluid pressures has been something like that which follows:

a. Pressures in the pipes in the home and school. (Observations, diagrams, and experiments.)

b. The city or village water-supply system. (Observations and diagrams.)

c. Standpipes and tower tanks. (Observations, diagrams, lantern slides.)

d. Equality of pressure and multiplication of force in the hydraulic press. (Study of a model and diagram.)

e. The idea of Pascal's principle developed from the similarity of behavior of water in all these cases reviewed and organized.

f. Verbal statement of the principle. (Drill on applying principle to the facts already considered. Review of inductive approach.)

g. Hydraulic punches and shears as further useful applications similar to the hydraulic press in principle. (Lantern slides or advertising pictures.)

h. Barber's and dentist's chairs which work on the hydraulic principle — their similarity to *d* and *g*. (Reports of inspection by pupils.)

i. Behavior of air in inflated bicycle tires and footballs. (Recall of familiar experiences.)

j. Numerical problems on the transmission of pressure and multiplication of force in presses, punches, hydraulic elevators, water pipes; on dams, walls of tanks, standpipes, etc. (Not all after, but some *along with* the cases and topics named above. In each case attention to be given to deducing consequences of the assumed principle.)

Now if opportunity has been given through the observations, experiments, reasonings, and discussions, for all these association connections to be made, we may suppose that, at least in the case of every interested and diligent pupil, an interlocking group of memory bonds has been formed, which might be represented diagrammatically by a figure resembling a spider web. In this figure all of the main ideas *a, b, c,* — *j,* might be pictured as a group of dots with *e* and *f* at the center and the others grouped around them, and the association or memory bonds of various strengths might be represented by heavy lines joining *e* with *f,* and also by lighter lines joining *e* and *f* respectively with all the others. Also, since each of these other ideas would have been connected in thought one with another as well as with *e* and *f,* there would be still lighter lines in the diagram connecting each of the dots with all the others. This web-like or net-like diagram would be purely schematic, but will perhaps give increased concreteness to the idea of an interlocking system of associations such as the teacher should aim to have built up in the minds of his pupils. Each such system has for its nucleus or center a general principle; and each of these principles should also be linked in a similar way with other principles that are related to it. For example, the principle of Archimedes follows directly, by reasoning that is comparatively simple, from Pascal's principle; so that with good teaching the latter principle

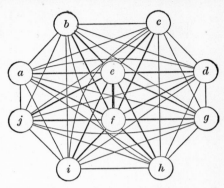

with its related facts should become associated with the former and its related facts.

When such an interlocking system of memory bonds has been built up in the mind of a student, each bond with "vividness, frequency, and resultant satisfaction," the presentation of any one of the experiences represented by the dots of the diagram should enable him to recall by means of the association bonds several of the others with which it has been thus associated, and also to recall the principle and its verbal statement with which all of them have thus been firmly connected. Conversely, the recall of the principle would in time be a stimulus for remembering all the experiences that are thus related to it. It must therefore be quite clear that if the pupils are to learn the principle so they may be able to recall and use it outside the schoolroom we must arrange their experiences in some such manner as has been described. There will then be many chances that the presentation of any one of the experiences a, b, c, — j will act as a stimulus to which the pupil will mentally respond by recalling some or all of the others. Thus if a new problem presented itself to him that was like any one of these, the principle would have many chances of being recalled by means of some one or more of the bonds of the interlocking system; and it might therefore be applied in solving the new problem.

Concepts, and the symbols that stand for them. — This explanation may perhaps have served to make clear the following principle, —

Words, definitions, statements of laws and principles, algebraic formulæ, are mere symbols. They are indispensable in science for economy in thought; but they are almost absolutely useless to any individual unless he himself has a clear and precise notion or concept of the things or relations for which each symbol stands.

A thorough and intelligent appreciation of this fundamental psychological principle is absolutely essential for real success in teaching anything, but it is more likely to be fatally overlooked by teachers of physics and chemistry than by teachers of some other subjects, because of the highly symbolic, condensed, and technical language in which these sciences are set forth in the treatises. The very excellence of logical organization to which these fascinating sciences have attained is on the one hand a source of the gravest danger to all attempts to teach them to young people, and on the other hand, if rightly used, a means of the highest value in forming habits of straight and connected logical thinking.

Some intuitive notions described. — What are the common sense notions or intuitive judgments that constitute so important a part of the mental raw materials with which the physics teacher must begin? We know no logical order in which to name them; and, as Mach shows,[1] it is useless to try to ascribe either priority or higher authority to one of them in preference to another; for they are all, as it were, *sui generis*, each being derived from a fund of experiences which is as worthy of confidence as any other. Hence the order in which they are here set down is not significant. Neither is it claimed that the enumeration is complete. It is intended only to be suggestive.

1. *The continuity of Nature*, the notion that things that have always been so will always be so *under similar*

---

[1] *Loc. cit.*, p. 80 ff.

conditions.[1]   In the teaching, the examination of conditions is the process on which a great part of any given
problem turns.

2.   *The causal notion,*[2] the intuitive habit of connecting
in thought two things that always go together, either
in sequence or simultaneously, and to look for a similar
relation which intelligibly connects a strange thing or
event with things or events that are familiarly known.
This intuitive tendency finds an outlet in the ubiquitous
question of the young child, " Mother, what makes it do
that? "   The teacher who can revive and foster this
naïve desire of the children to know the why of things —
a desire which is universally crushed by our conventional
social and educational procedure in dealing with them —
may know by this token that his methods, at least to
that extent, are right methods.

3.   *The notion of balancing,* and of a connection of
balancing with symmetry about the point or line of
support.   Here is a guiding intuition for all problems
about center of gravity, equilibrium, stability, levers, and
so on.   Every child who has played with a seesaw, played
store with toy scales, balanced his body, " trimmed " a
boat, carried packages in two hands, and the like knows
something about these problems and will be keen to
know more, if his interest is not stifled by making him
begin with reciting a book lesson about gravity or the
law of the lever.

4.   *The notion of force,* derived from the sensations of
muscular exertion in pushing and pulling things with
the hands, striking balls with bats, chopping with hatch-
ets, driving nails and pegs with hammers and stones,

[1] Cf. Mann, C. R., and Twiss, G. R., *Physics,* Scott, Foresman & Co., Chicago, 1910, p. 17.

[2] For a complete but simple discussion of the logical and scientific uses
of this notion, see Jones, A. L., *Logic, Inductive and Deductive,* Henry Holt &
Co., N. Y., 1909, pp. 79–109; cf. also Mach, *op. cit.,* pp. 483–485 and 579.

supporting weights, and the like. This notion again is usually clear enough in the pupil's mind if instead of trying to *define* force he is asked how it can be measured.

5. *The notion of work*, derived from lifting weights, pushing and dragging things against resistance, and so on. This notion, again, is made clear not by defining it metaphysically, but by showing in many cases that work can be measured by the numerical product, pounds force multiplied by distance.[1]

6. *The notion of inertia*, derived from running and dodging, from starting and stopping massive bodies, riding in vehicles.

7. *The correlative idea of mass*, expressed in the common saying that " large bodies move slowly." This idea is usually confused with those of weight and volume; and some care and a good deal of time and regulated experience in making the proper distinctions are needed to clear it up. Much of the difficulty here will be avoided if the teacher *always* makes the distinction correctly in his own speech *and does not insist on having the pupils understand and make it before they have had sufficient experience with the phenomena in which mass and weight can be differentiated.*

8. *The impossibility of a perpetual motion against a resistance,* derived from the continuous exertion required to keep bodies moving, and their tendency to stop when the urging force is relaxed, and from observation of swinging bodies which never rise to higher levels than those from which they started. This intuition is commonly expressed in the saying that " water never rises higher

---

[1] Cf. Mann, C. R., *The Teaching of Physics*, The Macmillan Co., N. Y., 1912, pp. 225–233. *No teacher of physics, experienced or otherwise, can afford not to read this book, and reflect on the vital questions respecting physics teaching that are discussed therein.* It has the almost unique advantage among books on science teaching of being written from the standpoint of modern psychology and is free from the taint of the discredited faculty and formal discipline psychology.

than its source " or that " you cannot get more work out of a machine than you put into it." The interest of many boys in suggested conflicts with this intuitive notion is striking. They will often think hard and argue keenly with one another in an endeavor to find the fallacies that lurk in such perpetual motion propositions.

The questions of Tyndall's boys. — In a lecture on Physics as a Means of Education [1] Tyndall gives a few questions selected at random from among those asked by his boys, students at an agricultural school in Hampshire. These questions were asked and discussed by the boys and their teachers at the meetings of a scientific club that they had formed. There were all sorts of questions, most of them asking for the causes of things. They exhibit the spirit of wonder that is so important for the science teacher to foster; and a few of them are just such problems as best serve for starting points from which to arrive at important physical principles.

" What are the duties of the Astronomer Royal? What is frost? Why are thunder and lightning more frequent in summer than in winter? What occasions falling stars? What is the cause of the sensation of 'pins and needles'? What is the cause of waterspouts? What is the cause of hiccup? If a towel be wetted with water, why does the wet portion become darker than before? What is meant by Lancashire witches? Does the dew rise or fall? What is the principle of the hydraulic press? Is there more oxygen in the air in summer than in winter? What are those rings that we see around the gas and the sun? What is thunder? How is it (*sic*) that a black hat can be moved by forming around it a magnetic circle, while a white hat remains stationary? [2] What is the

---

[1] In *Culture Demanded by Modern Life*, Edited by E. L. Youmans, Appleton, N. Y., 1875, pp. 59–85. Science teachers who have not read this eloquent and inspiring presentation of the culture value of science, by probably the most gifted teacher of physics that ever lived, should do so. The same volume contains a lecture by Liebig on "The Development of Scientific Ideas" which shows the close natural connection between science and the industries.

[2] This might have been some conjuring trick or a mere superstitious tradition; but it would seem unlikely that such a teacher as Tyndall would neglect the opportunity to incite the boys to find out in this case the relative merits

cause of perspiration? Is it true that men were once monkeys? What is the difference between the soul and the mind?[1] Is it contrary to the rules of vegetarianism to eat eggs? "

These are but a few from the many that were asked; but they suggest countless nodes of interest from which problems may be made to bud out at the command of a sympathetic and resourceful teacher. Tyndall then selects the questions of the wetted towel and the deposition of dew, and in his truly wonderful way shows how they can be explained by means of a few simple physical principles. The following quotation[2] will suggest the way in which such principles were led up to and enforced through some problems that enabled his boys to apply their knowledge of arithmetic and geometry, not to " recite " for the teacher, but to find out something that they were keen to know. The class he describes was supposed to be studying geometry; but it is evident that no watertight bulkheads existed between mathematics and science for such a teacher as Tyndall. The selection also exemplifies that infectious enthusiasm that is indispensable to successful science teaching.

"It was often my custom to give the boys their choice of pursuing their propositions in the book, or of trying their strength on others not to be found there. Never in a single instance have I known the book to be chosen. . . .

"And then again, the pleasure we all experienced was enhanced when we applied our mathematical knowledge to the solution of physical problems. Many objects of hourly contact had thus a new interest and significance imparted to them. The swing, the see-saw, the tension of the giant-stride ropes, the fall and rebound of the football, the advantage of a small boy over a large one when

of credulity and knowledge by putting this question to the test of experiment. Cf. Hall, G. Stanley, *Adolescence*, Appleton, N. Y., 1904, Vol. II, pp. 154–159, wherein the author calls attention to the neglected field of scientific toys and conjuring tricks as sources of problems possessing strong motivating power for study of the principles of physics.

[1] This is a poser, but is instructive as showing the range of questions over which some children ponder.

[2] Youmans, *op. cit.*, p. 80 ff.

turning short, particularly in slippery weather, all became subjects of investigation. Supposing a lady to stand before a looking-glass, of the same height as herself, it was required to know how much of the glass was really useful to the lady, and we learned, with great pleasure, the economic fact that she might dispense with the lower half and see her whole figure notwithstanding. We also felt deep interest in ascertaining from the hum of a bee the number of times the little insect flaps its wings in a second."

Economy of time and effort. — It is often objected that the problem approach requires too much time, — that there is so much ground to be covered that conditions will not admit of it. But of what use is covering the ground by a cramming process which leaves the pupils with confused and detached ideas, and a distaste for the subject? On the other hand, a reorganization of the subject matter about the larger and more general principles, and the exclusion of topics that are either too difficult for pupils to comprehend or are lacking in significance to them because of not making intelligible connections with their experiences, makes it possible to save much time. Everybody admits that the current textbooks are overloaded; then why try to have the pupils swallow them whole? [1] Let us see what can be done by better organization.

Organization in the study of mechanics. — Instead of having the pupils learn as discrete ideas a separate law for each of the traditional simple machines — the three different classes of levers, the wheel and axle, the capstan, the pulley — all these machines can be shown to come under two general statements, *the principle of moments* and *the work principle*, (*i.e.* neglecting friction, the work got out of the machine equals the work put into it); and by a very elementary and obvious algebraic substitution any case coming under the

[1] Each author during the past twenty years has had to include all the topics covered by his predecessors and add a few more, in order that his publishers' agents might meet the "talking points" of their competitors. For the manifest absurdity of the result, see Mann, *op. cit.*, p. 208.

former principle can be brought under the latter. **Out of the work principle** directly we get the efficiency equation also. So one single principle, or two at most, covers all these cases or any others similar to them. To this principle add that of the parallelogram of motions, — which explains all cases of the inclined plane and its variants — Newton's third law, and add also clarified statements of the intuitive notions of gravity, inertia, mass, and uniform speed; and you have practically all the principles under mechanics of solids that it is worth while to try to teach to pupils of high school age. All the other details will be more easily remembered because associated with these few principles, well understood, instead of being scattered in many discrete groups.[1]

In the mechanics of fluids, all the static phenomena of pressure in liquids and gases can be organized under three general principles in addition to those already enumerated, — that of Pascal, that of Archimedes, and the law of Boyle. The second principle may be deduced from the first as well as established independently by experiment. The third applies to gases, and is made manifest through their compressibility within certain limits; but since liquids are not appreciably compressible with forces that are available in the elementary laboratory their behavior is in sharp contrast with that of gases, and this contrast may be made of assistance in remembering the properties and behavior of both kinds of fluids. Here both resemblances and differences should be clearly brought out in the process of comparison.

Organization in the study of heat. — Again, in the subject of heat, the additional principles are few. The process of transfer of heat by convection, for example, is merely the result of difference in weight between two equal columns of fluid, one of which has been expanded more by heat than the

---

[1] To see how this reorganization has been effected in a plan that is working successfully in many schools examine the first three chapters of Mann and Twiss, *op. cit.*, pp. 17–67.

other has and is therefore less dense. The process is easily
understood and becomes of great practical interest, if led up
to from such a live and simple question as, Why does the
smoke come out into the room instead of going up the chimney, when you start a fire in the grate or furnace in early fall?
Here immediate connection is made between familiar experience and the principles of fluid pressure; and by means
of a few simple experiments and some careful elementary
thinking, the entire process is made clear. When the principle has been grasped through practical experiences with
this simple and familiar case, it is easily applied in other problems that grow naturally out of it, such as those pertaining to
the construction and management of cookstoves, hot-air and
hot-water furnaces, hot-water system for kitchen and bath-
room, and so on. It is easily extended to land and sea breezes,
monsoons, cyclonic storms, and ocean currents as distributers
of heat, resulting from similar circulation on a grander scale.
The utility of the general principle as a means of economy in
thought and as a guide in controlling the materials and forces
of nature thus becomes manifest to the pupils and can be
appreciated by them.[1] These problems also raise others
pertaining to the conduction of heat, such as the relative efficiencies of thermos bottles, teakettles, fireless cookers, refrigerators, flatiron holders, and many other common conveniences. Questions arising from these problems, and the
related ones pertaining to cold storage and artificial ice making,
lead directly to the conditions of boiling and evaporation, to
methods of measuring heat, and to the new principles of
specific heat, the heat of melting, and the heat of vaporization.
These in turn lead to the relative heats of combustion of different kinds of fuel, and also to the history of the growth of
the steam engine. In considering the steam engine, its horse-
power and its efficiency, we come upon one of the fundamental concepts of modern physics, the principle of Mayer

[1] Cf. pp. 113–117, ante.

and Joule, or the first law of thermodynamics. When we produce heat by doing mechanical work, and measure the work in foot pounds and the heat in British thermal units and, (after correcting for the known experimental errors), divide the former by the latter, we always get the same ratio or quotient, namely, 778 foot pounds equal 1 British thermal unit, (or, if metric units are used, 42,700 gram centimeters equal 1 gram calorie). Since 778 foot pounds of work can always be converted into one unit of heat, they must be the same thing, only in different form and therefore measured in different units; and this thing which we can measure objectively is what we call energy. This the pupils will readily grasp if they have not been first muddled by speculations about molecules and kinetic energy. Molecular physics and kinetic energy problems, if introduced at all in a beginner's course, should come near the end of it. The subject can be developed in a perfectly logical manner without them.

So again in the study of heat we have only a few leading principles under which we can organize all the facts and information that the pupils are able to acquire; and by such careful organization we may save much valuable time for the more efficient strengthening of the memory bonds that are most important to be formed in this field of thought.

Organization in the study of electricity. — The subject of electricity may be begun with a simple problem about an electric bell. How is it that a doorbell sometimes refuses to act? This usually brings the answer from some one that the battery runs down, or the bell gets out of adjustment. So here we have a motive for studying the construction of voltaic cells and electromagnets. Telegraph instruments and electric motors are fundamentally electromagnets or combinations of electromagnets, and hence their construction, action, and efficiency follow directly from the study of the doorbell.

Each new step can be taken through a question or problem that arises in the solution of some preceding one; and sustained interest and effort may thus be secured. The motor at once suggests the question, " How does the dynamo work," and necessitates the repetition of Faraday's experiments with induced currents, and discovery through them of the laws of electromagnetic induction. The induction coil, the alternating current transformer, and the telephone come in naturally here; and their essential kinship with the dynamo and motor, if brought out, will help the student to remember these four important devices and also the laws of induced currents, which give an economical, generalized description of their action.

Since the dynamo absorbs mechanical energy and yields an output of electric current, and the motor does just the reverse, these two machines suggest questions of economy of conversion and transmission. How can the efficiencies of these machines be measured? This question starts us into the problem of measuring the current and of comparing the resistances of various kinds of conductors, and also necessitates finding out the numerical relations of electrical pressure, current strength, and electrical resistance (*i.e.* Ohm's law). Further, since we put energy into the dynamo and get energy out of the motor through the intermediation of an electric current, we are led to the almost obvious inference that the current is a carrier of energy. It now becomes evident that in order to measure the efficiencies of the dynamo or motor we must have a unit in which to measure the energy of the electric current, and we find that such a unit has been devised on the analogy of flowing water or working steam. This unit is the watt second or its commercial multiple the kilowatt hour. Again Joule was the scientist who determined for us the ratio between the kilowatt hour and the British thermal unit, and thus enabled us by a simple arithmetical calculation to find the desired ratio between the kilowatt hour and the foot pound, or its multiple used by steam engineers, the horse-power hour. This ratio is $\dfrac{1000}{746}$, or approximately, $1\frac{1}{3}$ horse-power hour equals 1 kilowatt hour.

Now it thus appears that we can supply energy to a steam engine in the form of heat, and it reappears as mechanical energy which we can transfer by a belt to a dynamo, that the dynamo can take the mechanical energy from a steam engine, or a water wheel, and convert it into electrical energy, that this electrical energy can be driven along a wire, can produce heat and light, can decompose metallic compounds, and can operate a motor which turns it back into mechanical work.

When the pupils have reached this point, and not until then, they are ready to grasp comprehensively the great unifying principle of physical science, the principle of the conservation of energy. This principle includes the work principle, the first law of thermodynamics, and the principle of the conversion of electrical energy into heat — all of which previously have been encountered by the pupils. Since the telephone receives sound vibrations and reproduces them again after carrying them in the form of electrical oscillations, and since light and radiant heat can produce mechanical rotations in a radiometer, this is the place to recall the telephone and to show the radiometer. Thus the generalization is arrived at not as the dogmatic dictum of the teacher or the textbook, but as a summation of a considerable number of convincing experiences. This is the only way that a generalization can become meaningful. Acquired by any other process, it is a string of empty words, a series of symbols without significant mental content.

Here again we have a large body of facts grouped around a few principles and associated with them. All of these can be recalled more readily because they have been so associated, and not taught as discrete facts each associated only with conventional schoolroom cues in the form of teacher's questions.[1]

Organization in the study of sound. — In the realm of sound it is easy to arrange a set of experimental problems that will bring out and establish the few main principles and associate them with the most important facts. What kinds of bodies give rise to sounds, and what is their common physical condition while producing the sounds? What are the kinds of media through which sounds are transmitted? Must it always be an elastic substance? What is the speed of sound? Can one sounding body set another sonorous body to vibrating? What are the necessary conditions in order that this phenomenon (resonance) may occur? By this time the question as to the precise mode of transmission will have occurred to the pupils; and having successfully sought the answer to the preceding questions through experiments, observations, and appeals to experience, they will be keen to search for the answer. If they are challenged to enumerate the various ways in which they have found that energy is transmitted from one place to another as they have found that sound is, and they are asked to venture a hypothesis, they will probably eliminate promptly moving masses and currents, and select wave motion as the only likely hypothesis. A study of wave motion in water and in elastic cords then becomes necessary in order that they may learn the general characteristics of wave motion; and in this study they may learn that the common phenomenon of resonance points to a close kinship between the mechanism of sound transmission in air and the wave motions in water and in elastic cords. After they have recalled that air is elastic when subjected to compression stresses, they may be assisted in inferring that the transmission of sound may be accomplished by waves that consist of condensations and rarefactions in the air, and if so might be de-

[1] Such for example as "Define electromagnet," "Describe the dynamo," "State Ohm's Law," "Give the formula for the heat of an electric current," etc.

x

tected by means of a sufficiently quick and sensitive pressure indicator. The teacher may then suggest a gas jet fed by a stream of gas that passes through a chamber with an elastic wall (Koenig's vibrating flame), and also a revolving mirror for stringing out the image of the flame so that rapid changes in its height can become easily apparent to the eye. If the experiment is led up to in this way instead of being all formally and didactically explained at the outset, it will become the object of absorbing interest. It will also carry conviction, and establish confidence in the results of carefully safeguarded inductive inference.

Next will follow a study of the piano, guitar, or violin as a type of stringed musical instruments; and interest will be centered on the functions of sounding boards and the behavior of vibrating strings. Some consideration also will be given to the organ pipe and reed pipe as types of wind instruments, which depend for their utility on the behavior of vibrating air columns. In connection with these studies, the causes of differences in loudness, pitch, and timbre will be brought out, and an elementary discussion of the basis of our musical scale will naturally occur.

All these phenomena are thus naturally and easily grouped through a consecutive series of experimental problems around the simplest principles of wave motion, resonance, partial vibrations, interference, and the simple whole-number ratios of harmonizing tones. Instead of memorizing without thought or intelligence, and with indifferent success, a hopeless aggregation of unrelated and isolated facts and laws, the pupils thus taught will have possessed themselves of a consecutive, orderly, organized procession of facts. Furthermore, these facts will be clearly apprehended and firmly associated with the aid of a short series of simple principles each of which has been logically related to those that were learned before it.

Organization in the study of light. — Similarly in the study

of light we may create a problematic situation of absorbing
and stimulating interest by forming through a small opening
in a closed shutter of the darkened classroom an inverted
image in its natural colors of the scene outside.   It may be
displayed on the opposite wall or on a white screen.   Out of
this situation such questions as the following arise for solution : What is the cause of this image?   What conditions
determine its size and intensity?   What information does this
experiment and its underlying principles offer as to the question of how we judge the sizes, distances, and relative directions of objects?   Can a photograph be made with a camera
minus its lens (pinhole camera experiment)?   Is it true that
the smaller the hole, the clearer the image, but the less its intensity and the greater the time of exposure to make a photograph?   Why?   What are the geometrical relations that determine the size of the image as compared with that of the
object?   All the information that grows out of the study of
these questions may be associated with the principle of the
rectilinear path of light (in a homogeneous medium), and
organized about it.   The applications of the simple geometry
of straight lines, vertical angles, and similar triangles to the
solution of these problems are of great educational value, since
they give motivated practice in the use of mathematics, and
demonstrate its value as a convenient tool in reaching valid
conclusions that can be further tested by experiments.   Why
are expensive lenses needed in making photographs, when we
can make photographs without them?   This question will
have come up by the time the pupils have gone thus far ;
and the first step in working it out is to repeat the initial
experiment, placing a long-focus lens in the shutter-aperture,
and note the change in the size, distance, distinctness, and
illumination of the image.   These observations clear up the
facts, but do not answer the question ; and so a careful experimental study of the properties of lenses becomes necessary.
This study reveals the fact that the photographic lens is useful

because it causes a diverging or parallel beam of light to converge at a focal point, and so forms an image made up of
small intense points of light instead of by large overlapping
patches.

The close optical kinship between the camera and the eye
suggests an elementary study of the latter as the next problem
involving the principle of a converging lens.   This leads to the
use of the magnifying glass and the objectives of the opera
glass, telescope, microscope, and stereopticon, and to an elementary consideration of the relation of the size, distance,
and position of the image as compared with those of the
object.

Related to these problems also are those of spectacles, as
aids to vision either myopic or hyperopic.   The elementary
theory of refraction may follow here in answer to the question
as to how the lens causes the rays to converge, or it may better
be considered in connection with the general review near the
end of the course, with many other matters that are best deferred because of their difficulty until the pupils have gained
the knowledge and skill in reasoning that several months'
training on easier subject matter may be expected to have
given them.

Next will arise the questions concerning images formed
by plane mirrors, the use of diffuse reflection, and the measurement of light intensity by the photometer.   The subject
of color is always one of absorbing interest; and it is easy
to start inquiries about the reasons for the colors of the rainbow, of stained glass windows, of three-color process prints,
and of various other objects of nature and art, and to group
these about the principle of the prism and that of selective
absorption, which serve to explain them.

Finally the question as to the mechanism by which light is
transmitted may be raised, and the wave theory set up as a
hypothesis.   The discovery by Roemer that light requires
time to travel from the sun to the earth may now be recounted

and explained. The fact that light and radiant heat are energy, proved by the radiometer, and the resemblance of light to water waves may be discussed with reference to their common property of being reflected, refracted, and affected by interference. The interference fringes, made by two glass plates or by a soap film in sodium light and white light, may then be shown and the argument for the wave theory clinched. Then and not till then has the time come for mentioning the luminiferous ether.[1]

Thus all these phenomena of light may be organized with reference to the principle of rectilinear propagation, the geometry of similar triangles, the simple fact of convergence or divergence of light " rays " in passing through convex or concave lenses, the law of reflection, the law of inverse squares, and the principles of prismatic analysis and selective absorption.

Organization of the whole body of subject matter. — From the foregoing discussion, it may be seen that each one of the less comprehensive principles of mechanics, heat, electricity, sound, and light may be approached through simple, interesting problems, some qualitative, and more of them quantitative, all of them starting with knowledge that the pupils already

---

[1] This fundamental principle of science teaching — withhold theories until they are needed to explain the facts, and allow them to be used only as working hypotheses until the accumulated evidence forces conviction — is flagrantly violated in some of the most widely used texts in both physics and chemistry. In one physics text the wave theory of light comes almost at the beginning of the subject, and the molecular theory is introduced before the phenomena of heat are taken up. In several of the chemistries the authors take the shortest possible cut to the atomic theory. The result is muddy and vague talk by the pupils about what molecules and ether do, when plain statements of fact are required. It leads them inevitably toward a dogmatic, deductive attitude; and it fails to train them in distinguishing between fact and inference — an ability that is absolutely essential to any clear and scientific thinking. If the reader is not convinced that first teaching a theory and then deducing the facts therefrom is a pedagogical misdemeanor, if not a crime, let him read carefully Smith and Hall's *Teaching of Chemistry and Physics*, Longmans, N. Y., 1902, Chapter VI.

possess, and proceeding by consecutive steps of experimentation and reasoning toward the goal. These in turn can be shown to be comprehended by a few larger and more inclusive principles which make up the theoretical framework of the whole subject.

Fundamental concepts of physics. — Thus we have the few fundamental concepts of physics, *time* and *space, mass* and *inertia, electricity* and *ether,* all related to one another and made apparent through the transformations and transferences of *energy* that take place in connection with phenomena that are described by them. So also we have the great comprehensive principles of action and reaction, of the conservation of energy, of the degradation of energy, and of relativity, which serve to sum up and connect all the facts and phenomena which the beginner in physical science can successfully examine and fairly master. The molecular and electron theories may perhaps be given at the end of the course, but are not needed for the effective organization of the most important and significant facts. The earlier introduction of these theories will certainly serve only to confuse the pupils and draw them away from the safe and firm ground of facts that they can grasp through first-hand observation and experimentation into what, at least for them, must remain a treacherous atmosphere of speculation.[1]

QUESTIONS FOR FURTHER STUDY

1. How would you teach a physical principle so that a pupil would be able to apply it to a new problem? Choose one, and outline your plan.

2. For your plan (Question 1) make a diagram representing the association bonds, and tell how you would go about forming them.

3. Explain what you understand by building up a concept, and connecting its meanings with the symbols that stand for it.

[1] For suggestions as to a detailed elaboration of such a course as has been indicated see the chapters on the various divisions of the subject in the Mann and Twiss *Physics* and read Mann's *Teaching of Physics,* Part III.

4. Select some physical principle or concept and explain how it contributes to economy in thought.

5. For each of the intuitive notions listed, describe some way in which you have, at one time or another, assumed its truth and acted accordingly.

6. What is your opinion as to the utility of reciting the customary "definitions" of force, mass, and inertia, as compared with possessing knowledge of how bodies *behave* under various conditions and how force, mass, etc., can be measured?

7. What ideas of value in teaching physics do you get from the discussion of Tyndall's methods?

8. Argue either for or against any one of the plans proposed in this chapter for the organization of the subject matter of physics.

9. Discuss the rule, "Withhold theories until they are needed to explain facts."

10. How should the "fundamental concepts" of physics be used in teaching physics in the high school?

REFERENCES

In addition to the references given in the footnotes the reader will find titles on methods and content in the list at the end of Chapter XVIII, and a list of books for teachers and pupils in Appendix A.

CHAPTER XVIII

METHODS IN PHYSICS

Division of the course into two parts. — Most of the writers of physics textbooks have been so bound to the logical order of treatment that has been handed down from the books of their predecessors that they insist on mixing up topics of widely different degrees of difficulty, in order that all the applications of a given principle may be treated before they pass to the next principle. That such a mode of organization is the best and most logical for a reference book to be consulted by a mature student, who already has a good knowledge of the elementary facts and principles, may be frankly admitted; but in a course or a textbook intended for beginners it is psychologically wrong. The most difficult topics — those that require the closest and longest-sustained attention and the most difficult reasoning — should come near the end of the course, after the pupils have gained facility and confidence in reasoning, and the habit of distinguishing clearly between fact and inference. Let the facts that are gained be organized and logically connected with the general principles that coördinate and explain them, as the course is developed. Let the advance be orderly and sequential; but let the materials used at the successive stages be fitted to the progress of the pupils in ability and understanding, rather than to an abstract scheme which is the final product of the trained adult mind. There is no *one* logical order; there are many, and the one to be chosen is the one that best serves the purpose in hand, which is the instruction and training of the pupils. A lawyer organizes his materials so as to carry conviction to the jurors, not to mystify and perplex them. He cares nothing for the logical classifications of his lawbooks while he is addressing the jury, although he is glad that the materials are so arranged in the books for his own convenience in preparing his case. His speech is none the less logical for that. It is more so, because he had reorganized his materials with reference to the case under consideration. Why should not the textbook writer and the teacher do the same thing? It is therefore just as logical, and far better psychologically, to arrange the course in two parts, the first part containing a presentation that is both logical and psychological of those facts and principles that are easily comprehensible by a beginner, and the second part containing additional materials that are important, but that have been proved by long experience in the classroom to be difficult to the pupils. These more difficult facts and principles may then be organized and presented through a series of problems in connection with a general review near the end of the course and may thus be fitted into the general scheme of the year's work. This plan has the very great advantage of making it possible to expand or contract the course to fit the varying abilities of classes and individuals, — a pedagogical principle which is now insisted on by the leading authorities in school administration.

Following out this principle, composite machines, solid and fluid friction, the explanation of the kite and aëroplane; the changes of gas volumes with changes of both temperature and pressure; the gas engine; electrical resonance, wireless telegraphy, and the telegraphic relay; the formation of images by the combination of lenses in the various optical instruments; concave and convex mirrors; the discussion of kinetic energy, accelerated motion, and the measurement of forces in absolute units; and the molecular, ion, and electron theories — all these should be relegated to the second part of the course. Thus all or only part of them may be taught in connection with the general review, according to the interests, aims, and abilities of the class. The selection, of course, should be made by the teacher according to his best judgment; and he should take care when he is teaching them, and in the final review, that they are incorporated with the related facts given in the first part of the course, and under the general principles where they logically belong in the finished organization of the subject matter.

The authors of at least one beginner's textbook in physics,[1] convinced of the soundness of this principle of adapting the material to the progress of the pupils, have had the courage to depart from the beaten track, and put the principle into practice by dividing their book into two parts in the manner indicated; and the results with the classes where this book is used have justified the departure.

Syllabi. — To those teachers who are in such circumstances that they must conform to the content of the syllabi of the College Entrance Examination Board or those of state authorities, it may be said that the plan of organization and teaching here outlined can be followed under these syllabi if careful attention is given to *relative emphasis* on the various items that the syllabi call for. None of their makers ever intended that the syllabi should be followed slavishly as to order of topics, or that the same emphasis should be placed on every item. Even if this really had to be done, better results could be obtained by devoting the bulk of the year to real teaching after the manner here described, and devoting three or four weeks at the end of the course to a " cramming " review for the examinations.

The North Central Association's unit in physics. — This statement of an outline for a year's work in elementary physics was formulated in 1910 by a committee of the association com-

[1] Cf. Mann and Twiss, *Physics*, Revised Edition 1910 (compare Part II with Part I).

posed of physicists, psychologists, and school men who were
also members of the National Commission for the Teaching of
Physics. This commission, organized and led by Professor
C. R. Mann of the University of Chicago, was composed
of representatives elected by all the important organizations in the country interested in the teaching of physics.
With the coöperation of this commission, Dr. Mann conducted a careful research on the condition of physics teaching
in the United States extending over a period of two years.
The progress of this work was reported from time to time in
School Science and Mathematics. The work of the commission was known as " The New Movement among Physics
Teachers " and was widely discussed in educational magazines
and in meetings of physics teachers. Its organized work
was responsible for giving force and direction to the present
tendency to " bring physics closer to the daily lives of the
pupils," and to make use of modern psychological principles
in the methods of teaching it. Another direct result of this
commission's work was a revision toward greater freedom for
the teacher in the present college entrance requirement of
the College Entrance Board of the Middle States and Maryland.[1] The unique characteristic of the North Central unit
in physics as compared with that of the College Entrance
Board, and that of the New York Regents, and the so-called
" National Physics Course " is that it provides for the utmost
liberty of choice, emphasis, and arrangement by the teacher,
*and contains no topic to which any member of the National
Commission on the Teaching of Physics objected.* In other
words, it contains those topics and those only which this
representative body unanimously regarded as essential to an
elementary course. It is given in full below.

[1] For references, see list at end of this chapter.

PHYSICS

Definition (1 unit)

1. The unit in physics consists of at least one hundred and eighty periods of forty minutes each (equal to 120 hours) of assigned work. Two periods of laboratory work count as one of assigned work.

2. The work consists of three closely related parts; namely, class work, lecture-demonstration work, and laboratory work. At least one fourth of the time shall be devoted to laboratory work.

3. It is very essential that double periods be arranged for the laboratory work.

4. The class work includes the study of at least one standard text.

5. In the laboratory the student shall perform at least thirty individual experiments, and shall keep a careful notebook record of them. At least twenty of these should involve numerical work and the determination of such quantitative relations as may be expressed in whole numbers. Such quantitative work should aim to foster the habit of thinking quantitatively, but should not attempt to verify laws with minute accuracy nor to determine known physical constants with elaborate apparatus. The list of topics covered by these quantitative experiments should not differ widely from the list of starred topics in the syllabus.

6. The class work should aim to build up in the student's mind clear concepts of physical terms and quantities, and an intuitive appreciation of the general principles which make up the syllabus. He must be trained in the use of those principles in the solution of simple, practical, concrete numerical problems.

7. Examinations will be framed to test the student's understanding of and ability to use the general principles in the required syllabus, as indicated in 6.

8. The teacher is not expected to follow the order of topics in the syllabus unless he wishes to do so.

Syllabus of Required Topics

This list of required topics is not intended to include all the material for the year's work. It is purposely made short, in order that each teacher may be free to supplement it in a way that fits his individual environment. It does include those topics which all agree are essential to a first course in physics, and which are capable of comprehension, at least to the extent specified in number 6 of the definition of the unit, by boys and girls of high school age.

*1. Weight, center of gravity. *2. Density. *3. Parallelogram of forces. 4. Atmospheric pressure; barometer. *5. Boyle's law. 6. Pressure due to gravity in liquids with a free surface; varying depth, density, and shape of vessel. *7. Buoyancy; Archimedes' principle. *8. Pascal's law; hydraulic press. 9. Work as force times distance, and its measurement in foot-pounds and gram-centimeters. 10. Energy measured by work. *11. Law of machines: work obtained not greater than work put in; efficiency. *12. Inclined plane. *13. Pulleys, wheel and axle. *14. Measurement of moments by the product, force times arm; levers. 15. Thermometers: Fahrenheit and Centigrade scales. 16. Heat quantity and its measurement in gram calories. *17. Specific heat. *18. Evaporation; heat of vaporization of water. *19. Dew point; clouds and rain. *20. Fusion and solidification; heat of fusion. 21. Heat transference by conduction and convection. 22. Heat transference by radiation. 23. Qualitative description of the transfer of energy by waves. 24. Wave length and period of waves. 25. Sound originates at a vibrating body and is transmitted by waves in air. *26. Pitch and period of sound. *27. Relation between the wave length of a tone and the length of a string or organ pipe. *28. Resonance. 29. Beats. 30. Rectilinear propagation of light; pin-hole camera. *31. Reflection and its laws; image in a plane mirror. *32. Refraction, and its use in lenses; the eye, the camera. *33. Prisms and dispersion. 34. Velocity of light. 35. Magnetic attractions and repulsions. *36. Field of force about a magnet. 37. The earth a magnet; compass. 38. Electricity by friction. 39. Conductors and insulators. *40. Simple voltaic cell. *41. Electrolysis; definition of the ampere. *42. Heating effects; resistance; definition of the ohm. *43. Ohm's law; definition of the volt. *44. Magnetic field about a current; electromagnets. *45. Electromagnetic induction. *46. Simple alternating current dynamo of one loop. *47. Electromagnetic induction by breaking a circuit; primary and secondary. 48. Conservation of energy.

Library work. — The amount of library work that can be done in connection with a year's course in beginning physics is doubtless limited because of the large amount of textbook and laboratory work that should take precedence of it. Nevertheless, it ought by no means to be wholly neglected. It will naturally take the direction of references to the biographies of great physicists, and of readings for pleasure, inspiration, and additional fullness of information, from classical presentations of physical facts, theories, and discoveries. Biographical facts about Galileo, Copernicus, Newton, Boyle, Watt, Galvani, and Volta; about Franklin, Faraday, Tyndall, and Rowland; about Bell, Edison, Marconi, the Wright Brothers, and other illustrious physicists and inventors; stories of how they made their discoveries; and occasional selections from the lectures by Davy, Faraday, Tyndall, Fleming, Lodge, Dewar, and others at the Royal Institution, or from those delivered in this country by eminent physicists at the Franklin Institute and Cooper Union — all these may be of great inspirational value, as well as highly instructive. Some of these lectures are classical examples of expository English writing and should be read in the English classes with the two-fold purpose of inspiration in Science and appreciation in English literature. They might well take the place of a classic that has so little appeal with most pupils as the De Coverley Papers have.

References of another sort that may be of very great value when used with wisdom and caution can be found in some of the notes on their original discoveries by Faraday, Roentgen, Arrhenius, and others that have been collected and prepared for students of physics.[1]

Finally, such books as Hopkins's "Experimental Science," describing experiments that can be contrived with apparatus to be made by the boys at their homes or in the school shop, and such periodicals as *The Scientific American, The Scientific American Supplement, Popular Mechanics, The Popular Science Monthly,* etc., will be found very interesting and stimulating to the practical-minded pupils, while their reports to the class may be of great interest to those of a less mechanical type of mind — even to the girls.

Many voluntary assignments may well be given out; but

[1] The Series of *Scientific Memoirs,* edited by J. S. Ames, Editor-in-Chief, and a number of leading American physicists, and published by the American Book Co., N. Y. Volumes 75 ¢ to $1.25.

required references should be few and very carefully chosen; and when given out, the latter should be conscientiously followed up, and reports insisted on; so the teacher may know that his orders have been carried out, and also whether the assignment proves to be profitable or otherwise. If there is a science club in the school, much of this sort of reference work may be done voluntarily by pupils in performing their parts in the work of the club.

Laboratory work. — The method for physics outlined in these chapters will not necessitate discarding immediately the laboratory equipment that the school has on hand. A number of the experiments usually made in the laboratory are lacking in significance for high school pupils, and are not worth the time that is spent on them; but the greater part of them may be made valuable if they are presented in a better way. For example, take one of those on specific gravity. Approached in the customary way, the purpose of the experiment is usually stated as follows, " To find the specific gravity of a solid that sinks in water." Stated thus, it has no significance. There is no motive. Why should the student care to find the specific gravity of " a solid " that he is not going to *do* anything with? Suppose, on the other hand, we raise the question as to how much work will be required to lift a large block of stone to its position in a neighboring building under construction. The answer, of course, can be obtained by multiplying the weight by the height to which it is to be lifted; but how are we to find the weight? A little questioning will usually elicit from the pupils the suggestion that the dimensions can easily be measured and the volume calculated. Then if we knew the weight of a unit of volume of the stone we could multiply this by the total volume and get the weight of the block: also the weight for unit volume of the stone can be found by determining the specific gravity of a sample of it.

Again, suppose that instead of assigning an experiment

" to determine the specific gravity of a liquid " the teacher proposes that the pupils find out whether the milk that they are receiving at their homes has been watered. There will then be a real motive for finding the specific gravity of the milk and for making a hydrometer which they can use for that purpose at home.[1] Other changes in attitude of the same sort can easily be made by every teacher for himself. Thus pupils need no longer make an experiment " to find the electrical resistance of a wire," but can find out " whether a tungsten lamp if substituted for a carbon lamp will save more than its increased cost," and so on. *Under this sort of teaching, the laboratory experiment, instead of being abstract, formal, and meaningless to the pupils, becomes a necessary step in the solution of a live human problem that the pupils have some real, sane reason for desiring to solve.*

Types of live laboratory problems. — For further illustration of what may be called the live or dynamic attitude in the framing up of laboratory problems, as contrasted with the formal method, a few more laboratory projects and propositions are here enumerated.

　　1. In geometry we learn that the medians, or lines drawn from the vertices of a triangle to the middle points of the opposite sides, meet in a point. Cut a triangular figure out of a piece of board, sheet iron, or pasteboard. Where is the center of gravity of this triangle located with reference to the intersections of the medians of its two faces? Give the reasons for your answer, and supply proof by experiment.[2]

　　2. Will the amount of work that must be done in pushing this loaded box up this inclined plane from the floor to the table be equal to that required to lift it vertically to the same height? If not, how much greater or less? Account for the difference. How may the efficiency of the inclined plane method be increased? Find by experiment the per cent of increase in efficiency by your proposed improvement. Describe some of the most useful ways in which

---

[1] For such an experiment see Twiss, G. R., *Laboratory Exercises in Physics*, Scott, Foresman & Co., Chicago, 1906, p. 88.

[2] See Mann and Twiss, *op. cit.*, p. 19 ff., and Twiss, *op. cit.*, pp. 52–54.

you have seen the principle of the inclined plane applied outside the schoolroom.[1]

3. With the same body to be lifted, what effects do changes in the steepness of the inclined plane have on the amount of work done? On the amount of force exerted along the plane? Answer by measuring the force and the work with different slopes and comparing results.[1]

4. With this set of pulleys (or this wheel and axle) can you lift the loaded box (Exp. 2) to the table with less work than with the inclined plane, or is more work required? How much? Measure the efficiency of this machine and compare it with that of the inclined plane. Find out whether the efficiency varies with the load, and show the relation by plotting a graph, with loads as abscissas and efficiencies as ordinates.[2]

5. Find how much force is exerted by each hand when holding a shovel filled with coal preparatory to throwing it into the furnace. See how long a list of the practical applications of the principle of moments you can make in fifteen minutes.

6. Considering a hand tack-puller as a lever, find out by experiment and calculation the forces with which a tack resists being drawn out of different kinds of wood.

7. Find the efficiency of this water motor by means of a brake test. Find out how the efficiency is related to the water pressure, and to the amount of the load.[3]

8. With a straight lamp chimney, corks, sheet rubber, pins, a wooden rod, and glass tubing, make a model of a lift pump. Make it over into a force pump.[4]

9. With a lamp chimney, corks, and glass tubing make a model of a kitchen hot-water tank. Fill and operate it. Find and describe the convection currents with the aid of scrapings of blotting paper.

10. Is the burner of this gas stove more or less efficient than this Bunsen burner? Calculate the relative cost per quart of water raised from tap temperature to boiling point.[5]

11. Is this copper teakettle more or less efficient than this aluminum one? After the water has begun to boil, is the "simmer-

[1] See Mann and Twiss, *op. cit.*, pp. 33–37, and Twiss, *op. cit.*, pp. 33–37.

[2] See Mann and Twiss, *op. cit.*, pp. 36–40, and Twiss, *op. cit.*, pp. 23–27, 46–48.

[3] See Mann and Twiss, *op. cit.*, p. 104 ff.

[4] See Mann and Twiss, *op. cit.*, p. 76 ff., and Twiss, *op. cit.*, pp. 52–54.

[5] See Mann and Twiss, *op. cit.*, pp. 141–143.

ing burner" more efficient than the regular burner turned low? How much?[1]

12. Is the specific heat of copper greater or less than that of aluminum? How much?[2]

13. In this sectional model of a house install and test an electric bell system as described in the directions.[3] Make a sketch for improvements in the wiring of your home.

14. With these instruments and supplies set up and operate a two-station telegraph line. Make a working diagram and write a clear description of all that happens when a key is opened and closed.[4]

15. At present rates in this community, does it cost more to boil a quart of water with this gas burner or with this electric stove? How much more?

16. Find out which of these two electric motors is the more efficient, and how much more.[5]

17. How many vibrations does this tuning fork make per second when it is sounding?

18. How long are the air waves made by this tuning fork?[6]

19. With this sonometer find out the vibration-frequency ratios of the tones of a major chord, and the first and the second octave. What is the relation between the length of a string and the frequency of the tone that it gives?[7]

20. How many and what overtones can you get out of this sonometer string?[8]

21. What is the focal length of your camera lens (or of the objectives of your opera glass, or of your eye glass lenses)?[9]

22. Can you make a telescope with this pasteboard mailing tube and these lenses and corks?

23. Find by measurement and compare the energy-consumption and cost per candle power hour for this fishtail and this Welsbach gas burner and for this carbon and this tungsten glow lamp.

These problems and projects are not by any means necessarily the only or the best ones. They are proposed as being suggestive of hundreds of others that present to the pupil a

[1] See Mann and Twiss, *op. cit.*, pp. 141–143.
[2] See Twiss, *op. cit.*, pp. 108–112, and Mann and Twiss, *op. cit.*, pp. 132–133.
[3] See Twiss, *op. cit.*, pp. 135–138.   [4] *Ibid.*, pp. 129–135.
[5] See Mann and Twiss, *op. cit.*, pp. 210–212.
[6] See Twiss, *op. cit.*, pp. 165–167.   [7] *Ibid.*, pp. 173–176.
[8] *Ibid.*, pp. 168–173.   [9] *Ibid.*, pp. 198–200.

live motive by giving him something to do that will afford interest of itself, because it makes direct connection with other things that he is likely to care to think about. To solve them he must *do* something, and do it in order to find the answer to a question that seems to have some direct connection with daily life. There are many others of the same sort that can be used. Some very good experimental problems can be got out of the household, commercial, and industrial applications of physics, such as fireless cookers, electric flatirons, sewing machines,[1] pressure cookers, electric and mechanical vacuum sweepers, lathes, drills, electric fans, scissors, can-openers, fruit presses, thermometers, stoves and furnaces, gas and water meters, ice cream freezers, thermos-bottles, household and school plumbing and heating, refrigerators, stills, gas engines, annunciators, electric gas-lighters, bells, fuses, automatic fire sprinklers, electroplating, electrotyping, and a hundred others. In this connection the reader should review what is said about laboratory work in Chapter VIII of this book, and read Chapter XI of Mann's "The Teaching of Physics."

In advocating more experiments of this kind the author does not mean to be taken as placing no value whatever on the formal experiments that have been so long in vogue. Many of them are very well worth while, and will continue to stand the test of time; but when using such experiments, the teacher should test them carefully as to the effect that they have on the pupils' interests and enthusiasm for further investigation, and on their understanding of the principles which these experiments are intended to teach. Does the experiment interest the pupils in some principle of physics, and increase their ability to apply it in other cases? *This is the practical pedagogical test.* He should weigh all experi-

[1] See Singer Sewing Machine Co., *Mechanics of the Sewing Machine* (free). Address the company at New York, or J. A. Randall, Chairman Joint Physics Committee, Pratt Inst., Brooklyn, N. Y.

ments, and if he finds them wanting from this point of view he should courageously discard them for something better. Many can be re-stated in more vital ways, as has already been illustrated in the case of specific gravity, specific heat, and electrical resistance.

Danger of overemphasis of the practical. — The danger of going to extremes in the matter of using exclusively experiments that have to do with home and industrial applications is that the underlying principles may not be brought out in the teaching with sufficient clearness, force, and reiteration, and that the student's knowledge may be left in a scrappy and unorganized condition, because the principles have not been carefully and repeatedly associated with the facts that lead up to them and the facts that may be seen to be further applications of them. *No new methods can take the place of eternal vigilance and careful instruction and drill by an alert teacher.*

It should be borne in mind that the immediate and material interests of the pupils should be taken advantage of in order to lead up to more remote and higher interests. We should lead up to and establish interest in intellectual activity and intellectual achievements. We should go from the concrete to the abstract; but we should always remember that *real knowledge of abstract principles means the ability to apply them to concrete personal work and conduct* and that they are useless to the individual unless he has the ability and the will so to apply them as to make himself in some way useful to mankind.

Qualitative and quantitative experiments. — So much has been said about the importance of qualitative experiments on the one hand, and about the overemphasis of accurate quantitative experiments on the other, that the young teacher may be led to go either to one extreme or the other. The important matter in making the choice is not so much whether the experiment is quantitative or qualitative as whether it tends logically toward an important conclusion and requires carefully regulated, methodical procedure and guarded reasoning. A pupil may get as much in the way of good training in physics out of making a lift or force pump that will work neatly, and writing a careful description of its construction and action, as he can get out of measuring the watts per candle power of a glow lamp. It all depends on the spirit, attitude, sustained attention, and thoughtful thoroughness with which the thing is done. One purely qualitative experiment that the author has always believed second to no quantitative one in the training in logical skill and experimental initiative and resourcefulness that it affords is the investigation of the laws of induced currents as outlined in his laboratory manual.[1] The great advantage of this experiment is that it is logically exhaustive. The pupil can do himself everything that is needed to establish completely the truth of the qualitative statement of the laws.

The progressive program. — The foregoing discussion leads toward a number of conclusions, which help to define the pedagogical problem and indicate the steps to be taken in the improvement of the teaching.

1. The content of the modern physics course is not objectionable in itself, but is too bulky and needs to be cut down.

2. The highly abstract and theoretical, the incidental and insignificant — whatever is entirely foreign to the pupils' present purposes, present knowledge, and daily experiences, and cannot be connected up with them through significant problems in whose answers they can be vitally interested, — should be dropped out.

3. There must be a change in emphasis that will result in paying most attention to the "big dynamic things"[2] in physics, and to those facts and minor principles which have a human bearing, which are exemplified in the

---

[1] Twiss, *op. cit.*, p. 138 ff.   [2] Cf. Mann, *op. cit.*, Chapter **X.**

pupils' own locality, and which are therefore significant because they raise questions in whose answers the pupils can see some use.

4. Minor and special principles and definitions must be *justified* before the pupils are required to learn them. This can be done only by putting the pupils in situations where the need for these definitions or principles is apparent in connection with the work they are doing.   In other words, definitions, principles, and generalizations are justified by leading up to them inductively through concrete problems that arise out of the pupils' previous knowledge and their spirit of wonder or intellectual curiosity.

5. There should be a constant grouping of similar phenomena under the definitions or laws or principles which describe them, and a continuous process of organization, showing how each group of phenomena takes its place with other groups under a broader principle or generalization.   Thus the content of the science may be built up in the pupils' minds as a unified and classified whole.   This means a reorganization of the courses usually given, and an entire change in the mode of approach so as to arrive at the abstract and general by the way of the concrete and particular, instead of vice versa.

6. No opportunity should be neglected by the teacher that will enable him to aid the pupils in forming association bonds between the physical ideas acquired in the schoolroom and the various kinds of problems of everyday life which those principles assist in solving.   In other words, let them learn to apply their physical knowledge *by practice in applying it.*

If these principles are applied in the teaching, lack of interest in the subject will be rare; and the outcome is almost certain to be satisfactory.

QUESTIONS FOR FURTHER STUDY

1. What are the arguments for a division of the physics course into two parts, deferring the most difficult parts of the subject until near the end? What are the arguments against it? Which plan do you think has the better of the argument?

2. Do you think that the "North Central" syllabus represents as much work as outside influences should be permitted to prescribe for a school? Compare it with that of the Regents of the University of the State of New York, and that of the College Entrance Examination Board. Under which of these three prescriptions would you prefer to do your teaching? Why?

3. How much of the kind of library work indicated in this chapter do you think it would be practicable to attempt?

4. What advantages, if any, do you think would result from the recasting of laboratory problems after the manner indicated by the examples given?

5. Make out a list of five or ten problems or projects, other than those given, which you think could be successfully used. Write detailed laboratory directions for at least one of them, and present it to the class for criticism.

6. Should the teaching of pure physics be entirely abandoned for project study of practical applications? Support your answer by argument.

7. Discuss the statements made under the heading "The Progressive Program." Which of them do you regard as the most essential?

REFERENCES

Methods, Subject Matter, Textbooks

ABRAHAM, H. Recueil d'Expériences Elémentaires de Physique. Gauthier-Villars, Paris, France. 1904. 2 vols. 247 and 433 pp. A complete illustrated manual of physical experiments and manipulation. Very valuable.

BRADLEY, MILTON. Color in the Schoolroom — Manual for Teachers. The Milton Bradley Co., Springfield, Mass. 1890. 99 pp. 75 ¢.

CREW, HENRY. Elements of Physics. Macmillan, N. Y. 1901. 347 pp. $1.10. A model of logical presentation for study by the teacher and reference for the pupil. Approach largely inductive.

CREW, HENRY, and JONES, F. T. Elements of Physics Revised. Macmillan, 1908. A more conventional presentation than the preceding.

DUFF, A. WILMER, Editor, and others. A Text-book of Physics. Blakis-

ton, Philadelphia. 4th Ed. 1916. $2.75. An authoritative and up-
to-date general and college text. One of the best for teacher and
ambitious pupils.

FARADAY, M. Experimental Researches in Electricity. Dutton, N. Y.
(Everyman's Library.) 332 pp. 35 ¢. Extracts from the original
edition. Mostly on electrochemical relations. Illustrates well
the scientific method. Excellent for teacher and pupils.

FLEMING, J. A. Principles of Electric Wave Telegraphy. Longmans,
N. Y. 1910. 906 pp. $7.50. Complete, recent, and authoritative.

FORDYCE, EMMA J. Physics for Girls, by the Scientific Method. Proc.
N. E. A., 1914, p. 750.

FRANKLIN, W. S. The Study of Science by Young People. N. Y. State
Dept. of Education Bull. No. 431. September 15, 1908.

FREEMAN, F. N. Manual Training in the Service of Physics. School
Review, Vol. 7, November, 1909, p. 609 ff.

FULLAN, M. THOMAS. Correlation of Physics and Manual Training.
Proc. N. E. A., 1915, pp. 996–1000.

JACKSON, D. C. and J. P. Alternating Currents and Alternating Current Machinery. Macmillan, N. Y. 1913. 968 pp. $5.50.

KENT, W. Mechanical Engineer's Pocket-Book. Wiley, N. Y. 1916.
1526 pp. $5.00.

KIMBALL, A. C. Physical Properties of Gases. Houghton, Mifflin & Co.,
Boston. 1890. 238 pp. $1.50. For teachers and pupils.

LINCOLN, J. C. Practical Electricity. Cleveland Armature Works,
Cleveland, O. 1904. 286 pp. 4th Ed. $2.00. The best simple
discussion of dynamo, motor, and electric transmission arithmetic
that is known to the author.

LODGE, SIR O. J. Mechanics. Van Nostrand, N. Y. 1892. 208 pp.
$1.50.

LODGE, SIR O. J. Modern Views of Electricity. Macmillan, London
and N. Y. 1907. 518 pp. $1.75.

LODGE, SIR O. J. Signalling across Space without Wires. London
Electrician Printing & Publishing Co. Van Nostrand, N. Y. 1909.
154 pp. $2.00.

MACH, ERNST. Tr. McCormack, T. J. The Science of Mechanics.
The Open Court Pub. Co., Chicago. 1893. 3d Ed. 1907. 22 +
605 pp. $2.00.

MACH, ERNST. Popular Scientific Lectures. Open Court Pub. Co.
3d Ed. 1906. 415 pp. $1.50. Paper, 50 ¢.

MANN, C. R., and TWISS, G. R. Physics. Revised Ed. Scott, Foresman & Co., Chicago. 1910. 417 pp. $1.25. (Applies the prin-
ciples advocated in this book.)

MANN, C. R. The New Movement among Physics Teachers. School Science and Mathematics, March, November, and December, 1906; April, 1907; June, 1908.

MANN, C. R. The Teaching of Physics. Macmillan, N. Y. 1912. 289 pp. $1.00.

MAXWELL, J. C. Theory of Heat. Longmans, N. Y. 1902. 12 + 333 pp. $1.50. This is one of the classics of physics that should be read by every teacher.

MICHELSON, A. A. Light Waves and Their Uses. University of Chicago Press, Chicago. 166 pp. Illus. $1.50.

MILLER, D. C. Laboratory Physics. Ginn, Boston. 393 pp. $2.00. Very clear and comprehensive advanced manual.

MILLER, D. C. The Science of Musical Sounds. Macmillan, N. Y. 1916. vii + 286 pp. Illus. Diag. $2.50.

PERRY, JOHN. Applied Mechanics. Van Nostrand, N. Y. 1898. 686 pp. $2.50.

POINCARÉ, L. A. The New Physics, and Its Evolution. Appleton, N. Y. 1907. 15 + 344 pp. $1.75.

PULLEN, W. W. F. Mechanics. Longmans, N. Y. 1902. 378 pp. $1.50. Very suggestive, for both teacher and pupils.

RANDALL, J. A., Chairman Joint Committee on Physics. Monograph Series. 1. Announcement. 2. Elementary Electrical Testing. 3. Edison Storage Batteries. 4. Experimental Electrical Testing. 5. Mechanics of the Sewing Machine. Free copies on application to J. A. Randall, Chairman, Pratt Inst. Brooklyn, N. Y. Every teacher of physics should study these monographs and other literature of this committee.

RANDALL, J. A. Heat. A Manual for Technical and Industrial Students. Wiley, N. Y. 1913. 325 pp. $1.50. A clear and excellent presentation. Useful to both teacher and pupils.

SCHUSTER, A. The Progress of Physics during Thirty-three Years. University Press, Cambridge, Eng. 1911. 164 pp. 12 diag. Putnam, N. Y. 1911. $1.25.

SINCLAIR, ANGUS. The Twentieth Century Locomotive. A. Sinclair Co., N. Y. 1904. $2.00.

STALLO, J. B. The Concepts and Theories of Modern Physics. Appleton, N. Y. 1897. $1.75.

Symposium on the Purpose and Organization of Physics Teaching in Secondary Schools. Avery, L. B.; Baldwin, J. Mark; Butler, Nicholas Murray; Chute, H. N.; Crew, Henry; Dewey, John; Hall, G. Stanley; Michelson, A. A.; Millikan, R. A.; Strong, E. A.; Terry, H. L.; Twiss, George R.; and Woodhull, John F.

School Science and Mathematics, December, 1908; January, February, 1909. (Also in pamphlet.) Smith & Turton, Chicago. 2059 E. 72d Place.

TAIT, P. G.   Properties of Matter. Macmillan, N. Y. *$2.25.*

TAIT, P. G.   Heat. Macmillan, N. Y. *$2.00.*

TAIT, P. G.   Light. Macmillan, N. Y. *$2.00.*

TAIT, P. G.   Lectures on Some Recent Advances in Physical Science. Macmillan, London. 1885. 368 pp. *9s.* A great book from which to gain scientific insight.

TAYLOR, SEDLEY.   Sound and Music. Macmillan, London and N. Y. *$2.50.*

TERRY, H. L.   The New Movement in Physics Teaching. Educational Review, 37 : 12–18, January, 1908.

THOMSON, J. J.   Electricity and Matter. Scribner, N. Y. 1904. 162 pp. *$1.25.*

THORNDIKE, E. L.   Science Teaching as Seen from the Outside. Bull. No. 34, N. Y. State Dept. of Education, August, 1907.

TIMBIE, W. H., and HIGBEE, H. H.   Alternating Current Electricity. Wiley, N. Y. 1914. 523 pp. *$2.00.* Excellent practical text, for the teacher and the more ambitious of the boys.

TWISS, G. R.   Laboratory Exercises in Physics. Scott, Foresman & Co. Chicago, 1906. 231 pp. 80¢.

TWISS, G. R.   The Correlation of Physics and Manual Training. Proc. N. E. A., 1915, pp. 1000–1005.

TWISS, G. R.   Physics, Nomenclature and Formulas. Proc. Central Asso. of Teachers of Mathematics and Science, Chicago, 1911, p. 12 ff.

TYNDALL, JOHN.   Six Lectures on Light. Appleton, N. Y. 1893. 17 + 272 pp. *$1.50.* A classic. Every teacher should read it.

TYNDALL, JOHN.   On Sound. Appleton, N. Y. 1891. 448 pp. *$2.00.* The teacher should read this for the insight it gives into the scientific method. Useful to the pupils for reference.

TYNDALL, JOHN.   Heat as a Mode of Motion. Appleton, N. Y. 1892. 19 + 591 pp. *$2.00.*

URQUHART, JOHN W.   Electroplating. A Practical Handbook. Van Nostrand, N. Y. 1905 and later. 224 pp. *$2.00.*

VANDERPOEL, EMILY C. NOYES.   Color Problems. Longmans, N. Y. 1902. 137 pp. 117 illus. *$5.00.* Very interesting.

WATSON, W.   Textbook of Physics. Longmans, N. Y. 1903. 951 pp. *$3.50.* Readable and well balanced college text. One of the best for the teacher's reference.

WHETHAM, W. C. D.   Recent Developments in Physical Science. Blakiston, Philadelphia. 1904. 347 pp. *$2.00.*

WOODHULL, JOHN F. Science for Culture. School Science and Mathematics, 7 : 83–93, February, 1907. School Review, February, 1907.
WRIGHT, LEWIS. Light. Macmillan, London and N. Y. 1882. 367 pp. $2.00. Unique and attractive treatment.
WRIGHT, LEWIS. Optical Projection. Longmans, N. Y. 1891. 8 + 426 pp. $2.25. A practical treatise by an expert.
WRIGHT, LEWIS. The Induction Coil in Practical Use. Macmillan, N. Y. 1897. 171 pp. $1.25. Clear and interesting.

History and Biography

BURNS, E. E. The Story of Great Inventions. Harper, N. Y. $1.25.
CAJORI, FLORIAN J. History of Physics. Macmillan, N. Y. 1899. 305 pp. $1.60. Excellent for both teachers and pupils.
CARNEGIE, ANDREW. James Watt. Doubleday, Page & Co., Garden City, N. Y. 1905. 241 pp. $1.40.
ELLIS, G. E. Memoir of Benjamin Thompson, Count Rumford. Am. Academy of Arts and Sciences, Boston. $5.00.
GARNETT, W. Heroes of Science — Physicists. S. P. C. K. London. Gorham, N. Y. 1895. $1.00.
GLAZEBROOK, RICHARD T. James Clerke Maxwell and Modern Physics. Macmillan, N. Y. 1896. 224 pp. $1.25.
GRAY, ANDREW. Lord Kelvin, an Account of His Scientific Life and Work. Dutton, N. Y. 1908. 319 pp. $1.00.
JONES, F. A. Thomas Alva Edison. Crowell, N. Y. 1908. 362 pp. $2.00.
THOMPSON, S. P. Michael Faraday, His Life and Work. Macmillan, London and N. Y. 1898. 308 pp. $1.25.
THURSTON, R. H. Robert Fulton, His Life and Its Results. Dodd, Mead & Co., N. Y. 1891. 194 pp. $1.00.
THURSTON, R. H. History of the Growth of the Steam Engine. Appleton, N. Y. 1891. 481 pp. 163 illus. $2.50.
WILLIAMS, HENRY SMITH. The Story of Nineteenth Century Science. Harper, N. Y. 1901. 475 pp. $2.50.

CHAPTER XIX

EQUIPMENT FOR PHYSICS TEACHING

Building up the equipment. — As in the case of other science subjects the equipment of apparatus for physics should be as good and as generous as, in view of all other needs, the school can afford. Where rigorous economy is necessary, the principle should be to eliminate from the list those articles that are most expensive and least used, such as the traditional " air pump and accessories " and the static electric machine. These are the things to which the school man who knows little of physics usually first points with pride; and yet all the necessary experiments that are made with them can easily be provided for by ingenious cheap substitutes, and the money that they would cost invested in things that cost less and are used more. The thoroughly competent teacher, who if he is such will be something of a mechanic, will recognize that a workbench with a minimum outfit of hand tools for working in wood and metal, and a judicious assortment of supplies in the form of planed boards and strips of wood, and of nails, brads, screws, wire, sheet metals, solder and soldering tools, glass and rubber tubing, corks and rubber stoppers, constitute an important part of the fundamental equipment for all science work in a small school, and an indispensable means of supplementing and keeping in order the equipment of a large school. A teacher going to any school to take charge of the work in physics will almost always find there physical apparatus of some sort; and usually the problem is not to equip *de novo*, but to convert an inadequate

332

equipment into an adequate one or to supplement from time to time an equipment that is already fairly satisfactory.

In any case the teacher should first prepare a list of the experiments that he expects to make during the year, in the order in which they are to be put on. These should be divided into two classes, those that are to be made by the teacher at the demonstration table, and those that are to be made by the students in the laboratory. For the performance of the experiments of the first list only one outfit of apparatus will be needed for each experiment; while for the laboratory experiments, the best conditions will usually require one outfit for each experiment for each pupil, in order that each may work independently, and not lean on others. For experiments requiring apparatus that is relatively costly, such as galvanometers, voltmeters, and ammeters, Boyle's law tubes, and the like, one piece may be supplied for each two, three, or four students; and the students may be allowed to work together in such groups. For some few experiments it is really better that they should thus coöperate. For the organization of the work in the manner that has been advocated in this book it is almost imperative that all the class should be working on the same experiment, or on a set of closely related experiments, at one time. This question has been practically settled by a consensus of opinion of experienced and successful teachers from the experience of the past twenty years. The classroom and laboratory work cannot be properly correlated unless this plan is followed. Hence, in making up the list of laboratory apparatus the number of outfits to be provided for each experiment on which pupils are to work singly is equal to the number of pupils in a working division, which should not exceed twenty-four if it can be avoided. For pieces that can be used by groups, then, the number required would be twelve, eight, or six, according to the sizes of the groups in which the pupils are to work on the experiment.

How to order. — Since all the apparatus dealers furnish free illustrated priced catalogues of their wares the teacher can easily attach the prices to his list and find the approximate cost of the whole. Then if paring down is necessary he can do the paring on the things that are least essential. When the final list is ready copies of it may be sent to two or three dealers, who will return it with the prices filled out in detail, and a statement of the total cost at which they will furnish the entire order. The prices of reliable dealers on standard types of apparatus are in most cases much the same. They usually give a discount averaging about ten per cent from their list prices. It is not wise to try to beat them down through competitive bidding. It is far better to pay their prices, letting them understand that quality and reliability are preferred to cheapness, and that they are expected to stand behind every piece with their honor and good name. The best houses all do this, and are perfectly willing to take back any piece that is not satisfactory. The close competition between dealers has caused them to make great efforts toward the improvement of their apparatus, and hence a comparative study of the latest catalogues of the leading dealers is advisable in making selections. In selecting any one piece of apparatus one should aim to get the best of its kind; hence the discriminating teacher will not award the entire order to any one dealer. Where purchases are made through a purchasing agent of the school board or through a contract with a local firm, as is insisted on in some cities, the teacher should so word his specifications as to get the exact article that he wants. Thus if a later and improved form of one kind of apparatus is manufactured by only one of the firms and is better than those made for the same purpose by other firms, the specifications can be so worded that only the one wanted will fit them. In such cases the purchasing agent or contractor should be informed as to who is the manufacturer of this particular form. This does not preclude competitive bidding, where it is legally required.

Shop outfit. — A small carpenter's bench and a fairly efficient set of woodworking tools will cost approximately $25. In addition, there should be an assortment of metal-working tools, including ball hammer, hack saw, gas pliers, round nose pliers, flat nose cutting pliers, snips, an assortment of coarse, medium, and fine files, round, half round, and flat, of two or three sizes each (4, 6, and 8 inches), a set of drills and drill stock, and a small vise and anvil. A soldering-copper and heater, with rosin and chloride of zinc fluxes, a blast lamp and bellows for glass working, glass cutters for sheets and tubing, a set of cork borers, and a gluepot will complete the minimum outfit. The cost for the latter will be about $30, making the total shop outfit about $55. In addition, a set of taps and dies is also very useful.

A large school where much work is to be done and where a generous equipment can be afforded may advantageously be equipped with a good screw-cutting engine lathe, a grinder and buffer, a sensitive drill-press, a circular saw, and a motor to furnish the power. The motor may be used also to operate a direct current dynamo to furnish current for the lantern and for numerous experiments. Of course the power tools should not be bought unless the teacher has the disposition and ability to make profitable use of them. If the school has a manual training shop, the latter will contain most of the tools that any teacher of physics would want to use; but even in such cases there should be a bench in the laboratory where he can make quick repairs without leaving the pupils who are under his care.

Homemade and improvised apparatus. — If the teacher is given the necessary time, and can interest and train some of the boys to help him, there is almost no limit to the amount and kind of apparatus that he can improvise and make. With a generous shop outfit and plenty of raw materials, the only limitations are those imposed by lack of time and mechanical skill. If the teacher of physics and the teacher of manual training work enthusiastically together much valuable apparatus can be made in the manual training shop. If the disposition to do so be present, the needed pieces can be planned as a series of projects, the making of which will teach the principles underlying the use of the tools, develop the skill in using them, and at the same time produce the goods and a considerable amount of enthusiasm in the pupils for both subjects, all at the same time. In some schools much of this kind of coöperation has been carried out; but in most schools it has been almost wholly neglected.

Among the things that are needed and can be easily home-made are the following :

Plumb-bobs and pendulums, tumble-jack, inclined planes, levers, weights for levers, model jackscrew, model of a traveling crane, second law of motion apparatus, equilibrium of liquids tubes, open manometer, lift pump and force pump models, demonstration barometer tubes, Boyle's law tubes, model water wheels, model turbine, air thermometer, convection apparatus, model of hot-water tank, distillation apparatus, suspended coils and Ampere frame (to show effects of magnets on currents), helices mounted in boards (to show the magnetic fields with filings), sheet-iron strips (to be used as cores for the helices), electromagnets, telegraph sounders and keys, resistance coils, primary and secondary coils (for experiments with induced currents), Wheatstone bridges, simple voltaic cells, cells for electrolysis of water and metallic solutions, Leyden-jars, discharger, electrophorus, electroscopes, demonstration electrophorus, sonometers, bell-in-vacuo, Rumford's or Bunsen's photometers, optical benches, mirrors (for reflection experiments), rectangular blocks for blocking up and supporting apparatus, pinhole cameras, color tops, refraction bottle, and *porte lumière.*

Besides these, with machine tools, almost any of the ordinary pieces that are bought from dealers by most schools can be made. Other things being equal, these will be productive of more interest if so made, and if used, than if bought dressed in mahogany and lacquer, and kept under lock and key to be gazed at through glass doors.

Apparatus that must be purchased. — No matter how ingenious or industrious the teacher may be, there is always need for supplies and raw materials that must be obtained by purchase; and in view of other demands on the teacher's time, and the need of his influence and coöperation in connection with the general activities of the school, the problem often arises as to whether it may not be better economy to buy apparatus ready to use than to improvise or manufacture it. It is practically certain to be better to buy in case the required apparatus is cheap because manufactured in large quantities, and in the case of precision apparatus. There should always be a few carefully selected experiments in which a considerable degree of precision is required, and for these the apparatus should be of accurate and substantial construction and of neat and workmanlike finish. When possible this should be such as is in actual commercial use, as, for example, the Weston voltmeters and ammeters.

The standard commercial apparatus has many advantages. It impresses the pupils with the actual utility of the principle because it is applied in the school experiment just as it is applied in the working world outside. Its accuracy and substantial finish impress the pupils with the need of correspondingly accurate and methodical procedure, and with the necessity of giving the apparatus careful and respectful handling. Since it enables them to get accurate results it also impresses them with the true spirit of science, which implies precision, carefulness, and skill of hand and eye, as well as logical exactness in reasoning. For many experiments improvised apparatus will answer perfectly, but not if the apparatus be slovenly in construction and finish or if it be handled in an awkward and bungling manner.

Among the things that belong to an adequate stock of apparatus the following may usually be bought to good ad-

z

vantage from local department stores or dealers in hardware
and electric supplies :

> Pulleys and cords, small water motor, lemonade shakers (for
> dew point and calorimetric experiments), dry cells, gravity cells,
> electric doorbells and push buttons, annunciator-wire, sheet zinc,
> copper, and glass tumblers (for simple voltaic cells), miniature
> and standard electric glow lamps, toy motors.

Among the most important items of apparatus and supplies
that should be ordered from the regular apparatus dealers
are those in the following list :

> Spring balances, beam balances and weights, meter sticks,
> wheel and axle, cars for inclined planes, dissectible Swiss clock,
> Hall pressure gauge, cylindrical graduates, small steam gauge for
> gas and water pressures, spirometer, or seven-in-one apparatus,
> mercury, standard barometer, air pump, Magdeburg hemispheres,
> "hand-glass," Florence flasks, water motor, speed indicator, stop
> watch.

> Boilers or hypsometers for heat experiments, psychrometer,
> copper and aluminum wire or clippings for specific heat, Junker-
> calorimeter and Thorpe gauge or gas-meter (for heat of combustion
> of gas), Bunsen burners and rubber gas tubing, thermometers,
> sectional model of steam engine.

> Bar magnets and iron filings, small pocket compasses, D'Arson-
> val galvanometers, bare and cotton-covered copper and German
> silver or Manganin wires (for making magnet and resistance coils,
> etc.), double connectors, Weston voltmeters and ammeters, "St.
> Louis" demonstration dynamo and motor with electromagnetic
> field attachment.

> Hand or motor rotator, siren, Galton's whistle, tuning-forks,
> manometric flame capsule and revolving mirror, organ pipes,
> set of demonstration lenses, cheap lenses for laboratory experi-
> ments (10 to 15 c.m. focal lengths), laboratory prisms, radiometer,
> Newton's rings, Maxwell color mixer.

Economical substitutes. — However, the teacher who is
ingenious will recognize in this list many things for which
substitutes may be found if necessity requires. For example,
gear wheels may be illustrated by the works of a wornout
79-cent clock, a laboratory rotator can be improvised out of

a ten-cent revolving egg beater, or better, a hand drill-stock, or still better, a junk-shop sewing machine. A splendid experimental wheel and axle, a gyroscope, or a torsion pendulum can be made from a discarded bicycle wheel. With flasks, rubber stoppers, glass and rubber tubing and screw pinchcocks, nearly all the experimental phenomena ordinarily demonstrated by air pumps and expensive accessories can be shown very effectively, using only mouth suction. Cars can be made out of old roller skates, boilers out of oil cans or varnish cans, gasometers out of garbage cans, bar magnets out of broken clock or watch springs that the jeweler throws away, manometric flame capsules out of wooden pill boxes, and so on. It is astonishing how many illustrations of physical principles and problems can be found at the ten-cent store and the toy or trick store, if one has imagination and eyes to see. For example, an inexpensive shaving mirror will do very nicely for experiments with images formed by concave mirrors; a cheap glass lamp reflector answers as well for the same purpose, and the back of it makes a good convex mirror; so does a large silvered glass ball, such as is used for decorating Christmas trees. The ten-cent stores sell spectacles with lenses of various focal length, with which one can make nearly all the laboratory experiments with concave and convex lenses. Many of the phenomena of vibrating air columns and wind instruments can be demonstrated with a toy tin whistle.

Apparatus that is desirable but more expensive. — There are many pieces that may be omitted where economy is imperative, but which ought to be available in schools where a liberal equipment is justified. Such articles may be accumulated by judicious purchases from year to year; and such a progressive development of the physical equipment of a school has many advantages. Thus, mistakes are less likely to be made, and the chances of getting the latest and best are increased. The accession and trying out of new additions to the equipment can always be made a special occasion of community interest, and a stimulus to the work of the pupils in the department. Since, if properly cared for, such acquisitions are permanent, they should be looked on as a permanent investment of the community for education. From this point of view, $100 worth of apparatus represents an initial *investment* of $100, and the real expense is an annual charge for interest and deterioration of about $8. The question then to be decided is, " Is this annual charge justified? " It ought not to be difficult to get a business man who is a member of a board of education to look at investments in apparatus from this business point of view.

A list of such apparatus as is here referred to is given below, with comments.

The Hartl optical disc. — This is one of the most widely useful and convincing pieces of demonstration apparatus with which the author is familiar. With it one can demonstrate with ease all the important phenomena of refraction by liquids, glass plates, prisms, and the various forms of lenses, determine indices of refraction, prove the law of regular reflection by direct measurement of the angles, demonstrate total reflection, demonstrate the critical angles of the different colored lights, measure the angle of a prism, and demonstrate the spectrum, the principle of the rainbow, and of many other things covering nearly all the phenomena of light that he may wish the class to study. It is a source of never-failing interest to both class and teacher, and is equally useful at the demonstration table and in the laboratory. With other attachments and accessories the phenomena of diffraction with a grating, and of polarized light, including the interference figures by uniaxial and biaxial crystals, and so on, can be shown. The price without the latter accessories, but including the diverging ray attachment and the liquid refraction tank, is $26.05 (Central Scientific Co. Catalogue, 1910, pp. 224–226).

Every school should have this outfit if possible. In selecting the apparatus for light, it should be the first to receive consideration.

Porte lumière. — This is one of the pieces of apparatus that should be regarded as among the essentials; though there are many schools in which it is not found, and many teachers who are not familiar with its many uses. Various forms of this instrument are sold, each dealer having one that he particularly recommends. One of the best forms known to the writer is that made by Stoelting, because of the many uses to which it can be adapted in connection with other projection apparatus and accessories made by the same manufacturer. Essentially it consists of a mirror attached to a metal plate and capable of being inclined forward or back by turning a screw head. The same screw head serves as a knob by means of which the flange to which the mirror is attached may be rotated so that the mirror follows the movements of the sun. When the metal plate is mounted on a board that fits between a south window and the lower part of its frame, the apparatus may be used to throw a cylindrical beam of sunlight into the room. As described, it is listed at $9.

With the addition of a metal cap fitted with suitable metal diaphragms or slides, the beam of light may be cut down to various smaller diameters, or may be admitted through a rectangular slit which can be made as narrow as desired. The beam may thus be used for many kinds of experiments in reflection and refraction, and with the aid of the slit and prisms, may be used to project a spectrum on the screen. The optical bench-rod is of a standard size and takes the mountings for all the accessories needed for a complete projection apparatus. These accessories can thus be added to the outfit at any time.

At an additional cost of $11 this *porte-lumière* becomes a complete solar projectoscope, including the bench rod, a plano convex condensing lens of 4½-inch diameter and 6½-inch focal length, a condenser cell, a stage for slide holder, a double slide holder, adjustable objective holder, and a " ¼ plate," 6-inch equivalent-focus projecting lens with rack-and-pinion focusing adjustment and flange to fit holder (Stoelting Catalogue, 1912, No. 4014, p. 171).

With such apparatus anything can be done in optical projection that can be done with the best electric lanterns, and far better, so long as the sun remains unobscured. For projection, if the distance of the screen is more than 25 feet, a " ½ plate," 10-inch equivalent-focus projection lens should be substituted, else the projected picture will be too large for a 12-foot screen. The change willl increase the cost about $10 if a high-grade lens is used.

Directions for making a very efficient solar lantern, and for performing a wide range of experiments in light, may be found in "Light" by Mayer and Barnard. (See Appendix A.)

Projecting lantern for artificial radiants. — There are many good lanterns for sale by reliable dealers at very reasonable prices. For a small school where only one lantern can be afforded, and may have to be carried from one room to another, lightness and compactness are much to be desired. In such cases the Bausch and Lomb Model C Baloptican is one of the best lanterns made. It may be used to project lantern slides, for which it is primarily intended, and since the stage is open, all kinds of apparatus can be lined up in the optical axis; so that it is adaptable for the projection of all kinds of physical experiments, excepting vertical projections. One of the best features of this instrument is the lamp-box, which is so well ventilated that it does not become uncomfortably hot — a very common fault. The price is $35 with a 6-inch objective and $40 with a 10-inch objective. For vertical projections a suitable attachment can be added at a cost of $15. This lantern is fitted with a right-angle hand-feed electric arc lamp [1] and requires the use of a rheostat, preferably an adjustable one, which costs from $20 to $30, according to the amount of current to be carried. If the attachment for opaque projection is to be added later, the rheostat should be chosen to carry a maximum current of 35 amperes to get the very best results; although 25 amperes with a good lens, good pictures, and a thoroughly darkened room will give results that are very satisfactory.

To complete the equipment, a double-pole, double-throw switch, rubber-covered twin cable, fuse block, and fuses are required, and will add from $2 to $5 to the cost, according to quality.

Other radiants that may be used where a 110-volt current is not available are the oxyhydrogen (calcium) light, and the alcolite, or the acetylene burner. (For full information write to the dealers.)

If the Stoelting Solar Projectoscope is selected, it can be converted into a complete electric Projectoscope by using the bench rod, objective and slide carrier along with the bench supports, the proper double condensing system, the lamp-box and the hand-feed arc lamp. One great advantage of the Stoelting equipment for a school just beginning to accumulate projection apparatus is that all parts are interchangeable so that the firm's Universal Projectoscope (No. 4002) can be finally acquired complete by successive purchases of the various parts. With the Universal Projectoscope one can change almost instantly from lantern slides to opaque pictures or microscopic objects, or to vertical projection; and the dark chamber can be very quickly removed, leaving the stage clear for lining up apparatus for physical and optical projection.

The list price of the Stoelting Electric Projectoscope (No.

---

[1] Stereopticon dealers are now selling a new high-power electric glow lamp for projection apparatus, which is said to be very satisfactory for ordinary projection, and which requires no attention while operating the lantern.

4020) is $31.50, and all the parts of both the solar and the electric projectoscope together come to less than $45.

When purchasing a lantern with a view to the projection of microscopic slides and living animalcules in the biology work the teacher should see to it that it is adapted for the use of a cooling cell in the optical axis, for this is necessary in all such work and also in the projection of transparencies made by the three-color photographic process. In all projection work a suitable screen is necessary. The very best screen is a white wall. Where this is not available a white or aluminum coated cloth screen mounted on a spring roller, with a protecting strip of enameled cloth at the bottom, is the best substitute. Such a screen 9 by 9 feet (with a $\frac{1}{2}$-plate lens at 30 feet) is large enough for any schoolroom, and costs $12. For the large assembly room a 12 by 12 foot screen will be needed, and costs $20.

For the projection of spectrum experiments a pair of carbon bisulphide prisms will be required, and should be of the best quality. These are listed at from $5 to $7 per pair.

The Von Nardroff color mixer. — Projection experiments with this color mixer, used in connection with either the solar or electric projector, are among the most fascinating and instructive in the whole range of optics. With it the primary hues can be mixed in all proportions; and all hues, tints, and shades can be produced on the screen with extraordinary purity and brilliancy. It never fails to delight and interest both pupils and adults; and it makes for clear understanding of all the phenomena of color vision that can be taught in the high school. Unfortunately it is expensive, costing $25, but it is worth the money. An evening lecture attended by 250 people at 10 cents each would enable it to pay for itself.[1]

Lecture table galvanometer, voltmeter and ammeter combined. — This is a very useful instrument for many kinds of demonstration experiments with electric currents of various pres-

[1] Sold by the L. E. Knott Apparatus Co., Boston. Send for circular.

sures and strengths. It is built on commercial lines, but with all parts and connections open to view, and has many other points of merit. This instrument is listed at $40 (Stoelting's Catalogue 1912, No. 2886, p. 134). A less elaborate lecture table instrument, which cannot be used as a volt-ammeter, but is very satisfactory as a galvanometer, can be bought at from $12 to $15, according to pattern and maker (Stoelting No. 2866, p. 131, $13.50). If the school already has good commercial voltmeters and ammeters for both battery currents and the regular 110 volt service currents, the latter instrument will do as well in connection with them as the former would without them.

Weston voltmeters and ammeters. — The Weston Electrical Instrument Co. of Newark, N. J., in coöperation with the National Joint Committee on the Improvement of Physics Teaching,[1] has issued monographs describing experiments that can be made with types of their commercial voltmeters and ammeters designed especially for school work and sold at very reasonable prices. The instruments are of the well-known standard construction of this firm and of guaranteed accuracy characteristic of their work. It is better to put money into such instruments than into the cheap toys that are so widely bought for school laboratories, and that soon become useless because of their flimsiness and inaccuracy.

Sympathetic tuning forks. — The experiment of sympathetic vibrations is so important that it ought not to be omitted; and unfortunately it cannot be made impressively without the use of a pair of large and accurately synchronized tuning forks mounted on tuned resonance boxes. Such a pair of forks costs from $10 to $15, according to quality and working distance. A perfectly satisfactory pair should respond

[1] Address Prof. J. A. Randall, Chairman, Pratt Institute, Brooklyn, N. Y., for free circulars concerning new apparatus and experiments in successful use, and for copies of the Weston Monographs or the Singer Sewing Machine Monograph. The committee invites coöperation.

audibly when separated from 25 to 40 feet. The vibrations may be demonstrated to the eye by means of a reflected light beam or by a small glass pendulum-bob resting lightly against it. The demonstration is particularly impressive and pleasing to a large audience when the movements of the pendulum are shown greatly magnified by projecting them on a screen with the lantern. These forks must not be carelessly handled, or they will get out of tune. When not in use they should be covered with a film of pure vaseline to prevent rusting, and should never be exposed to the fumes from chemical experiments.

Models of ear and eye. — For a satisfactory understanding of the mechanism by which sound and light sensations are perceived, large dissectible models of the ear and eye are very much needed. These models, of course, can be used also by the department of biology. The eye costs from $7 to $30 and the ear from $7 to $10 according to size, quality, and number of parts into which it can be dissected. The prices are much lower when the models are imported duty free (Kny-Scheerer Biological Catalogue, pp. 33–34).

Dissectible dynamo-motor. — An excellent apparatus is sold by Stoelting under this name (No. 2751, Catalogue 1912, p. 122). It is built on commercial lines, with drum armature and ironclad field, and can be easily taken apart and reassembled. With the hand power furnished it is claimed to give a maximum E. M. F. of 15 volts and a maximum current of 25 amperes, and can be used for electroplating and all sorts of experiments where such a current is required. It can be changed to a series dynamo by throwing a switch, and to an alternator by changing the brush connections of the external circuit. It may also be used as a rotary transformer. With a current of 10 or 12 volts pressure it can be run as a motor, and is said to develop $\frac{1}{10}$ horse power. It is, therefore, useful for furnishing light power or for making brake tests of its efficiency. With suitable accessories this machine

can be used as a laboratory rotator in either a vertical or a
horizontal position, or as a drilling machine, buffer, and polisher.
The list price with all accessories is $59. This is recom-
mended where a larger dynamo operated by a motor on the
commercial circuit is not available.

Induction coil. — For practical work with X-ray and vacuum tubes, and for wireless telegraphy over considerable
distances, a spark-coil is necessary. A standard make
commercial instrument giving a 6-inch spark costs about
$75. With it practical X-ray and wireless telegraphy work
can be done; and many interesting and instructive experiments with electric waves, high-pressure discharges, and
vacuum tubes can be made. Such a coil, however, should
not be purchased unless the other accessories to such work
are to be added from time to time, and unless the teacher
intends to make use of them for the benefit of the school
and community, and is competent or can become competent
to do so. A dissectible coil that will give a $\frac{1}{4}$ to $\frac{3}{8}$ inch spark
can be bought for from $4.50 to $7.50, and can be used for
laboratory experiments with wireless apparatus, for small
vacuum tubes, for giving shocks, and for demonstrating the
principle of the coil.

Static machine. — An excellent and reliable little Töpler-
Holtz or Voss machine costs about $20 to $25, or less if
imported duty free. A more powerful and also more reliable
machine of the Wimshurst type costs from $40 to $50. The
latter will operate X-ray tubes and vacuum tubes, produce
electric waves, puncture wood and glass (when used in connection with a bank of Leyden jars), and do many other
interesting things of a spectacular nature, all of which may
be made instructive and interesting to a good-sized company.

Wireless telegraphy apparatus. — A practical wireless outfit for one station, including a specially designed spark-coil,
or an adjustable alternating current transformer, can be
bought for from $55 to $75, according to power demanded

(Stoelting, Catalogue, 1912, No. 2683, pp. 115 C ff.).   The expense of installing the antenna will depend on the presence or absence of substitutes for the necessary masts.   If the school has a tower surmounted by a flagstaff the expense of installing the antenna on it will be very small.   With such an outfit communication can be held with schools having similar outfits in neighboring towns, and the messages of distant commercial stations can be picked up.   Many schoolboys have manufactured wireless outfits of their own, and have obtained endless pleasure and instruction from them.   If such boys are in attendance in the school their coöperation in the instruction of the class should by all means be obtained.

Röntgen ray tubes, and other vacuum tubes. — X-ray tubes cost from $7 to $15, and fluoroscopes from $8 to $15, according to size and quality.   The tubes should be bought with reference to the coil or machine by means of which they are to be operated, and from the same dealer, in order that their satisfactory performance may be assured.   Geissler tubes, fluorescent tubes, Crookes' tubes, and other vacuum tubes of various sorts may be had at prices ranging from 50 cents to $8 or $10 each.   These are very attractive and instructive for special lectures and community entertainments, but have little place in the regular course of instruction.

Switchboard. — In a large city school where a generous equipment is provided, and where a dynamo is installed, it is desirable to have the switchboard installed behind the lecture table a little to one side of where the teacher stands. It should be of standard commercial construction, and besides the necessary switches and fuse blocks it should carry a large station voltmeter and ammeters for the direct and for the alternating current.   It would be well if a wattmeter were also added.   The effect on the students of seeing the switchboard in use and of being able to read the current strengths and voltages of all the currents used for the demon-

stration experiments, and for lighting the room, is likely
to be very good; and it is also desirable that the teacher
should be able to know at all times what voltage and amperage he is getting. With commercial currents all electromagnetic and current effects can be shown much more impressively than with battery currents, and experiments with them
are productive of more respect and more interest. It makes
the whole atmosphere of the experimental work partake
more of the nature of serious business than of formal instruction or of play.

Rectifying alternating currents. — If the school has no
large dynamo, and yet is equipped with the alternating current for lighting, this current may be changed into a direct
pulsating current with either a mercury rectifier or a " Nodon
Valve." The former, if used, may well be mounted on the
switchboard. The Nodon valve can be " homemade " at
relatively small expense.

A few practical hints. — Before closing this chapter it
seems desirable to add a few hints from the author's experience
about some things not generally known among the younger
generation of physics teachers.

Beam balances and weights. — Much money is wasted in schools
where it cannot be afforded by purchasing expensive "laboratory
balances" or "Harvard trip scales" or "hydrostatic balances"
for work that can be done just as well with the inexpensive but
sufficiently sensitive and accurate "German hand balance."
This balance with 6-inch beam costs but $1.65 and with 7½-inch
beam $2, and a set of suitable weights from $2.25 to $3.50.
Twenty-four of these hand balances have been in use in the Central High School of Cleveland for over twenty years, and are still
practically as good as new. They are supplemented by a few
trip scales with larger weights, for use with heavier and bulkier
bodies than are ordinarily weighed, and by an accurate Sartorius
balance for testing the cheaper weights and adjusting them if
necessary, and for making the smaller weights from sheet aluminum to replace those that inevitably get lost. These hand balances are mounted for use by hanging them on laboratory support

rods by means of ordinary retort clamps, which are useful for many other purposes.[1]

With these hand balances and one of the laboratory balances or trip scales referred to, to supplement it, all the needed work can be done.

Hydraulic press. — A good working model of a hydraulic press is a very valuable but expensive piece of apparatus. A good substitute for it for purposes of illustration and study can be improvised by mounting the "spirometer or seven-in-one apparatus" inverted, on an iron ring-tripod, and joining it, by means of a rubber tube, to a glass model of a force pump. The ease with which the small model pump will lift weights of many pounds when blocked up on the spirometer piston is very impressive. The motion of the rising mass is very slow, but can be impressively demonstrated by means of a blackboard pointer mounted as a lever, with the short arm resting on the load of weights.[2]

Bell-in-vacuo. — This experiment is one of the most to be desired and yet usually the least satisfactory in the whole range of acoustic phenomena. The author has tried every known way to demonstrate it, with air pumps of the best makes; but it has never been satisfactory to him when performed otherwise than in one particular way. Persistent cross-examining of high school and college teachers for many years has satisfied him that his lack of success with the usual methods is not unique. The one apparatus that can be depended on always to give success consists of a large glass fruit jar with a ground rim, closed by a metal cover, also ground smooth, and fitted with a flat rubber washer. From the lower face of this cover a forked metal support projects into the bottle. A small sleighbell is supported between the prongs of the fork by means of several strands of *soft yarn*. The metal cap is perforated by a tubulure with a stopcock, which can be attached to the air pump. When the jar is closed and shaken without exhausting the air, the tinkle of the bell can be plainly heard by the class; but after the cover has been securely clamped down and the air has been exhausted, no amount of shaking will extract from the bell an audible tinkle. This apparatus is so simple that a successful home-made substitute can easily be made with a large wide-mouthed bottle and a rubber cork to fit it. The tubulure and stopcock can be replaced by a glass tube, rubber tube, and

[1] For method of suspension and use see illustration in Twiss, *op. cit.*, pp. 66, 72, and 219.

[2] Cf. Stoelting Catalogue, 1912, No. 942 and 1107, and No. 948.

screw pinchcock. The forked support can be made from a slender brass rod, by any good amateur metal worker. In the apparatus recommended, it is the soft yarn suspension that refuses to transmit the sound independently of the air, and this is the one vital part of the apparatus that makes it different from others. The trouble with the apparatus of all other types, when good air pumps are used, is that the sound travels out either through the pump plate, the bell-jar, or the wire or rod that makes the connection, electrical or otherwise, with the outside.

Air pumps. An air pump, to be really worth the money spent on it, must be capable of producing a respectable vacuum. The modern oil-seal pumps, such as the well-known "Geryk" make will do this. Unless a Geryk pump or one of the other standard oil-seal pumps can be bought, it would be better to be content with one of the small exhausting and condensing pumps of the bicycle pump type (Stoelting Cat. No. 1007), which is as useful as a $20 lever pump, and costs but $3.75. The Geryk pump No. 2 with a 9 inch glass-top plate costing $57.50 duty free is recommended. For larger schools, where power is available, the duplex A for either hand or power operation is worth the extra cost. For a school that can afford to spend but $30 for an air pump the Geryk No. 0 is recommended as satisfactory, though it is much slower than the larger pumps and the vacuum obtainable is not so high.

These pumps require careful treatment. No oil should be used with them excepting that furnished especially for them, and no acids or mercury should ever be allowed to get into or even touch them. If they do not work satisfactorily they should be sent for overhauling to the dealer from whom purchased. The teacher should not take them apart nor let any one else do so. All the prominent dealers sell this pump.

A good wax for use on the pump plate and all air-tight joints is made by melting together equal parts of beeswax and tallow. For permanently sealing joints air-tight, use a cement made by melting together equal parts of beeswax and rosin.

QUESTIONS FOR FURTHER STUDY

1. Make up a list of tools for a shop outfit for your high school. If it comes to more than $25, select from it a new list which you would recommend to a teacher who was allowed only that amount for tools.

2. Make up a list of demonstration apparatus which shall include what you regard as practically indispensable.

3. Supposing that you are advising a school board that can spend only $300 for a physics equipment, what amounts would you advise putting into laboratory apparatus and demonstration apparatus respectively? Make out priced lists of the apparatus that you would recommend to them for purchase with these sums.

4. What is your opinion as to home-made apparatus? Discuss the topic from whatever standpoint appeals most to your judgment.

5. Give your opinion with regard to the advantages and disadvantages of using apparatus of commercial types.

6. What do you think of the plan of having apparatus made in the school through coöperation with the manual arts department? What advantages may accrue to the pupils from the standpoint of the school as a socializing agency by following such a plan?

7. Supposing the manual arts teacher were opposed to coöperating for the equipment of the physics rooms, make a brief statement of the arguments you would use in trying to persuade him.

8. Make a list of the more expensive items of equipment that are mentioned as being desirable; and place them in the order of their desirability, taking price and possible frequency of use into consideration.

9. Which of these articles could be made to pay for themselves? Which would be of most value in connection with the use of the school as a community center?

REFERENCES

See end of Chapter X and XVIII, also list of books for the library, Appendix A.

CHAPTER XX

CHEMISTRY. PRINCIPLES AND METHODS

The psychological basis. — Chemistry is *par excellence* the experimental science, inasmuch as little chemical knowledge of consequence can be learned without making experiments. Observation here plays fully as important a rôle as in the other sciences; but very little can be observed of the chemistry of substances without first *doing something* with them. Thus chemical experiments appeal directly to a fundamental instinct. " To do something and have something happen as the consequence is, other things being equal, instinctively satisfying, whatever be done and whatever be the consequent happening." [1] This is fortunate for the psychological teaching of chemistry because perception of its facts and acquisition of its concepts are not favored so highly as the other sciences are by familiar experiences and common sense intuitions in terms of which the facts and relations that are presented in the teaching can be interpreted; and it is therefore not so easy to make obvious connections between chemical lore and everyday life situations as it is to make such connections in presenting the other sciences. But although the chemistry teacher is thus at a disadvantage, he has strong allies in the original tendencies to manipulate [2] and experiment.

In the case of chemistry, then, if we are to start our teach-

[1] Thorndike, E. L., *The Original Nature of Man*, Teachers College, Columbia University, N. Y., 1913, p. 142.
[2] *Ibid.*, pp. 135–138.

ing with a problem growing out of the child's experience we must let him *get* the necessary experience by making chemical experiments himself.   In the beginning we must depend for motivation largely on his original tendencies toward manipulation and toward " doing things to have something happen," plus whatever liking for purposeful experimentation he may be fortunate enough to have acquired through previous scientific training in school or out.

If this be true, then two conclusions follow, which might indeed have been inferred from common sense considerations, apart from psychology, namely: (1) it is of little avail to attempt to teach chemistry without a large amount of individual laboratory experimentation; and (2) *the very first lesson and every succeeding lesson in which a new topic is taken up, should be an experimental problem in which the pupil himself is the experimenter, guided and assisted, of course, by the teacher.*

How to begin. — Many teachers and many textbooks make the traditional mistake of beginning with general observations about chemistry, its value, and its relations to the other sciences, with definitions of physical and chemical changes, of elements, compounds and mixtures, *and even of atoms and molecules!* This is not only productive of gross waste of time, but tends also to form the habit in the pupils of depending for their facts on books and authority instead of forming in them the habit of making their own judgments on the basis of what the facts themselves have to reveal to them through their senses. *To create such an attitude at the start is fatal to the scientific spirit which it is the mission of science teaching to engender.* Furthermore it is of course impossible for pupils to form any conception of the meaning of a generalization or definition unless they have become acquainted through first-hand experience with a considerable number of the specific facts of which it is a general or condensed statement.   The wise teacher then will seek at once for some problems that can be solved only by experiments, — experiments that are simple enough for the pupils themselves to carry out, and that at the same time lead straight toward some of the important facts and principles of chemistry. A number of these can be found which lead directly to the preparation of oxygen, and which grow naturally out of common experience.

For example, why is iron always nickel plated, or covered with paint? If rusting is not at once suggested, let the teacher then show some specimens of badly rusted iron; and if the students think they have solved the problem when they have said that the nickel plating or painting is to keep the iron from rusting let him ask them why. If they answer that the covering keeps the air away from the iron let him ask them why they think the air has anything to do with it. If they are sharp enough to answer this question logically, let him ask them how the air causes the iron to rust. Here their experiential knowledge will stop unless perchance some one suggests that iron does not rust in a dry attic but does rust in a moist cellar. Obviously the next question is, "If the rusting of the iron is connected with the presence of moist air, does the iron take something from the air to make the new substance, rust; or does the air take something from the iron?"[1] The answer can be obtained by inverting over a dish of water a test tube into which some moist powdered iron has been introduced so as to stick to its walls near its closed end. The iron soon rusts; and water rises and occupies about a fifth of the volume of the tube, when the action stops, leaving some of the iron unrusted. The obvious inference is that the iron takes away one fifth of the air, and that when it

[1] For the detailed procedure in solving this problem so as to get to the bottom of it, see Smith, A., and Hall, E. H., *The Teaching of Chemistry and Physics*, Longmans, N. Y., 1904, p. 107 ff. The Chemistry section of this book should be read and re-read by every teacher of chemistry. It is the soundest, most thorough and most helpful discussion of the pedagogy of chemistry that is known to the writer.

has done so that portion of the air which was capable of taking part in the rusting process was used up, so no more iron was rusted. If the tube be removed and a lighted taper plunged into it, the flame is extinguished, showing that the part of the air used up was that part which supports combustion. Powdered iron on a watch glass counterpoised on a balance and left in a moist atmosphere gradually rusts and is seen to increase in weight. Thus it is proved conclusively that something from the moist air is added to the iron to make it rust. These experiments may be followed by heating weighed mercury, tin, and lead in porcelain crucibles, noting the respective changes in properties and the increases in weight. The early historical knowledge of these changes can then be recounted, oxygen prepared from mercuric oxide like that obtained by heating mercury for a long time in air, and the experiments of Priestley and Lavoisier explained. The pupils will then be keen to prepare oxygen in larger amounts from potassium chlorate and " do things with it to find out what will happen." In this way their memory bonds between oxygen and its properties will be formed and may be firmly established by later reviews and drills. Also they are more likely to catch the scientific spirit than if they began with definitions and formal experiments " to illustrate and make clear " the difference between physical and chemical changes, and the difference between compounds and mixtures.

The teacher who knows how to work experiments for all they are worth, will bring out these differences clearly in connection with the experiments described; and if so brought out they will be better remembered because learned in connection with problems that can be seen to lead to some significant goal. The advantage lies in the mental attitude of the pupil. The formal and didactic approach tends to make him lean on the crutch of authority, while the problem approach tends toward the open-minded scientific attitude and the desire to know and prove truth for its social utility.

The experiments suggested are by no means the only mode of problem approach. Oxygen can be led up to in connection with building fires, the burning of candles,[1] lamps and Bunsen burners, putting out fires, respiration, the useful properties and constitution of water, and so on.[2]

How to use the textbook. — Many of the modern textbooks of chemistry, though excellent in other characteristics, do not present the facts in an order that suggests the problem approach. This however need not prevent the teacher from giving the pupils the benefits of this method. If the teacher remembers the true function of the textbook as a reference book for facts that cannot be easily obtained by direct experiment either at the demonstration table or by the students themselves, and as a guide in the logical organization and review of facts, principles, and theories, he will use his ingenuity in devising suitable problematic situations through which the different topics can be approached. *He will not send the pupils to the book beforehand to find out from the printed page what they should find out with their own eyes, noses, and hands.* It is wrong to suppose that in the early stages of scientific study time can be saved by learning facts from books. The pupil does not *learn* the facts thus. He merely learns words and formulæ which for him can have no content because he lacks the experimental knowledge which alone can enable him to apperceive them.[3] Later on, after he has

---

[1] For suggestions see Faraday, Michael, *The Chemical History of a Candle*, Harpers, N. Y., 1899. This classic example of lecture presentation of chemical facts and principles to youngsters should be read by every teacher of chemistry.

[2] For an approach through an experiment to detect cotton in alleged woolen cloth and leading inductively to certain fundamental distinctions of chemical science, see Smith, Alexander, *Elementary Chemistry*, The Century Co., N. Y., 1914. The entire method of this intensely modern text ought to be given serious study by teachers.

[3] Cf. Thorndike, E. L., *The Principles of Teaching*, A. G. Seiler, N. Y., 1906, p. 42 ff., and Bagley, W. C., *The Educative Process*, Macmillan, N. Y., 1907, Chapter V., or James, William, *Talks to Teachers on Psychology*, Holt, N. Y., 1905, Chapter XIV.

accumulated a considerable amount of facts through first-
hand experience, has perceived their relations, and has formulated these relations, largely for himself, in the form of laws,
principles, and generalizations, he is in a position to use chemical books, articles, and reports with the right attitude. It is
then safe to assign him book lessons, and references to such
articles and reports. *The teacher however can never be too
careful about hammering in the notion that every one of the chemical facts that is to be learned from a book is simply a statement
of results attained by experiment, observation, and measurement
and by reasoning founded thereon.*

The content of chemistry, and methods of teaching it. —
Like other scientific subject matter, chemical information
consists of facts, laws, hypotheses and theories, and their
history; and this body of information has been built up and
is being extended by the use of the scientific method. Like
the other sciences, chemistry has its own peculiar special
methods of procedure, which are found to be most expedient
in the solution of chemical problems. The facts of course
are first and fundamental. The laws are merely convenient
condensed statements under which like facts and like relations between groups of facts are summed up. The hypotheses and theories are merely convenient ways of describing
the facts by conceiving them to be *like* facts with which we
are better and more intimately acquainted.

Since the laws and theories, if they are thoroughly understood, are very helpful for economizing time in memorizing
facts and recalling them when needed, and in drawing valid
conclusions about them, it is very important that the student
should know the laws and theories that he is capable of com-
prehending. But he cannot comprehend the laws and theories,
and they cannot therefore be helpful to him, unless he first
knows at least a considerable portion of the facts which
the laws resume or the theories explain.

The teaching of chemical facts. — These facts consist

largely of the physical properties of the various elements and
compounds, their chemical behavior and its practical applications under various conditions, such as addition or with-
drawal of heat, presence of light, application of electricity,
intimacy of contact and relative amounts of the substances
reacting, concentration of solutions, relative solubility, relative volatility, temperature, pressure, and so on. These
things are the essence of chemical knowledge and the basis
of chemical theory, and they are valuable in proportion to
the extent to which knowledge of them can be applied for
useful purposes. It follows, therefore, that facts that are
most closely related to the pupils' previous and concurrent
experiences, facts about the behavior of those substances
when reacting on one another, — especially facts that pupils
are most likely to meet with and need to use in their daily
lives, now or after they have finished with school, are the
ones that should receive first consideration when choice of
content for the course is made. Such facts should have preference over those that have value only as illustrating the
theoretical side of chemistry. It should be almost self-evident
that a usable knowledge of such facts cannot be learned to
any great extent from books. The pupil must get them and
fix them in memory by subjecting the substances to critical
observation and thought under various conditions, in experiments which he makes himself with whetted senses and an
alert mind, — by doing things with them to find out what
happens, and then practicing himself in interpreting the hap-
penings in the light of his knowledge gained from other experiments of a similar nature. One can learn chemistry
effectively from books only after he has had a good deal of
chemical experience of this intimate first-hand sort. The
fundamental principle in teaching chemistry, then, may
be stated in this homely fashion, — Have the pupils do things
with the common chemical substances whose reactions are
not too complex, and see to it that they observe accurately

what happens, and correctly interpret their observations.
Give them only so much of theory as will help them better to
interpret and organize the facts that they become acquainted
with in the laboratory, at the demonstration table, and in
the world outside, in the home, on the streets, in the factories,
or on the farm.

Some of the essential facts of chemistry. — The following are
some of the items of chemical knowledge that may be assumed
to have been generally agreed on as essentials.

> Occurrence, preparation, physical properties and chemical
> behavior of oxygen, hydrogen, water, chlorine, sulfur, phos-
> phorus, and nitrogen; formation of oxides by direct union; and
> the hydration of the oxides, forming acids and bases.
>
> The common properties of acids, of bases, and of their salts,
> and the differences in their activities and the stabilities of their
> salts; the general characteristics of metathetical reactions, and
> their uses in the preparation of commercial salts from the raw
> materials.
>
> The different relative solubilities of salts, and the use made of
> these facts in the separation and identification of the basic elements.
>
> Carbon, its oxides, and the simpler hydrocarbons and carbo-
> hydrates; sulfur, its oxides and acids; ammonia; the common
> metals and the general methods of their reduction from their
> ores; and the manufacture, general behavior, and uses of the com-
> monest acids and bases.

In the teaching of all this material a serious mistake will be
made if the significance of such substances as are studied,
and of their chemical behavior be not emphatically brought
home to the pupils by showing their relations to the common
minerals, rocks, and soils, to drinking water, foods, and medi-
cines, to building materials, and to the raw materials from
which their clothing is made. There should be abundant
and generous correlation, especially on the practical side,
with the high school geography, biology, and physics. Furthermore, the pupils should be led to appreciate the fact that
the energy-changes which accompany chemical changes are
especially important. For example:

"When we buy a ton of coal, or a cord of wood for fuel, the whole weight of that coal or wood is so to speak thrown away. We need to build costly flues to carry off the gaseous products of combustion of our furnaces, and labor must be expended to remove the ashes.   The only thing that we pay for in the case of the wood or coal is so much possible heat.   Similarly in the food that is eaten by the animal, all is finally eliminated from the body in one form or another; and what has been paid for really in the food is so much possible energy, that is to say, so much energy as can be set free in the complicated process that we call the life of the animal."   It is well to have the students make collections of the rocks, soils, building materials, woods, and various organic compounds of the neighborhood, and, "What such things do when heated to various degrees of temperature ought to be observed by them.   Simple experiments of this kind will teach a great deal about the nature of such substances; and moreover, but very simple means are required for performing such tests. . . .

"When properly taught to a high school student, chemistry is a powerful aid toward getting him to think in logical and organized ways.   To make high school chemistry merely descriptive is fully as fatal as to restrict it to discussions of atoms, molecules, and various questionable theories connected with them.   A high school course in chemistry should endear the study of natural phenomena to the student, and lead him to see the important relationships between the chemical changes that are going on about us all the time, and the other phenomena of our everyday existence."[1]

It is to be feared that the latter end, though universally regarded as a prime desideratum, is not reached by overmuch attention to the theoretical side of chemistry.   Those who have overheard as many as the writer has of the expressions of utter detestation directed against the chemistry course by pupils in schools where the theories of chemistry hold prominence over its phenomena, are doubtless as firmly convinced of this as he himself is.

[1] Quoted from the paper of Professor Louis Kahlenberg, University of Wisconsin, at the St. Paul meeting of the Dept. of Science Instruction of the N. E. A., July 9, 1914.   Unfortunately, as Professor Kahlenberg was absent on account of illness, the paper under the rules could not be published in the proceedings.

The teaching of chemical laws and theories. — It has been contended that a very valuable course in chemistry can be given without cramming the pupils with symbols and theories. Let anyone who is not convinced of this read the book of Professor Armstrong,[1] already cited, and ponder carefully on the arguments that are to be found in it, and on the valuable chemical knowledge and training which he contends can be given without resort to the formal statements of theory which make up so large a part of most American textbooks. Yet the habit of emphasizing chemical theory has become so strongly fixed in this country that comparatively few teachers will have the disposition to give a course without considerable of it; and all of us agree that it is desirable that the pupils should know as much of it as they can readily learn. Doubtless much of the ill success in teaching the laws and theories comes from the attempt to teach them before the pupils have become possessed through sufficient first-hand experience, and sufficient opportunities for review, grouping and comparison, of the facts that the laws resume and the theories interpret. It seems desirable, therefore, to consider carefully the manner in which these laws and theories may be inductively approached.

The law of definite proportions. — Instead of giving the law of definite proportions dogmatically at the beginning of the course, it will be found to be more in the spirit of real scientific training to withhold it until the students have become familiar with a considerable number of compounds. From the very beginning, whenever a new compound is taken up, its exact percentage composition should be given, with the statement that these proportions have been accurately determined with the aid of the balance, and of appropriate methods known under · the general names of chemical analysis or synthesis. In the case of some compounds at least, the method of determining the weight

[1] *The Teaching of the Scientific Method*, Macmillan, N. Y., 1903.

of the elements in a given amount of it can be clearly explained.[1]

Thus when mercuric oxide is decomposed by heating in an ignition tube, the pupils actually see the mercury and have convincing ocular evidence [2] for *inferring* the presence of the oxygen and estimating its volume; and it will be easy for them to understand how with suitable provision for accuracy the mercuric oxide used, and the mercury liberated, could be carefully weighed, while the weight of the oxygen could be calculated from its measured volume and density.

So it easily can be made clear in connection with the experiments of Lavoisier, for example, that 1 gram of the mercuric oxide is always found to contain .926 gram of mercury and .074 gram of oxygen, and that this same proportion, 92.6 parts (or 92.6 per cent) mercury to 7.4 parts (or 7.4 per cent) oxygen, has always been found to hold when any number of grams of mercuric oxide have been accurately analyzed. In several other compounds the method of determining the proportion of at least one of the constituents can be shown experimentally, or described in such a manner as to be com-

---

[1] Several experiments that can be made by the pupils in the laboratory are mentioned in Smith and Hall, *The Teaching of Chemistry*, op. cit., 113–121. Before the pupils are required to learn and apply the law, at least one of these should be made by them or demonstrated by the teacher.

See also Schoch, E. P., *Chemistry in High Schools*, Bulletin of the University of Texas, Austin, Tex., No. 210, December 8, 1911, p. 52; and Armstrong, Henry E., *The Teaching of the Scientific Method and Other Papers on Education*, Macmillan, London and New York, 1903, pp. 226–231. Here and elsewhere in this book, quantitative experiments of great educational value are clearly described.

[2] If the teacher ask the pupils if they *observed* the oxygen, probably nearly all will blithely answer in the affirmative. Here is one of the countless opportunities to train them in the logical habit of making the distinction between observation and inference. If they are brought face to face with the logical absurdity of reciting that oxygen is a colorless, invisible gas, and then asserting that they observed it, they will be somewhat chagrined; and doubtless they will think hard in order to extricate themselves. Probably they will succeed in stating clearly what they do actually see, and what they so confidently infer from their observations. Such lessons in the logic of science are easy to give, and are so salutary in their results that they should by no means be neglected.

prehended. This information should be given along with the other characteristics of the compound. After several compounds have been studied, and the definite and invariable nature of their composition has become familiar along with their other physical and chemical properties, the pupils will begin to wonder whether this is the case with all compounds that are known ; and it will then be time to give them the law. In all probability they can be made to state it correctly themselves, in response to one or two skillfully worded questions ; and they certainly should be given the opportunity. In this way no time whatever need be lost ; and the generalization will come to the pupils naturally as a *résumé* of previously acquired knowledge with which they already feel somewhat at home. Coming thus from their own knowledge, that has been gained at least partially through their own experiences and formulated by their own thought, the law will have peculiar interest and convincingness ; and its implications are much more likely to be appreciated and applied later on. How much better this is than to kill their interest in the law at the beginning by compelling them to swallow it as a mysterious oracular dictum whose truth must be accepted on faith or authority, and whose origin lies in some nebulous realm of speculation outside the field of their experience !

The law of multiple proportions. — So again with the law of multiple proportions, if the teacher wait until the pupils have become familiar with some of the properties and the percentage compositions of water and hydrogen dioxide, of carbon monoxide and carbon dioxide, and of sulfur dioxide and sulfur trioxide, calling attention, when the compounds of each pair are studied, to the two different percentages of oxygen in the two members of the pair, the pupils may very likely discover for themselves that in the first pair the ratio of the percentages of oxygen is exactly two to one. If the opportunity has not been spoiled by telling them beforehand instead of putting them in the way of discovering it for themselves, this will strike them as rather remarkable, as in fact it really is.

When they discover that the ratio of the percentage of oxygen in carbon dioxide to the percentage of the same element in carbon monoxide is again exactly two to one, it will probably put them into a healthy condition of wondering. Very likely they will begin to suspect that there is some regularity about the relation; and perhaps they will surmise that oxygen forms two compounds with every element, and that the ratio of its percentage in one to its percentage in the other is always two to one. If the teacher have enough self-restraint to keep himself out of the situation until the pupils have learned and noted that the percentages in the two sulfur oxides are in the ratio, not of two to one, but of three to two, they will find that they must modify their first conjecture, but that there is some regularity about the proportions in which oxygen combines with any given element. In the meantime if they have raised the direct question as to whether there is a law of wider application with reference to oxygen and to other elements as well, they should not be told what the law is and made to learn the words in which the books state it, but they should be told to keep on thinking about it and await further facts. It would be wise even to caution them that if they find out more about this question they must refrain from telling it abroad in order that they may let their classmates get the benefit of practice in independent thinking. When the oxides of sulfur have been studied and the three-to-two ratio discovered, the teacher may then have the pupils tabulate the percentages on the blackboard and ask them if they can frame a statement about the proportions in which oxygen combines in its compounds with hydrogen, with carbon, and with sulfur. After they have made a correct statement limited to these six compounds, if they do not themselves ask whether similar relations exist in the case of all other compounds the teacher may put this question to them. Of course they should not be able to answer it with any confidence, for they are not in possession of sufficient data. If they do so answer it, let the teacher show them the logical absurdity of generalizing without facts sufficient to warrant generalization. Let him then ask them what sort of facts they would need to know in order to answer the question with confidence. If they have ordinary acumen they will suggest that they need to know the percentage compositions of a large number of other compounds. If they do not hit on this suggestion within a reasonable time, let the teacher suggest it, and ask their judgment on it. If they agree that this is the sort of information needed in order to find out whether there is a general law which holds in such cases, the time is ripe to assign them the task of looking through the textbooks for the percentage compositions of other pairs or series of compounds into which one of the elements enters in different proportions (*e.g.* the oxides of phosphorus and nitrogen, the chlorides of iron and copper, and so on), and tabulating the percentage compositions of the compounds and the ratios of the percentages of the varying elements in the compounds of each series. If the textbook in use or books in the library do not give the percentage compositions of the different compounds, the teacher may calculate them from the formulas and atomic weights, and give them to the class, preferably in a chance order. The pupils may then tabulate them in order. They will see that the simple whole-number ratios apply to all the compounds in which one element combines with another in more than one proportion; and they will then be in a position to frame a general statement of the law. When they have done this with the proper tentative, inductive attitude, the teacher may tell them that this law has been found to apply in every known case, and has been of service in the gaining of new knowledge.

Superiority of inductive teaching. — Note that up to this time atoms and molecules are not supposed to have been mentioned. The whole time taken to teach the law in this way will be scarcely longer than that taken by the writer in setting down this description of it; but even if it be longer it will be infinitely better spent than if used by the pupils in memorizing and reciting the law without having grounded it firmly on their own study and thought, and without having realized in this intimately concrete and personal way its purely experimental and inductive origin. It is the belief of the author that if the subject matter of chemistry were so organized in a textbook as to approach the chemical laws and theories consistently in this way, the subject would become so easy that many teachers of chemistry would refuse to use the book fearing that the pupils would not get the proper " mental discipline " out of it. As a matter of fact, there is always enough that is difficult in any science if the teacher insists that the pupils get to the bottom of the problems that inevitably arise; and if there is time it is never unprofitable to attempt the solution of such of these as involve data that the pupils can possess themselves of by the route of concrete experience, and of actual weighing and measuring. If the subject matter is so organized as to give such graded practice in logical thinking as is here suggested the pupils will learn to think so much better than they think under the old methods that they will be able easily to handle many theoretical matters that, otherwise approached, would be too difficult for them to comprehend.

If chemical laws and theories are not to be approached in some such inductive manner as has been described it would, in the opinion of the author, be better to omit the most of them and stick pretty closely to inductive studies of the natural history phases of the elements and compounds and such of their relations as can be determined by experiment. The pupils would know more of real chemistry at the end of the year than they would if they had been crammed with a formal textbook course consisting largely of *ex cathedra* statements of theory and of formal experiments without a compelling inner motive for investigation.[1]

The law of the conservation of mass. — In connection with the teaching of the two laws already mentioned and of the experimental facts that have led up to them, the basis will have been laid in experience for the law of the conservation of mass; and it can now be brought in at any time, and clinched. It may be done in a very interesting way, and in a short time, in connection with a brief review of the experiments of Black, Priestley, and Lavoisier. It is worth while to give the actual figures obtained in Lavoisier's famous experiment, and to call attention to the fact that the assignments of percentage compositions to all compounds that have been analyzed are necessarily based on the assumption that this law is true. The pupils will probably have assumed this without realizing that they have done so; and the occasion will furnish the opportunity for another salutary lesson in the logic of chemistry. It is only when we examine carefully the contents of our premises and the grounds on which we assume them, that we find out whether we have committed the common fallacy of slipping into our chain of reasoning, either without or with sophistical intent, some assumption that was not specifically recognized in the premises. There is no harm in letting the pupils assume a few things at first, in order not to crowd in too many new ideas all together at the start; but it is highly important that they be made to halt betimes and subject all assumptions to careful scrutiny, in order that they may know whether these assumptions are or not justified by the facts. In the case of the law of the conservation of mass, then, it is well to ask them a few questions that will lead them to realize that they have made this

---

[1] Read carefully Smith and Hall, *op. cit.*, pp. 52–84, and Schoch, *op. cit.*, pp. 44–56. Also for information as to the large amount of real chemistry that can be experimentally taught without resort to chemical symbols and theory, see Armstrong, *op. cit.*, pp. 219–234, 283–291.

assumption in accepting the percentage compositions as established facts. When they have seen this clearly they should be led by further questioning, suggestion, or explanation to understand that the law is an inductive inference based on a vast amount of accumulated experience, and that its justification lies in the fact that while thousands of analyses of compounds have been made, no chemical change has occurred, in connection with any of them, in which the sum of the weights of all the products resulting from the change was found to be greater or less than the sum of the weights of all the substances that entered into it.

In connection with this discussion and with all other quantitative experiments it should, of course, be made clear that small experimental errors are inevitable, but that these become smaller and smaller when the experiments are made with more accurate instruments and with greater care.

Gay-Lussac's law of combining volumes. — The pupils' knowledge of this law may be made to grow out of their experience with certain compounds in a manner similar to that suggested for the preceding laws. If they have been shown by experiment, as they should be, that when a given volume of oxygen taken as a unit is exploded in a eudiometer with two unit volumes of hydrogen, it forms two unit volumes of steam at the same temperature and pressure, and that one volume of nitrogen combines similarly with three of hydrogen to form two volumes of ammonia gas, they will be ready to accept the statement that one volume of chlorine combines with one of hydrogen to form under similar conditions two volumes of hydrogen chloride. This latter experiment is troublesome, and probably would better not be tried, on account of the violence with which these two gases unite; but if there is time for further quantitative demonstration before the law is formulated, the experiment of combining oxygen with sulfur to form sulfur dioxide can easily be

2 B

made,[1] and the fact shown that when one volume of oxygen combines with all the sulfur that it will take, two volumes of sulfur dioxide are formed.

If these facts are now tabulated graphically, letting small equal rectangles represent unit volumes of any of the gases, the pupils with the table before them and with the aid of a little questioning and suggestion, should be able to frame intelligently the statement that when these gases that have been experimented with combine, the volumes of them which enter into composition and the volumes of the gaseous compounds that are formed bear simple ratios to one another, — that is, they can be represented by the small whole numbers 1, 2, 3, etc. They may then be told that this statement holds good for all elements in the condition of gases or vapors and for all compounds formed by them as gases or vapors under constant conditions of temperature and pressure.   They are then prepared to memorize the formal statement of the law with some appreciation of its meaning.

The physical laws of gases and vapors. — The laws of Boyle and Charles and the law of vapor pressure must be made use of in correcting the measurements of gas volumes in the experiments to which we have just referred, and in all subsequent calculations in which the weights of gases are determined from their measured volumes. The pupils usually have little difficulty in reciting the verbal statements of these laws, but when they are required to make use of them in calculations they almost invariably have trouble.   The teacher may overcome this difficulty by carefully explaining and illustrating the behavior of gases, which the laws describe. He should do this at the demonstration table when the actual necessity for applying the laws occurs, as it does in these experiments.   Often the difficulties arise mainly because the

---

[1] For these experiments, see Schoch, *op. cit.*, pp. 55–56; and McPherson, W., and Henderson, W. E., *First Course in Chemistry*, Ginn, Boston, 1915, p. 50. See also, Smith, *op. cit.*, pp. 112–114, and pp. 48–49.   ·

teacher assumes that the pupils know these laws from their previous study of them in the course in physics. He perhaps overlooks the bearing, in this connection, of the psychological laws of memory and fails to appreciate the fact that because nearly a year's time has elapsed since the gas laws were learned, it is unlikely that they can be recalled and applied without relearning. A review of them, therefore, with some experimental demonstration is almost sure to be necessary in order that the pupils may be able to apply them intelligently. Other difficulties arise from the elevation of these problems (of the correction of measured gas volumes, and their translation to weights) into ends, instead of keeping them in their place as means to an end.

The author has found that the following statement of the laws of Boyle and Charles combined is altogether the most convenient and easiest for the pupils to remember and use:

" The product of the volume and pressure of a given mass of any gas is proportional to its absolute temperature "[1] or

$$\frac{P\,V}{273 + t} = \frac{P'\,V'}{273 + t'}$$

The language of fact vs. *the language of theory.* — Up to this point in the development of the theoretical aspects of chemistry, it is assumed that no mention has been made of combining weights, and especially of atoms. Only the direct results of chemical analyses are supposed to have been dealt with; and these in a purely matter-of-fact and inductive manner. This is very important if the true scientific attitude is to be established and fostered. If the pupils are allowed to begin talking and thinking in terms of the atomic theory before they have been inducted into the habit of starting their thinking with the facts of observation and experiment, the

[1] The experimental evidence, and the argument for this statement of these laws and for the law of vapor pressure may be found in Mann and Twiss, *op. cit.*, pp. 321–323, and pp. 128–129.

best part of the peculiar service that chemistry can render them through training in the scientific method of inductive inference will be lost, and they will form the habit of speculating on the affinities of atoms and the dance of the molecules, instead of thinking on the methods and results of chemical investigation.

This opinion of the author is based not so much on academic theories of scientific teaching as on his actual observation of the behavior of pupils in chemistry classes extending over many years. The attitude that is almost certain to be generated by introducing the atomic theory and chemical symbols very early in the course and by conducting the discussions in this highly condensed and artificial type of scientific language is the attitude of relying on belief instead of on knowledge. There is in chemistry classes too much talk of what " chemists tell us," of what " scientists believe "; too much arguing from prejudice and too little open-minded consideration of observed and recorded facts; too much jumping at conclusions and too little candid summing up of experience gained at first hand; and an atmosphere of mystery, unreality, and nebulous speculation pervades the whole procedure.

One can express himself so much more concisely in terms of the atomic theory, and with chemical symbols and equations, that the temptation is strong to introduce these very early, and few authors and teachers have been able to resist it. Nevertheless, in the opinion of the author it is pernicious to allow the pupils to juggle with symbols before they have gained some true conception of their meanings. " Chemistry as usually taught loses greatly in educational value because pupils are told, more often than not, that such and such *is* the case, instead of being taught *how it has been found out* that such is the case; indeed, that which has to be proved is usually taken for granted." [1] It is this tendency to make

[1] Armstrong, Henry E., *Suggestions for a Course of Elementary Instruction in Physical Science*, being the *Report on Teaching Chemistry* presented at the meet-

chemistry teaching a cramming process, instead of an opportunity for self-development, — for learning how to *do* and how to get to the bottom of a question, — that defeats the very purposes for which we profess to teach chemistry.

Combining weights. — After a considerable number of compounds have become familiar at first hand, and the preceding laws learned inductively in the manner indicated, the idea of combining weights may be gradually approached in a similar way. Let it be shown that since the relative weight of hydrogen that enters into various compounds is the smallest relative weight to be found in any of them, it was for a long time taken as a convenient unit for comparing the weights of the elements in all compounds. Thus the composition of water can be expressed as hydrogen 11.19 per cent, oxygen 88.81 per cent; or since $\frac{88.81}{11.19} = 7.94$, the same ratio may be more simply expressed as hydrogen 1 part, oxygen 7.94 parts, or a ratio approximately of 1 to 8. Similarly for hydrogen dioxide the composition may be stated as hydrogen 5.924 per cent, oxygen 94.076 per cent, or since $\frac{94.076}{5.924} = 15.88$, the same ratio may be expressed as hydrogen 1 part, oxygen 15.88 parts, or a ratio approximately of 1 to 16.

Again, if we reduce the percentage ratios of other hydrogen compounds in a similar manner so to compare the weight of the other element to that of the hydrogen when taken as unity we find the following :

For hydrogen sulphide — hydrogen 1, sulfur, 16.

For calcium hydride — hydrogen 1, calcium 19.88.

For ammonia — hydrogen 1, nitrogen 42.03, and so on.

Now since these ratios are always found to be the same for all quantities of these hydrogen compounds, we may calculate from the percentage compositions of these compounds as determined by analyses a set of numbers which tells how many grams of any element enter into combination with 1 gram of hydrogen.

Now a little further consideration of the relative weights of the elements in the compounds that have been studied reveals a remarkable relation; for if we calculate from the percentage composition of calcium

ing of the British Association for the Advancement of Science, Newcastle on Tyne, 1899, printed as Chapter XVI, (*loc. cit.*, p. 391) of the previously cited book by this eminent English chemist and educational leader. Every teacher of chemistry should read this entire report, and most of the other chapters as well.

oxide the number of grams of calcium that combines with 7.94 grams of oxygen, we find it to be 19.88, the same number of grams of calcium that combine with 1 gram of hydrogen.   Thus the weights, in grams, of calcium and oxygen that are found to combine with each other are the same as the weights in grams of these elements that combine with 1 gram of hydrogen; and the same proportions hold, whatever be the unit.

Similarly for sulfur dioxide — sulfur 16, oxygen 15.88 (*i.e.* 2 $\times$ 7.94): for calcium sulphide — sulfur 16, calcium 19.88.   Thus for the compounds mentioned we find that the ratios of the weights in which these elements combine with each other are the same as the ratios of the weights of them that combine with 1 gram of hydrogen.   When similar calculations are made for other compounds, and the results tabulated, we find the same thing to be true, namely, that we may choose for each element a number which we may call its combining weight, and which either by itself or when multiplied by a small whole number tells the proportion in which this element combines with a similarly chosen weight of any other element.

Chemical symbols and equations. — Although it is assumed that up to this stage no atomic or molecular symbols and formulas have been mentioned, the *idea* of the equation should have been introduced at the very beginning of the course, and continued by using names and percentage compositions to represent the chemical change in every experiment, thus —

$$\text{Mercuric oxide} \rightleftarrows \text{mercury} + \text{oxygen}$$
$$100 \qquad\qquad 92.6 \qquad 7.4$$

The pupils should be trained to read this, "100 parts of mercury, when heated in a hard glass tube, yield 92.6 parts of mercury and 7.4 parts of oxygen," and so for every reaction.   Also the idea of constant proportions should be given the necessary repetition for thorough comprehension and memorization by having one pupil state the proportion in grams, another in pounds, another in milligrams, another in tons, and another in percentages, until the concept of constant proportions has become concrete and has been fixed in their memories.   *The stating of proportions by weights should become a habit with them.*

After the laws of definite and multiple proportions and the concept of combining weights have been developed in such a manner as to make it clear that combining weights are more convenient than percentages, another step toward the atomic theory may be taken by representing all reactions on this basis, thus, for example,

$$\text{Hydrogen} + \text{chlorine} \rightarrow \text{hydrogen chloride}$$
$$1 \qquad\quad 35.37 \qquad\qquad 36.37$$

After this idea has sunk in, the pupils may be told that the chemists have found as a result of long experience and much experimentation that the combining weights of the elements came out with more whole numbers and fewer long fractions when the unit of combining weight adopted as the basis for comparison and calculation is taken as oxygen = 16 than they do if the unit combining weight is taken as hydrogen = 1.

On this basis, with oxygen = 16 as a unit, the proportions calculated from the percentage compositions of several compounds may be tabulated as follows:

oxygen	hydrogen	water
16	2.016	18.016
oxygen	hydrogen	hydrogen dioxide
32	2.016	34.016
hydrogen	chlorine	hydrogen chloride
1.008	35.46	36.468
hydrogen	nitrogen	ammonia
3.024	14.01	17.034
chlorine	oxygen	chlorine monoxide
70.92	16	86.92
sulfur	oxygen	sulfur dioxide
32.07	32	64.07

On comparing the combining proportions of the various elements in this table it becomes evident that the relative amount of hydrogen that enters into combination in the compounds here considered is 1, 2, or 3 times its least combining weight (1.008), and that the same thing is true for the other elements.

It is thus seen to be very convenient to regard the smallest relative weight of each of the elements that is found in any of its compounds as the unit of combining weight for that element (oxygen = 16 being the basis). We may then conceive that water is made up of one combining weight of oxygen (16) and two combining weights of hydrogen (1.008 × 2 = 2.016) and that hydrogen dioxide is made up of two combining weights of oxygen (16 × 2 = 32) and two of hydrogen (1.008 × 2 = 2.016), hydrogen chloride of one combining weight of hydrogen (1.008) and one of chlorine (35.46), and so on. Let the pupils finish by applying the principle to the other compounds of the table. After they have come to understand fairly well the use of combining weights as units in terms of which chemical changes can with convenience be quantitatively expressed, and after they have become habituated to writing chemical equations in the manner illustrated by the foregoing table, the pupils will be ready almost to *fall* into the use of symbols without further instruction. Let the teacher then ask them if they can think of labor-saving abbreviations to use instead of the terms one combining weight of hydrogen, two combining weights of oxygen, etc.; and probably they will suggest the initial letters of the names of the elements to stand for these names and a coefficient or subscript number attached to each initial to stand for the number of combining weights of that element that are present in a compound.

If they do not hit upon this idea at once, a little questioning and suggestion will bring it out. They may now be asked what shall be done in the case of two or more elements whose names have the same initial letter, as carbon, chlorine, and calcium; and after the symbols that have been adopted by chemists have been agreed on by the pupils as the best, the origin of Fe for iron, Hg for mercury, Na for sodium, and so on, may be explained.

At this point all the reactions that they have had should be grouped in a review according to their similarities, written with the symbols, and made the basis of a review of the elements, compounds, and processes involved.

During this review they may be told that the term, combining weight, as they are using it, is synonymous with *atomic weight;* and they may be made acquainted with the table of the atomic weights of the elements.

The atomic theory. — The pupils will now be ready for a real appreciation of the atomic theory. In presenting it, let the laws of definite and multiple proportions be recalled, and a table of combining proportions like that on page 375 be placed on the blackboard; then ask the pupils if the proportions of the elements in a compound should be expected to remain the same for the smallest quantities of those elements that can be conceived to enter into combination and still retain their peculiar chemical properties. When they have answered this in the affirmative, they may be asked if it would be consistent with the facts that they have thus far learned, if we were to suppose that these very tiny bits of the elements (which we may now agree to call atoms) go through all chemical changes as units, without losing their identity, and that when oxygen and hydrogen, for example, unite to form water each one of a certain large number of tiny oxygen atoms unites with two hydrogen atoms, and so on for other cases. If they are able to see that this supposition is consistent with all the facts, and to understand how it serves as a convenient interpretation for the laws of definite and multiple proportions and the law of combining weights, they ought to be prepared for the customary statement of Dalton's Atomic Theory.[1]

[1] For a very clear and simple statement, see McPherson and Henderson, *op. cit.*, pp. 67, 68.

From this point on, all reactions can be expressed in terms of chemical equations and interpreted in the language of the atomic theory; but the discussion should never be allowed to get far away from the facts of experiment. The pupils should be impressed with the idea that these equations are simply a concise means of stating facts determined by experiments; and they should never be allowed to deduce, by juggling with the equations, conclusions not based on the facts which the equations represent. The author has frequently heard chemistry classes discussing chemical equations and the proper observance of the rules for the "coefficients and exponents" as if they were handling algebraic equations, — and deducing consequences from them which they accepted with pathetic credulity — while no references were made to the actual substances and the process of their behavior when put together. Better no chemistry at all than trash of such a sort. A chemical equation is not something in itself from which a conclusion can be deduced. It is simply a condensed and very convenient statement of a conclusion itself, or of a set of observed facts. Deductions made with it, but without having in mind all the facts that it implies, and perhaps others besides, are almost certain to involve serious errors and misconceptions.

Molecules and Avogadro's law. — Since the pupils who study chemistry in high schools have usually had a previous course in physics, they will think they know somewhat about molecules; but it is best not to let them indulge in cock-sure statements about them at any time; and it is particularly desirable for fostering the scientific habit of mind in chemistry study that all mention of them be avoided until after the atomic theory has been inductively taught. After this the molecular theory may be reviewed with demonstration experiments in connection with the physical phenomena of gas volumes at varying temperatures and pressures, evaporation and vapor pressures, the phenomena of diffusion and solution, including osmotic pressure, and the effects of concentration on boiling and freezing points. Without such a review it is not to be expected that the pupils will have any clear conception of the theory. Their statements on the questions will be nothing but wild guesses and idle speculation. So if they have no clear conception of what molecules may be they can have none of Avogadro's law and its consequences. Unless this law and its consequences are *comprehended* it is useless to expect success in teaching the pupils how molecular and atomic weights, molecular formulæ, and valencies are determined. Neither can they understand the calculations that justify the correct balancing of equations, unless they understand this law. On the contrary the learning process will degenerate into unintelligent and uninterested memorizing, or become a mere guessing game, yielding no scientific training. If introduced at all, Avogadro's law should be approached inductively through suitable experiments. For the introduction of this hypothesis the following experimental problems are desirable, and, if possible, should be worked out by teacher and pupils at the demonstration table:

1. In what proportions by volume do oxygen and hydrogen combine to form water; and what is the relative volume of steam that is formed under the same pressure and temperature?[1]

2. In what proportions by volume do hydrogen and chlorine unite with each other; and what is the relative volume of the resulting hydrogen chloride[2] under the same conditions of temperature and pressure?

3. In what proportions do nitrogen and hydrogen unite; and what is the relative volume of ammonia gas thus formed (at the same temperature and pressure)?

4. When sulfur unites with a given volume of oxygen, what relative volume of sulfur dioxide is formed (at the same temperature and pressure)?

If any of these experiments have been made previously in connection with the study of water, oxygen, hydrogen, chlorine, or sulphur, or in connection with the law of combining volumes, it will here be necessary only to review them and tabulate graphically their results by volume as described in connection with the presentation of the latter law.[3]

When this tabulation has been done the basis for an understanding of Avogadro's hypothesis and its consequences is before the pupils; and it may then be explained to them how molecular formulæ are chosen, how molecular or reacting equations are written, and so on. And these theoretical matters may be made the basis of a review of

---

[1] The experiment of the electrolysis of dilute sulfuric acid is often used to demonstrate this proportion, and it is stated that since two volumes of hydrogen are liberated from the solution for every one volume of oxygen, this proves that water is composed of hydrogen and oxygen in the proportion of two to one. Strenuous objections are made to this statement by authorities in physical chemistry; and hence this experiment should not be used to demonstrate the composition of water. For arguments on this point see Schoch, *op. cit.*, pp. 47, 54, and 81–87. Professor Alexander Smith suggests the use of potassium fluoride, instead of acid, to increase the electrical conductivity of the water. In this case, no question can arise as to whether the hydrogen and the oxygen come from the water.

[2] For suitable substitutes for this troublesome experiment by direct union of H and Cl see Smith, *op. cit.*, pp. 111–114.

[3] Cf. p. 369 *ante.*

many previously learned facts on which they throw light. The writer, however, is skeptical with regard to the comprehension of these ideas, and ventures the opinion that the teacher as well as the pupils will be happier if he does not expect a very large measure of it, even under the best conditions and with the most careful approach. He should always remember that *getting the pupils to say the words is not necessarily getting them to understand what the words mean.* When the teacher thinks he has succeeded, if he "overhaul the pupil's conceptions" by doing a little probing and cross-examining he will more often than otherwise be disappointed; and he must not blame the pupil for it.

The ion theory. — Later, after a sufficient array of experiments and facts about electrolysis has been accumulated and organized, the ionic theory may be explained and some of its uses in ordering and interpreting chemical facts may be pointed out.

All this may be very well worth while; but it is very difficult, and if given, will be much more likely to be understood if it comes near the end of the course. It will be a rare teacher who can present it successfully unless he has mastered it himself through a laboratory course in physical chemistry; and it certainly should not be allowed to crowd out other more important and directly practical knowledge that the pupils can gain through experimenting themselves, and can more easily grasp. It may be argued that acids, bases, and salts cannot be understood without the ionic theory; but the answer to that is that very much of value was successfully taught about these bodies before modern physical chemistry began to filter into the high schools.

From the relatively large space devoted in this chapter to the teaching of chemical theory, it might be inferred that the author believes theory should occupy the major part of the pupil's time. The real case is quite the contrary, however. The purpose of the somewhat extended discussion is to make clear the uselessness of attempting most of the theoretical teaching at all unless it is done in such a way as to build up scientific habits of mind.

QUESTIONS FOR FURTHER STUDY

1. Outline your plans for the first three lessons of a high school course in chemistry.

2. Show how in your plans you have "psychologized" the subject matter and the method of instruction.

3. What error must be particularly guarded against in starting such a course?

4. Why is it psychologically wrong to talk about atoms and molecules early in the course?

5. Outline your ideas as to the proper use of a chemistry textbook, and support them by argument.

6. State clearly the distinctions between facts, laws, and principles, and hypotheses and theories. How shall you proceed in order to give the pupils clear notions as to these distinctions?

7. What are the principal types of chemical facts? What circumstances should govern the choice among these facts for teaching purposes?

8. How does a person become able to use chemical books in gaining chemical knowledge?

9. Discuss critically the list of chemical facts given as essential.

10. Explain how the relations to everyday things, of such facts, can be made clear and interesting to pupils. Why is it important to the pupil, both socially and psychologically, that this should be done?

11. What changes, if any, have occurred in your point of view or what new thoughts as to the teaching of chemistry have come to you as a result of reading the quotation from Professor Kahlenberg's paper?

12. What is your opinion of the soundness of the suggested method of teaching the law of definite proportions? Is the method feasible?

13. What is your reaction to the proposed approach to the law of multiple proportions? To the general comment on the inductive method of approaching generalizations?

14. Do you approve the proposed method of teaching the law of the conservation of mass? Why?

15. How would you teach the law of combining volumes? From your own experience in learning chemistry, do you think the proposed experiments and inductive approach are necessary?

16. Do you agree or disagree with the author in what he says about the teaching of the gas laws? Why?

17. Why have textbook authors introduced the atomic theory so early? In your own actual opinion are they pedagogically right or wrong in writing thus for beginners? Under the circumstances what can a teacher do who believes in withholding theories until their utility can be appreciated through knowledge of the facts that they explain?

18. Do you think the author of this book has overstated the bad effects on the pupils of introducing theories too early, and too dogmatically, and making them unduly prominent? If you disagree with him, what arguments can you advance to confute his statements?

19. Assuming for the time that your classmates are high school pupils, teach them the notion of combining weights, and ascertain by questioning whether they have grasped it with perfect clearness.

20. Teach them similarly the use of symbols and equations.

21. Introduce them to the atomic theory.

REFERENCES

Methods, Special Treatises, and Advanced Textbooks

BASKERVILLE, CHARLES. Municipal Chemistry. McGraw, N. Y. 1911. 526 pp. Illus. $5.00. Series of 30 lectures by experts.

BENEDICT, FRANCIS GANO. Chemical Lecture Experiments. Macmillan, N. Y. 1901. 436 pp. Illus. $2.00.

BLOXAM, CHARLES LOUDON. Inorganic and Organic Chemistry. Blakiston, Philadelphia. 1903. 11 + 848 pp. $6.00.

CARNEGIE, D. Law and Theory in Chemistry. Longmans, N. Y. 1894. 230 pp. $1.50. Historical development of chemical theory for teacher and pupils.

CHAPIN, C. V. Municipal Sanitation in the United States. Snow & Fornham, Providence, R. I. 1901. 970 pp. Illus. $5.00.

CLOWES, F., and COLEMAN, I. B. Quantitative Analysis. Blakiston, Philadelphia. 1911. 9th Ed. $3.50.

DANA, E. S. A Text-book of Mineralogy. Wiley, N. Y. 1898. 593 pp. $4.00.

FINDLAY, ALEXANDER. Chemistry in the Service of Man. Longmans, Green & Co., N. Y. 1916. 15 + 255 pp. $1.60.

FREUND, IDA. The Study of Chemical Composition. University Press, Cambridge, Eng. 1904. Putnam, N. Y. 650 pp. $5.50. An advanced account of the method and historical development of theoretical chemistry. Shows the true spirit and method of science.

GIBSON, JAMES H. Management of Laboratory Classes in Chemistry. High School Bull. No. 1. The University of the State of New York, Albany, N. Y.

JONES, HARRY CLARY. The Elements of Physical Chemistry. Macmillan, N. Y. 1907. 11 + 565 pp. $4.00.

JONES, HARRY CLARY. The Theory of Electrolytic Dissociation. Macmillan. 1900. 12 + 289 pp. $1.60.

JONES, HARRY CLARY. The Freezing-point, Boiling-point, and Conductivity Methods. Chemical Publishing Co., Easton, Pa. 1897. 64 pp. 75 ¢.

LASSAR-COHN, DR. Tr. by Smith, A. Laboratory Manual of Organic

Chemistry. Macmillan, N. Y. 1895. 403 pp. $2.25. Full and accurate treatment of laboratory methods in organic chemistry.

LEHFELDT, R. A. Text-book of Physical Chemistry. Longmans, N. Y. 1899, and later. $2.50.

LÜPKE, ROBERT. Elements of Electro-Chemistry. Lippincott, N. Y. 2d Ed. Illus. $2.50.

McPHERSON, W., and HENDERSON, W. E. A Course in General Chemistry. Ginn, Boston. $2.25. A college textbook.

MEADE, RICHARD KIDDER. The Chemist's Pocket Manual. Chemical Pub. Co., Easton, Pa. 1910. $3.00.

MENDELEEFF, D. The Principles of Chemistry. Ed. by Greenaway, A. J. Longmans, London and N. Y. 1901. 2 Vols. 611–462 pp. 3d Ed. $10.00. An elaborate treatise of great value to teachers.

MORGAN, W. C. The Relation of the Technical World to School Chemistry. School Science and Math., 8 : 645–56, November, 1908.

MUIR, M. M. P. Course of Practical Chemistry. Longmans, N. Y. 2 Vols. Each $1.50.

MUTER, JOHN. A Short Manual of Analytical Chemistry. Quantitative and Qualitative. Inorganic and Organic. Blakiston, Philadelphia. 1898. 228 pp. $1.50. "Adapted to use of both teacher and pupil."

NEWTH, G. S. Textbook of Inorganic Chemistry. Longmans, London and New York. 1897. 682 pp. $1.75. General text for teacher and pupils.

NEWTH, G. S. Elementary Inorganic Chemistry. Longmans, N. Y. 1899. 90 ¢. Note the development of theory in this book. It is intended for high school pupils.

NEWTH, G. S. Chemical Lectures Experiments. Longmans, N. Y. 1899. 344 pp. Illus. $2.00.

NEWTH, G. S. Chemical Analysis, Qualitative and Quantitative. Longmans, N. Y. 1898. 462 pp. $1.75.

NOYES, WILLIAM ALBERT. Organic Chemistry for the Laboratory. Chemical Pub. Co., Easton, Pa. 1911. 291 pp. $2.00.

NOYES, W. A. Elements of Qualitative Chemical Analysis. Holt, N. Y. 1893. 91 pp. 80 ¢. "A complete course for beginners. Directions explicit."

OSTWALD, WILHELM FRIEDRICH. Tr. by Walker. Outlines of General Chemistry. Macmillan, N. Y. 1890. 386 pp. $3.50.

OSTWALD, WILHELM FRIEDRICH. Tr. by McGowan. Scientific Foundations of Analytical Chemistry. Macmillan, N. Y. 1900. 215 pp. $2.00. Explains the applications of modern theory to analytical processes.

OSTWALD, WILHELM FRIEDRICH. Tr. by Muir. Solutions. Longmans, London and N. Y. 1891. 310 pp. $2.00.

PERKIN, W. H., JR., and LEAN, B. An Introduction to the Study of Chemistry. Macmillan, London and N. Y. 1897. 360 pp. 2s. 6d. The teacher should give this book careful thought. It exemplifies the scientific method of experimental study. Largely quantitative and inductive.

PERKIN, W. H., JR., and LEAN, B. Introduction to Chemistry and Physics. Macmillan, N. Y. 1902. (New Ed.) 2 Vols. 20 + 207 pp. and 12 + 216 pp. Each 50 ¢.

PERKINS, W. H., and KIPPING, F. S. Organic Chemistry. Lippincott, Philadelphia. $2.00.

PRESCOTT, ALBERT B., and JOHNSON, OTIS COE. Qualitative Chemical Analysis. Van Nostrand, N. Y. 1912. 254 pp. $3.50.

RAMSAY, SIR WILLIAM. Experimental Proofs of Chemical Theory for Beginners. Macmillan, London and N. Y. 1893. 143 pp. 60 ¢.

RAMSAY, SIR WILLIAM. A System of Inorganic Chemistry. Churchill, London. 1891. 15 + 700 pp. 15s.

RAMSAY, SIR WILLIAM. Modern Chemistry. Pt. I, Theoretical. Pt. II, Systematic. Macmillan, N. Y. 1901. Each 40 ¢.

REMSEN, I. Inorganic Chemistry. Holt, N. Y. 1890. 850 pp. $2.80. Standard college text.

REMSEN, I. Introduction to the Study of Compounds of Carbon. Heath, Boston. 1895. 12 + 387 pp. $1.30.

RICHTER, VICTOR VON. Tr. by Smith, E. F. Inorganic Chemistry. Blakiston, Philadelphia. 1900. 432 pp. 5th Ed. $1.75.

RICHTER, VICTOR VON. Organic Chemistry. Blakiston, Philadelphia. 1900. 2 vols. 1296 pp. $6.00.

ROGERS, A., and AUBERT, A. B. Industrial Chemistry. Van Nostrand, N. Y. 1912. 854 pp. 340 illus. $5.00.

ROSCOE, H. E., and SCHORLEMMER, C. Inorganic Chemistry. Appleton, N. Y. 1908. Vols. I and II. $7.50. The standard English reference work.

SCHÜTZENBERGER, PAUL. On Fermentation. Appleton, N. Y. 1889. 351 pp. $1.50.

SCHOCH, E. P. Chemistry in High Schools. Bull. Univ. of Texas No. 210, Austin, Tex. 1911. A very suggestive and instructive monograph.

SELLERS, J. F. A Symposium on Chemistry Requirements. Science, 23 : 730–36, May 11, 1906.

SENTER, G. Outlines of Physical Chemistry. Van Nostrand, N. Y. 1911. 401 pp. Illus. 12 mo. $1.75.

SMITH, ALEXANDER. Introduction to General Inorganic Chemistry. The Century Company, N. Y. $2.25. A new edition with comments on some phases of chemistry teaching is forthcoming.

SMITH, ALEXANDER. Some Possible Items, Old and New, for the Course in General Chemistry. New England Asso. of Chemistry Teachers, a recent address, with list of references.

SMITH, ALEXANDER. The Training of Chemists. Science N. S., Vol. XLIII, No. 1114, pp. 619–629, May 5, 1916.

SMITH, ALEXANDER. The Content, Method, and Results of the High School Course in Chemistry. School Sci. and Math., Vol. 16, 1916, pp. 289–302.

SMITH, ALEXANDER, and HALL, E. H. The Teaching of Chemistry and Physics. Longmans, N. Y. 1902. 370 pp. $1.50.

STIEGLITZ, J. O. Qualitative Analysis. The Century Co., N. Y. 2 vols. $1.40 and $1.20.

Symposium on High School Chemistry. School Sci. and Math., 1908–1910.

TALBOT, HENRY PAUL. An Introductory Course of Quantitative Chemical Analysis. Macmillan, N. Y. 1898. 125 pp. $1.50.

TILDEN, W. A. Hints on the Teaching of Elementary Chemistry. Longmans, London and N. Y. 1895. Crown 8vo. 2s.

TILDEN, W. A. Introduction to the study of Chemical Philosophy. Longmans, London and N. Y. 1902. 368 pp. $2.00.

THORP, F. H. Inorganic Chemical Preparations. Ginn, Boston. 1896. 238 pp. $1.50. Tells how to make one hundred pure chemical substances of technical importance.

VAN'T HOFF, J. H. Tr. by Smith, A. Physical Chemistry in the Service of the Sciences. Univ. of Chicago Press, Chicago. 1903. 126 pp. $1.50.

WAGNER, R. VON. Rev. by Fischer, F. Tr. by Crookes, W. Manual of Chemical Technology. Appleton, N. Y. 1892. 952 pp. $7.50. An elaborate reference work.

WALKER, JAMES. Introduction to Physical Chemistry. Macmillan, N. Y. 1907. 332 pp. $3.25.

WILEY, HARVEY W. Foods and Their Adulteration. Blakiston, Philadelphia. 1911. 641 pp. $4.00.

WILLIAMS, R. P. The Planting of Chemistry in America. School Sci. and Math., 2 : 75–82, 139–48, April, May, 1902. A historical survey of the teaching of chemistry in American schools.

History and Biography

BAUER, HUGO. A History of Chemistry. Longmans, N. Y. 1907.
232 pp. $1.00.

DAVY, SIR H. The Elementary Nature of Chlorine. University of
Chicago Press, Chicago. Alembic Club Reprints. 78 pp. 54 ¢.

MARTIN, GEOFFREY. Triumphs and Wonders of Modern Chemistry.
Van Nostrand, N. Y. 1911. 358 pp. $2.00.

MEYER, ERNST VON. History of Chemistry. Tr. by McGowan, Geo.
Macmillan, N. Y. 1891. 544 pp. $4.50. "The most complete
history of chemistry in English."

MUIR, M. M. PATTISON. Heroes of Science, — Chemists. S. P. C. K.
London, Gorham, N. Y. 1883. 350 pp. $1.00.

MUIR, M. M. PATTISON. The Story of Alchemy. Appleton, N. Y.
1903. 35 ¢.

PHILIP, J. C. The Romance of Modern Chemistry. Lippincott,
Philadelphia. 348 pp. Illus. $1.50.

PRIESTLEY, JOSEPH. The Discovery of Oxygen. 1775. University of
Chicago Press, Chicago. Alembic Club Reprints. 56 pp. 44 ¢.

RAMSAY, SIR W. Gases of the Atmosphere. Macmillan, N. Y. 1896.
240 pp. $2.00. Historical and descriptive, including the author's
discovery of argon.

RAMSAY, SIR W. Essays, Biographical and Chemical. Dutton, N. Y.
1909. $2.50.

RODWELL, GEORGE FARRER. The Birth of Chemistry. Macmillan,
N. Y. 1874. 135 pp. $1.00.

ROSCOE, H. E. John Dalton and the Rise of Modern Chemistry.
Macmillan, N. Y. 1895. 216 pp. $1.25.

SCHEELE, KARL WILHELM. The Discovery of Oxygen, 1777. University of Chicago Press, Chicago. 46 pp. 44 ¢. Alembic Club
Reprints. The Early History of Chlorine. *Ibid.* 48 pp. 44 ¢.

THORPE, SIR T. E. Essays in Historical Chemistry. Macmillan, N. Y.
1894. 381 pp. $2.50. Biographies of eleven famous chemists.

THORPE, SIR T. E. A History of Chemistry. Putnam, N. Y. 2 vols.
182 and 185 pp. + bibliography. 75 ¢ each.

THORPE, SIR T. E. Joseph Priestley. Dutton, N. Y. 1906. 228 pp. $1.00.

TILDEN, W. A. A Short History of the Progress of Chemistry in Our
Own Times. Longmans, London and N. Y. 1899. 276 pp.
$2.25.

TILDEN, W. A. Mendeleeff's Life and Work; the Career of a Great
Chemist. Scientific American Supplement, 69 : 250–51, 270–71,
April 16, 23, 1910.

2 C

VENABLE, F. P.   A Short History of Chemistry.   Heath, Boston.
   1901.   163 pp. $1.00.
WIECHMANN, F. G.   Science Sketches: Chemistry, Its Evolution and
   Achievements.   Jenkins, N. Y.   1899.   176 pp. $1.00.   "Very
   readable, and very good."

Elementary Textbooks

BLANCHARD, A. A., and WADE, G. B.   Foundations of Chemistry.
   American Book Co.   1914.   436 pp. $1.25.
BRADBURY, R. H.   An Inductive Chemistry.   Appleton, N. Y.   1912.
   415 pp. $1.25.   The teaching of this text is largely inductive and
   quantitative.   Its plan embodies many of the principles herein
   advocated, although its exposition of theory is not always consist-
   ently inductive.
BROWNLEE, R. B., and others.   Practical Chemistry.   Allyn & Bacon,
   Boston.
BROWNLEE, R. B., and others.   First Principles of Chemistry.   Allyn.
   1915.   Rev. Ed.   535 pp. $1.25.
BROWNLEE, R. B., and others.   Laboratory Exercises in Chemistry.
   Allyn.   1910.   147 pp.   50 ¢.
BROWNLEE, R. B., and others.   Chemistry of Common Things.   Allyn.
   1914.   624 pp. $1.50.
BROWNLEE, R. B., and others.   Experiments in the Chemistry of Com-
   mon Things.   Allyn & Bacon, Boston.   1915.   140 pp.   loose
   leaf.   45 ¢.
GODFREY, H.   Elementary Chemistry.   Longmans, N. Y.   1909.
   447 pp. $1.10.   With manual, $1.25.
HESSLER, J. C., and SMITH, A. L.   Essentials of Chemistry.   Sanborn,
   Boston.   1902.   430 + 110 pp. $1.25.   A combined text and
   laboratory manual.
IRVIN, F. C., RIVETT, B. J., and TATLOCK, O.   Elementary and Applied
   Chemistry.   Row, Peterson & Co., Chicago.   1915. $1.25.
KAHLENBERG, LOUIS, and HART, EDWIN B.   Chemistry and Its Rela-
   tions to Daily Life.   A textbook for students of Agriculture and
   Home Economics in secondary schools.   Macmillan, N. Y.   1913.
   379 pp. $1.25.
McPHERSON, W., and HENDERSON, W. B.   First Course in Chemistry.
   Ginn, Boston.   1915.   403 pp. $1.25.   Lucid and attractive,
   consistently quantitative and somewhat strongly inductive in
   attitude.
MORGAN, WILLIAM CONGER, and LYMAN, JAMES A.   Chemistry.   An

Elementary Textbook. Macmillan, N. Y. 1911. 429 pp. $1.25. With laboratory manual, 142 pp. Very full on the humanistic and industrial phases. Strong on type reactions.

NEWELL, L. C. Descriptive Chemistry. Heath, Boston. $1.40.

NOYES, W. A. Qualitative Chemical Analysis. Macmillan, N. Y. 1899. 5th Ed. 1916. $1.50.

OSTWALD, WILHELM, and MORSE, H. W. Elementary Modern Chemistry. Ginn, Boston. 1909. 285 pp. $1.00. The plan of this book favors the problem approach. Attitude quantitative and inductive. Teachers will do well to give it careful study.

SMITH, ALEXANDER. Elementary Chemistry. Century Co., N. Y. 1914. 439 pp. $1.25. Strongly inductive and quantitative. Language clear and simple.

WEED, HENRY T. Laboratory Manual of Chemistry in the Home. Amer. Book Co., N. Y. 1916. 199 pp.

CHAPTER XXI

CHEMISTRY. PRACTICAL SUGGESTIONS

Some common sense rules and principles for teaching chemistry. — Out of the foregoing discussion some rules and principles emerge, which, if they are followed out, will make for success in the teaching.

1. Begin with the facts of observation and experiment and stick closely to such facts throughout the course. When the facts involve quantitative relations, that have been determined by measurement, state them in quantitative terms; and show or describe the manner of making the measurements so far as it may be apprehended.

2. *Withhold laws until a sufficient number of the facts and relations that are specific cases of the law have been studied and have become familiar.* The law can then be appreciated as a device for the economy of thought.

3. *When a law has been once presented have the pupils connect the statement of the law with every new specific case that comes under it, until they habitually do this for themselves.*

4. *Withhold theories until they are needed to furnish explanations of observed facts.* Do not be in such a hurry to teach theories that the facts are subordinated to them. Laws and theories are man-made devices for describing facts. Facts are not to be degraded into *illustrations or examples* of the operation of laws and theories. Laws and theories do not "operate." They merely say what in general goes on under certain conditions. If at any time the facts shall be found

with certainty not to agree with them, then the laws must be altered to fit the facts as the facts are.

5. *If the students fail to understand a law or theory when it is presented, do not insist on their memorizing it so they can repeat it glibly at once.*   Give them time and more experience with concrete cases, and after a while they will have learned it.   They will all be too ready to substitute the memory of a few words for knowledge of facts unless they are made to form the contrary habit.   Generalizations are of supreme importance if the facts that they resume are comprehended and can be recalled and used with their aid; otherwise they are useless.

6. *Laws and theories, therefore, should be introduced gradually as the course proceeds, and the more difficult conceptions should come near the end of the course.*   This principle is recognized in greater or less degree in most elementary texts; and in some of them the highly theoretical matters — such as the atomic and molecular theories, Avogadro's law, the making of formulæ, valency, ionization — are placed in chapters by themselves so that they can be deferred or omitted altogether according to the judgment of the teacher.   In all cases when they are taught, these theoretical matters should be led up to through quantitative demonstrations or descriptions, and copious illustration.   Whenever chemical theories serve to muddle and disgust the pupils instead of interesting them, clarifying their ideas, and enabling them to make, tentatively, simple predictions, such a result is proof either that the conceptions are beyond the pupils' abilities or that the teaching is inefficient, or both.[1]

7. *The laws of chemistry should always be expressed in such language as clearly to imply that they are statements of the results of experiments.*   Thus for the law of definite proportions, " Every sample of any compound substance, formed or de-

[1] For a full discussion of this question of chemical theory read Smith and Hall, *op. cit.*, pp. 69–84, and also Schoch, E. P., *Chemistry in High Schools*.   Bull. Univ. of Texas, No. 210, Official Series 64, Austin, Tex., December, 1911, pp. 44–60 *passim*.

composed, *is always found* to contain the same constituent elements in the same proportions by weight." [1]

8. The law of definite proportions, the law of the conservation of mass, and Gay-Lussac's law of volumes are among the most important generalizations of chemistry; and fortunately they are not difficult for high school pupils to comprehend if they are carefully approached. The law of simple multiple proportions can usually be taught successfully, but is not especially important to beginners, and may be omitted with little loss. The law of combining weights, which is a more general statement of the two preceding, is important, but probably too difficult and doubtless should not be attempted with any confident expectation that it will be clearly and fully comprehended by the pupils.

Type reactions. — It is wise to develop strongly the type notion in chemistry and to show at every opportunity that the reactions encountered are types of many others that are like them. Thus instead of having the pupils learn that oxygen can be obtained from mercuric oxide or potassium chlorate by heating, a fine opportunity for the appreciation of science as economy of thought will be missed unless the teacher shows in connection with the experiment that similarly many other compounds of oxygen, such as BaO_2, PbO_2, KNO_3, MnO_2, break down in a similar manner when raised to high temperatures, and give up all or part of their oxygen. Thus the behavior of HgO or $KClO_3$ is typical of the other reactions shown. So when hydrogen is obtained by displacing it from hydrochloric acid by zinc, the reactions of other nonoxidizing acids with zinc and other metals should be shown and explained. This reaction then no longer remains a " method of making hydrogen," but in addition becomes a type of the general behavior of nonoxidizing acids with metals that stand above hydrogen in the list of the elements, when the latter are arranged in the order of their electrochemical

[1] Smith, A., *op. cit.*, p. 21. (Italics mine.)

activities. The type notion may be used with advantage
also in showing the many similarities in the methods of
reducing metals from their ores, and in connection with the
gradations in properties of the elements in the families or
groups into which they fall according to the periodic system.
If the teacher form the habit of emphasizing such groups
of similar reactions, pointing out their resemblances to one
chosen as a type, and concentrating the students' attention
on the general resemblances and specific differences among the
reactions of the group, he will find not only that he has saved
time in the end but that he has secured unlooked-for reviews,
stimulated interest, and formed in the student the valuable
mental habit of using the type notion to organize and relate
his chemical concepts.   Practice in thus forming generalizations that are true only within certain limits, and carefully
confining them in thought to those limits, constitutes a very
valuable part of the mental discipline afforded by science.[1]
Careful attention to the types of reaction would result in a
much more pedagogical arrangement of the subject matter
than is found in many texts ; for the simplest types of reactions
could be grouped at the beginning of the course and the more
complicated types near the end.   Such an arrangement would
bring in the reactions of combination and decomposition,
reversible reactions (which belong to both the preceding
classes), hydration, displacement, and double decomposition
approximately in the order named ; and it would leave until
later many of those involving oxidation and reduction, and
implying change of valence (such as the reactions of nitric
acid with the metals).[2]

Practical applications. — Though it is not feasible in most
cases to make the approach to new topics through household
and industrial applications of chemistry, this may perhaps
be done occasionally, when the reactions are sufficiently

---

[1] Cf. pp. 205 and 241 *ante*, the type notion in biology and geography.
[2] Cf. Schoch, *op. cit.*, p. 47.

simple.   The mistake is often made of straining a point by beginning with some industrial fact or process with which the students are totally unfamiliar and which at the same time is so complicated that it presupposes for its comprehension knowledge of chemical principles that have not yet been studied.   Nothing could be worse pedagogically than this. Again the mistake is often made in high school courses in so-called " applied " or " industrial " chemistry of requiring the pupils to memorize complicated details of processes in which no easily perceived applications of chemical principles are involved and out of which no clear chemical concepts can be gained.   All this with the notion that chemistry is thus being " brought close to daily life."   For example, the writer once shared for a recitation period the boredom of a class that was reciting the details of the processes of tanning various kinds of leather.   There was no evidence that any one of the class had ever seen a tannery or made a laboratory experiment in tanning, nor did any reference to a chemical principle or any experimental demonstration of whatever sort come out in the recitation or the notes that had been given out to be studied.   Another course in " practical " chemistry known to the writer contained fifteen or twenty recipes for removing stains and grease spots, and in direct connection with them not even a reference to the properties of solvents and solutions. On the other hand, experimental problems in removing real grease spots, known facts about unwashable colors, dry cleaning, softening of hard waters with washing soda and the like might be made a most simple and natural approach to the study of solutions, if rightly handled.   So chlorine and sulfur dioxide can be approached through problems connected with bleaching and disinfection, although these problems are not necessarily better or even as good for beginning these topics as problems that would grow naturally out of previous studies.   The teacher must go over all the possible methods of approach and choose the problem that arouses the most natural and real interest.

Although the industrial applications often involve complicated chemistry and unfamiliar substances, there are nevertheless in every community some applications that can be examined which are simple enough to be understood. So the teacher should make himself acquainted with these and should connect them with the chemical facts and principles that are applied in them, at the time when these facts and principles are being studied. There are many fairly simple chemical substances and reactions that are very common and very important to know about.

Some of these are: the prevention of industrial waste through the utilization of by-products in manufacturing processes; the chemistry of flames, raising of bread and biscuits; respiration, digestion, sanitation; fermentation; drying of paint, setting of mortar and cement; the making of glass, soap, coal gas and water gas, of domestic ammonia, soda-water, explosives and plastics, inks, dyes and varnishes; the nature and sources of alcohol and vinegar, of oils, petroleum and gasoline, of carbohydrates, fats, proteins, and cellulose in foods, of soils and fertilizers, and of insecticides.

How much or how little of these should be brought into the course depends on the knowledge and judgment of the teacher, the ease or difficulty of bringing the illustrations into the classroom or taking the class to them, the amount of knowledge and interest that the pupils bring to them, the closeness of their relation to the main features of the course, and many other considerations concerning which only the teacher himself can decide. Some of these things can be made the subjects of excursions, others of special home experiments and reports by those especially interested in them. Others still the teacher may merely explain and illustrate, leaving the seeds to fall on good ground when and where they may, without digging them up to see whether they have sprouted. It is certain that if the teacher is full of such information, and is enthusiastic about it, some of the pupils will be infected with this enthusiasm all the time, and all of them some of the time; and chemistry in that school will be rated as a popular and practical subject.

Time for practical applications. — To save time for such work, the less common elements and compounds may be omitted, and the most of the more highly theoretical parts of the subject can be carefully explained and illustrated by the teacher and informally discussed by the class, but passed over without requiring that it shall be mastered. If the writer's observations and those of most of the college chemistry teachers of his acquaintance are reliable he is justified in the opinion that only in rare instances are these theoretical parts mastered anyway. There is no sense in expecting that every student will know every part of the course as well as every other part. Such an ideal grows out of a very poor conception of thoroughness. One important element of thoroughness in teaching is drill in judging the relative importance of different kinds of information, and practice in selecting for thorough learning those facts and relations that have to do with one's aims and purposes. It is important that the pupils should know well and intimately a few of the chemical facts and laws that they are likely to meet with now or later in their active life or their leisure reading, that they should catch the spirit and method, and something of the logic of chemistry, that they should know how to plan and make an experiment that will get to the bottom of the relation sought, and that they should know where to find chemical books and how to get needed information out of them. It is not important that they should become walking encyclopedias of chemical information.

Practical hints on the conduct of the course. — Use experiments and demonstrations constantly. It is related of Faraday that in lecturing to children, whenever he spoke of gravity he dropped something in order to make the idea concrete. So when one speaks of copper sulphate or of sodium hydroxide, it is a good thing to pick up some of the substance and exhibit it, so as to connect the fact mentioned with the substance directly as seen, as well as with its name and its symbol.

Interest students in the chemical behavior of substances that they know something about. Things totally unknown are not interesting. No interest, no attention. Strange things are interesting only when meaningful, and meaningful only when having some discoverable relation to that which is known and valued for some reason. As far as possible without straining matters, whenever a new fact or principle is learned, show its *utility*, either in the industries or as throwing light on the understanding of other topics.

Qualitative analysis purely as such is a technical subject, and it is wrong to crowd out real chemistry to make a place for analytical processes. These, with young students knowing so little of chemistry that such processes must for them consist merely in following a recipe, must remain largely mechanical. Yet it is profitable in connection with solution to make clear the principles used in the separation of the metals, and in review to give some of the characteristic laboratory tests for identifying the metallic and the acid radicals.[1] Especially is this true of tests made in the dry way, when the pupils are made to get to the bottom of them and correctly interpret all the phenomena, so as to prove that the substance under investigation is that named and nothing else.[2]

Chemistry is a quantitative science, therefore present it constantly through quantitative descriptions; that is, always mention the weighings and measurings by which the facts and laws that are being taught were learned, give many easy numerical chemical problems, using live human ones involving commercial quantities expressed in pounds and tons whenever possible, as well as laboratory problems involving grams.

[1] Cf. Smith, *op. cit.*, Chapters XXX and XLII.
[2] For a description of such work, and an appreciation of its possibilities for training in logical reasoning, read Smith and Hall, *op. cit.*, pp. 171–182.

Thus, how many pounds of zinc and sulfuric acid will make sufficient hydrogen to fill a balloon that will hold 4000 cubic feet at 0° C. and 30 inches pressure? Do not overwork the numerical problems, but keep the quantitative relations constantly in the foreground.

Chemistry is a difficult subject. Don't be discouraged if the difficult parts are not understood. Remember what struggles you had with them yourself; be patient and review them at intervals. After a while they will clear up for the students, and all will go well. Give the ideas time to take root and grow. If you find yourself lacking in patience or charity take up and try to master a subject that is entirely strange and new to you, or read an advanced modern chemical work in German. You will come back from it with more patience and charity for the dull pupils.

QUESTIONS FOR FURTHER STUDY

1. Of the eight statements under the heading "Common Sense Rules and Principles," which seem to you to be debatable? Choose any one of them and argue for or against it.

2. Select several textbooks in chemistry and grade them in order according to what you judge to be their relative merits with relation to withholding theories until sufficient facts have been learned.

3. Regrade the same textbooks on the basis of their closeness of relation to daily life and social values.

4. Regrade the texts on the basis of their merits in presenting chemistry so as to lead to training in the scientific method of attacking and solving problems.

5. Compute the average rank of each book according to the three previous rankings, and arrange them in the order of these average ranks, the one getting the lowest number first, and so on.

6. After a careful study of what is said of type reactions examine a number of texts to see if they take advantage of this principle in their presentation. Make a list of the principal reactions that you think ought to be taught, and rearrange them in groups in accordance with this principle.

7. After doing the work suggested (Question 6) give your opinion

as to the feasibility and value of type studies of reactions after the manner indicated in this chapter.

8. To what extent would the teaching of practical home and industrial applications of chemistry be available in your home community?

9. Go through the chemistry texts again and for each of them make a list of the topics that could be omitted with least loss from the standpoint of a good elementary working knowledge and appreciation of chemistry.

10. What do you think of the author's statement that some of the more difficult portions of chemistry may be informally explained and passed over without requiring that they "be recited and examined on"?

11. Of the chemistry lessons that you have known, do you remember many in which the matter of making statements concrete by showing things when mentioning them, *à la* Faraday, was overdone? Can you recall any that would have been improved by more of that sort of thing?

REFERENCES

For references, on subject matter, methods, textbooks, etc., see list at end of Chapter XX, and the library list, Appendix A.

CHAPTER XXII

CHEMICAL EQUIPMENT

Principal items of expense. — The most expensive item of equipment for chemistry, ordinarily, is the furniture and plumbing; and the next item, if the equipment is high grade, is chemical balances. It is possible, however, with the exercise of ingenuity to reduce the cost of both these items so as to bring a good course in chemistry within the means of a small school. Most of the chemical glassware and most of the supplies that are needed are relatively inexpensive, and their cost, if necessary, can be covered by a small fee, which the pupils will pay cheerfully if they are given abundant opportunities for experimenting with what they pay for. The writer once equipped a good working laboratory for a class of twenty-four pupils, in which much profitable work was done at a cost for tables and all of less than $250. The room was provided with one sink, which was made to answer all purposes. The tables were made from his own drawings by a local planing mill. This was many years ago, however, when lumber and labor were cheaper than they are now. The pupils paid an assessment of 50 cents each, which approximately covered the cost of broken glassware and staple chemicals used up.

Students' tables. — The first demand is a place where the pupils can work. The minimum space is 3 feet by 18 inches for each pupil; hence a table with a top 3 by 12 feet in area will accommodate eight pupils at one time. The space beneath the tables should be divided and filled with drawers or lockers or both, in which the students' individual outfits can be kept, and perferably locked up so that each may be charged with his individual outfit and held responsible for it. This arrangement secures careful habits, and saves many administrative adjustments that otherwise would consume much of the teacher's time, energy, and patience. It is convenient to have a sink and two water taps for each four pupils, and it is necessary to have a gas cock with a hose nipple for each pupil. The water, gas, and drain pipes should run through the middle of the table from end to end and if laid under the floor should run parallel with the joists. It is better, however, to have them above the floor, if possible, so they may easily be accessible, and for this reason also the tables are best made in two longitudinal sections, which may be moved apart to get at the pipes. The best pipe for trunk drains is cast iron lined on the inside with asphaltum; and an open trough is far preferable to a pipe. If this is used it should empty into a hopper at the end of the table. It should, of course, be large enough to carry the flow from all the sinks at once, although it will seldom have to do this. Only one trap is necessary, — and that at the point where the main drain leaves the room, — unless the state laws or municipal plumbing rules dictate otherwise.

If shelves are placed on the table to hold reagent bottles they should be low, so the teacher can have an unobstructed view of the table tops. Since only a few reagent bottles are needed, now that qualitative analysis is not usually featured in the course, it is much better to have no shelves on the tables, but to keep the bottles in the lockers. It is very convenient to have trays lined with sheet lead, in which the bottles may always stand. These can be easily "homemade."

Each sink should be provided with a " standing waste pipe," so that it may be used as a " pneumatic trough " for collecting gases over water. The space under the table assigned for one pupil should have a drawer or a locker for each working division of pupils, and a common locker in which certain pieces that are used in common by the pupils of different divisions, who work at that space, can be kept. Sufficient space under the table should be left open for a stone jar for each two places, into which acids and waste other than pure water can be emptied. Pupils must be trained never to throw anything excepting water into the sinks. Some expense may be saved by having only two sinks, one at each end of each table, but the saving in money will cost in time all it is worth. It is desirable, though not necessary, to have the tables wired for electricity and provided with a plug and socket for each pupil, so that current can be distributed for electrolytic experiments. If the school is lighted by the 110 volt direct current this can be cut down by a suitable resistance to about 8 or 10 volts, or the current may be furnished by a 10 volt dynamo operated by a small 110 volt motor. If the current is alternating, it can be rectified and cut down to the proper voltage by means of a " Nodon valve " or electrolytic rectifier.[1]

The demonstration equipment. — The general features most desirable in demonstration tables have been described in Chapter X; and only a few remarks need be added. For demonstration work in chemistry, the teacher should have at hand on shelves, or in a convenient cabinet, next the wall behind him, a set of bottles containing all the reagents that he is likely to want to use in his experiments before the class. On a rack conveniently near there should be a supply of beakers, test tubes, flasks, etc., ready for instant use. There should also be a fume-hood in a position convenient for the teacher, and where the pupils can look into it. The ideal plan is to have it just behind the center of the lecture table, and between the classroom and the laboratory or the work-

[1] For a description of an efficient homemade rectifier see Schoch, *op. cit.*, pp. 117–119.

and stockroom, with windows opening into both rooms, so that apparatus can be passed through it from one room to the other. In order not to lose the blackboard space a sliding blackboard may be mounted in front of the glass door of the fume-hood.

If there is plenty of case room, the teacher should have a separate outfit of apparatus for each demonstration experiment already set up and ready for use. After the apparatus has been used at the demonstration table, it should be thoroughly cleaned and made ready for the next time it is to be used, and placed in its own proper place in an apparatus case, from whence it can be instantly transferred to the demonstration table when next wanted for use. The habit of thus having always in readiness an outfit for each demonstration experiment, instead of having to assemble it anew whenever it is used, will save the teacher during the year immense quantities of time which he can use to better purpose in improving his scholarship; and the saving in his time will be worth more to the school than the interest on the small extra outlay for apparatus standing unused.

Fume-hoods. — Some of the best tables from the special manufacturers of laboratory furniture are provided with draft tubes and hoods in the form of an inverted funnel, one for each student, and an extra large one for the demonstration table. These work well, and are the most convenient, if a special ventilating system with an extra strong draft is provided; but they will not work without such a system. Where these are not provided, there should be at least one hood at the wall for every six pupils. The essentials for successful operation in a wall hood are that it should be built well, so as not to be leaky; that it should not be too wide in proportion to the cross-section of flue; that its roof should have a steep slope, like a funnel, toward the flue; that the flue should be ample, and as nearly straight as possible; and that a large gas burner should be placed within the flue and kept burning

2 D

when the hood is in use. The hood should have glass sides and a good-sized glass door, fitting snugly and either sliding upward or hinged above so as to lift upward. The floor of the hood should be perforated to let in air from below, and should be at the same height as the tops of the work tables.[1]

Gas substitutes. — Little or nothing satisfactory can be done with alcohol lamps; and gasoline torches are troublesome unless given expert care, which consumes considerable time; but they are the only available substitutes for gas in some form. In a village not provided with a gas system, it is desirable that the school be equipped with its own gasoline-gas plant, information concerning which can easily be obtained from any enterprising hardware dealer. Directions for making a small gasoline-gas machine will be found in Professor Schoch's pamphlet.[2]

Balances and weights. — If a considerable amount of quantitative work is done, about four to six balances for a class of twenty-four will be needed; and these and the weights should be kept in a separate room away from the corrosive fumes of the laboratory. The best balances for students' use are those made by Becker, and costing, with suitable weights (50 g. to 1 c.g.) about $20 each. The German hand balances already mentioned[3] will answer all purposes for an elementary course if teacher and pupils are sufficiently ingenious to mount them in homemade wooden cases with glass slide-doors. These can easily be assigned as a project for the manual training class, if there is one.

Water still. — A good water still is a necessary adjunct to any chemical laboratory. If the school happens to be heated by steam, it may easily be improvised with the aid of a plumber by connecting a long slender pipe to a radiator. The pipe may be led through a water jacket consisting of a

---

[1] Cf. Schoch, *op. cit.*, pp. 11–13.
[2] *Loc. cit.*, pp. 20–25.
[3] *Ante*, p. 349. See also Smith and Hall, *op. cit.*, p. 116.

larger pipe; but this latter is not necessary, for if the steam cock or valve through which the steam escapes from the radiator into the pipe be kept nearly enough closed so that the steam will pass very slowly through the length of the pipe it will be sufficiently cooled by the air to condense before reaching the end. If a still is to be purchased from the dealers an automatic one, such as the " Peerless " or the " Jewell," is to be preferred when the laboratory is supplied with gas and running water. Otherwise, the " Ralston " still or an ordinary copper retort and worm condenser must be used, with a blue-flame oil burner as a source of heat.[1]

Ring stands. — In some of the best laboratories the common form of ring stand is replaced by nickel-plated steel rod which screws into a flush plate [2] permanently set into the table top. The advantages of this method are that it secures greater steadiness, eliminating entirely the danger of being over-turned, that the rod when unscrewed requires very little space for storing, and that labor is saved by eliminating the necessity of reënameling the base from time to time. The only disadvantage lies in the fact that it cannot be moved from one place to another on the table, which may at times be the cause of considerable inconvenience. This can easily be overcome by having on hand for use at such times a few extra stands of the ordinary type.

When the sinks are placed at the center of the 6 by 3 foot space occupied by four students, the best place for the flush plates and for the gas cocks is near the medial line of the table, and near the middle of the three feet occupied by each student. There should be for each stand three rings of diameters from $1\frac{1}{2}$ to 4 or 5 inches, and a burette clamp.[3] These burette clamps are useful for so many purposes that it is well to have in stock a few extra ones.

---

[1] See Stoelting's Catalogue, 1913, p. 220, and Central Scientific Co.'s, 1909, pp. 326 and 396.

[2] Stoelting's Catalogue, 1913, pp. 182, No. 4327.

[3] Stoelting's Cat. p. 215, No. 5389.

Individual apparatus. — Each individual must be supplied with a certain irreducible minimum of apparatus, including a Bunsen burner with 18 inches of rubber gas tubing, and a wing top for bending glass tubing; the ring stand and burette clamp already mentioned; a sand bath or square of thick asbestos board; a test-tube rack and six test tubes; a test-tube holder and a test-tube cleaner; a small watch-glass; a $2\frac{1}{2}$-inch glass funnel; a 3-inch porcelain evaporating dish; glass stirring rod; a small porcelain crucible with cover; a clay-covered wire triangle to support the crucible, and a pair of crucible tongs; two hard-glass test tubes; four 8-ounce salt-mouth bottles for collecting and holding gases, four corks and four small squares of glass for closing the gas bottles; a deflagrating spoon; a triangular file; a perforated rubber stopper to fit the test tubes; six inches of rubber connecting tubing, size to fit the glass tubing (4 or 5 m.m. inside diameter); a package of 2-inch filter papers; a small mouth-blowpipe; and a wash-bottle.

Other apparatus. — Additional apparatus that is very desirable for each pupil consists of two burettes with glass stopcocks (50 or 100 c.c.); a nest of beakers, 500, 250, 100, and 50 c.c. capacity; two Bohemian flasks (500 and 250 c.c. preferably flat bottomed) with rubber stoppers (perforated with two holes) to fit the flasks; two thistle tubes; one cylindrical graduate, 100 c.c.; one small wedgewood mortar and pestle ($2\frac{1}{2}$ to 3 inches diameter); and two platinum wires (B & S gauge No. 28, 2 inches long, mounted in glass tubing handles) for borax bead and flame tests. The teacher should show the pupils how to fuse the wires into the glass handles, and also how to assemble the wash bottles.

Where economy is imperative a supply of these things may be kept by the teacher in the stockroom and handed out to the pupils as needed. If the tables are not provided with sinks that can be used for collecting gases over water, a small pneumatic trough must be provided, at least one for every two students. There must also be a set of standard reagent bottles (blown with labels on them and fitted with glass stoppers) for each four pupils. Each set should include a bottle for each of the following reagents: concentrated H_2SO_4, HCl, HNO_3; dilute H_2SO_4, HCl, HNO_3; NH_4OH, and NaOH. One set for each one or two pupils is better.

General apparatus and supplies. — For demonstration and laboratory experiments certain general supplies must be provided, such as a few chemical thermometers, a stock of glass tubing; rubber and cork stoppers (of sizes to fit flasks, bottles, and tubes, etc.), some with one hole and some with two; rubber gas and connecting tubing; cork borers, glass stirring rods, large and small; drying tubes; pincers; pinchcocks and clamps for closing rubber tubes; lead dishes for etching with fluorine; plain flasks and distilling flasks of 1, $\frac{1}{2}$, and $\frac{1}{4}$ liter capacity; cylindrical graduates of 1, $\frac{1}{2}$, and $\frac{1}{4}$ liter capacity, for mixing solutions; evaporating dishes of various sizes up to 8 inches diameter; beakers, assorted sizes up to 1 liter capacity; funnels and filter papers of assorted sizes; a blast-lamp and bellows for glass working; a filter pump (Richards') which may be used also in place of a bellows for operating a blast-lamp where the water pressure is sufficient. A carboy, or two or three large mineral-water bottles, will be needed for storing distilled water.

A generous supply of test tubes, beakers, evaporating dishes, and crucibles should be always in stock to replace those that are broken.

Chemicals. — It would be useless to attempt here to give a list of the chemicals needed for a course. The needs must be determined by the experiments given and the number of pupils in the classes; but a few hints as to buying and storing the supplies may be useful. It seldom pays to buy from the local drug dealers. One can buy almost all chemicals cheaper and of better quality from reliable chemical supply houses. It is much better to buy chemicals of steady consumption in packages of from one to five pounds. In large schools it is an advantage to buy the common acids by the carboy. This obviates the risk of running out during the year; and the prices are proportionally very much lower, as will be seen by consulting the catalogues. The substances should be of the chemically pure quality rather than of the commercial.

Nearly all of the chemistries, or the handbooks that accompany them, give lists of the chemicals that will be needed for the experiments that they describe. They also give the minimum amounts that will be required. The teacher should make out his list with these as guides, making proper allowance for the relative number of pupils in the class. He should keep in a convenient place an order list; and when he finds that the stocks of any chemicals, or other kind of supplies, are getting low he should enter on the list a memorandum for an order of it. The list for next year's order should be completed, and the order sent in, a month or two before the summer vacation; so that all supplies for the next fall may be received and stored ready for the work of the fall term. Deliquescent and efflorescent salts should be kept in tightly corked bottles. The corks should be soaked in melted paraffin, and after opening should be resealed with a bit of paraffin which is to be melted and made to flow around the cork by means of a hot wire. Rubber goods of all kinds, and chemicals that are affected by light, should be kept in drawers or dark closets. The stoppers for the reagent bottles containing Na_2CO_3, $NaOH$, and KOH, should be dipped in melted paraffin, or rubber stoppers should be substituted for them.

Some economical devices. — In small schools, where the strictest economy is necessary, much may be done at very small expense. Pupils can make their own test-tube racks by boring holes of the proper size in sections of 2 by 4 inch scantling to set the tubes in, and inserting pegs on which they can be inverted to drain when not in use. A common block-tin preserving kettle makes an excellent pneumatic trough. A piece of sponge inserted in the loop of a doubled and twisted stout copper wire, or tied on to a stick, makes a good test-tube cleaner. A test tube fitted with a cork and delivery tube makes a gas generator that answers almost every purpose. A loop made of a strip of asbestos board 6 inches long and ¾ inch wide answers for a test-tube holder, or one can easily be made from wood. A small tin pie pan answers for a sand bath. Paraffined wood corks may replace rubber stoppers. A clay pipe bowl makes a good crucible for many purposes. A deflagrating spoon can be made from a piece of electric light carbon and a piece of copper wire. A cheap saucer makes a fairly satisfactory evaporating dish, and pickle bottles brought from home do very well for collecting gases. Not much money is saved by using such things; but in a community where science work is poorly appreciated and poorly provided for, if the teacher has the energy and enterprise to get some good work done with such devices, he can go a long way toward persuading the board of education to provide better facilities.

A few further hints. — The teacher should make himself competent to give promptly " first aid " in cases of cuts or burns or of acids splashed into eyes.[1]

The test tubes made by Whitall, Tatum & Co., Philadelphia, cost more than others, but the author has found them more economical, for they are more durable than those of any other make. This firm makes reagent bottles and nearly all kinds of chemical glassware. Thermometers and all kinds of chemical supplies of excellent quality are furnished by the Bausch & Lomb Optical Co. of Rochester, N. Y., and their prices are among the lowest. Eimer and Amend of New York City and Henry Hiel & Co. of St. Louis will also be found to be thoroughly reliable, and their prices are always low on large orders.

One of the great faults in many school laboratories is lack

[1] Cf. Smith and Hall, *op. cit.*, pp. 126–127, or consult a physician.

of sufficient storage room for chemicals and supplies. The stockroom should be of generous size and have only one window, so as to give wall space for plenty of drawers, shelves, and closets. Unlike those for physical apparatus, the shelves for holding bottles and most of the chemical glassware should be not over 8 inches in depth.

In the laboratory there should be side shelves placed so that they can be conveniently reached by all the students. On these the reagents and supplies to be used by the pupils, but not included in their individual outfits, should be placed.

Extra articles of glassware, thermometers, and the like should be given out to individuals only when they are to be used. A good plan is to give them out in exchange for signed tickets like the slips used for drawing books from the library, putting the ticket in the place from which the article is taken and returning it to the pupil, to be destroyed, when the article is returned.

When an apparatus with glass stopcock or stopper is put away the stopcock or stopper should be removed and tied to the apparatus with a string or soft copper wire.

Laboratory rules. — Clear and simple rules should be made regarding neatness, safety, and system in experimenting and the care of apparatus, and the teacher should see that these are scrupulously obeyed. Among the things which should be covered by the rules and which are overlooked in an amazingly large number of schools are the following:

See that the gas and water are kept shut off when not in use.

Never put matches, charcoal, or chemicals in drawers or lockers.

Never throw anything but water into a sink. Use the waste jars for all other waste.

When lighting a Bunsen burner hold the match three

inches above its mouth. If the flame " strikes back " into the burner, causing a yellow or greenish flame, turn off the gas and relight it after the burner has cooled.

When heating anything in an open test tube always incline it away from yourself and your neighbors, and heat it cautiously, moving it about in the flame. In heating liquids in glass vessels, never let the flame touch the glass above the level of the liquid.

If a glass tube is to be pushed into a rubber tube or through a cork, see that you have first rounded the sharp edges by fusing in the Bunsen flame. Always grasp the tube near the end that is to be inserted, and push it in straight, with a twisting motion, otherwise you may break it, and get an ugly cut. It is a good plan first to wrap the hand in a handkerchief.

Never handle phosphorus or sodium with the fingers; always use the pincers. Cut phosphorus only under water; and after burning a bit of it in a deflagrating spoon, hold the spoon in the Bunsen flame until you are sure that the last bit is burned.

Be careful to avoid burns; it is better to assume that a thing is hot until you know that it is cool.

Never lay down the stopper of a reagent bottle. Grasp and hold the stopper between the second joints of the second and third fingers of the right hand. You can use the hand freely for pouring from the bottle while doing this.

When experimenting, weigh or measure out the substances in strict accordance with the directions, and never use more than is necessary to produce the desired result.

Record results in the notebook as soon as they are obtained, and see that you write exactly what happened, without regard to what you expected.

These things belong to the A.B.C. of the art of chemical experimentation; and the author in inspecting schools has found that the observance of them by the pupils is a thoroughly trustworthy measure of the quality of chemical training that the teacher has had and is giving. If the pupils fail to observe them and are not promptly called to account, it is a rare experience to find on further investigation that the teacher is much of a chemist.

QUESTIONS FOR FURTHER STUDY

1. From the catalogues of several dealers in laboratory furniture (see list, end of Chapter X), select the best type of student tables for your school; make out specifications and order; and write a letter to your board of education presenting the need for the tables, and your reasons for preferring the type chosen.

2. If you are good at mechanical drawing, make working drawings for a laboratory table of your own design to be made by the pupils in the manual arts department, or by a local carpenter. Get out a mill bill, look up costs of materials, and figure out the cost per table, including the plumbing.

3. Make a plan for your chemistry rooms, providing for the demonstration equipment that is necessary.

4. Make a detailed drawing for a standard fume-hood.

5. Make out a list of chemicals, apparatus, and supplies for a class of a specified number of pupils.

REFERENCES

Consult the list of names and addresses of apparatus dealers at end of Chapter X, also the reference lists at the end of that chapter and of Chapter XX. Additional titles of interest to both teachers and pupils will be found in the list of library books, Appendix A.

CHAPTER XXIII

"GENERAL SCIENCE" COURSES

Huxley and introductory science. — The first consistently organized course in introductory general science which embodied in its spirit and mode of presentation the scientific method of inquiry was given by Professor Thomas H. Huxley as a series of illustrated lectures to London children at the Royal Institution in 1869, and was published later in book form under the title of "Physiography,"[1] which means literally a description of nature. The basis of organization used by Huxley was the problem of the relation between the physiography and geological history of the Thames basin and the activities of the people in the vicinity of London. It was frankly informational, and did not aim at technical scientific training, but was full of the method and spirit of science as set forth by one of its greatest exponents, in a way that appeals to imagination, arouses interest, and stimulates thought. The value of such a course, given by such a teacher as Huxley, would scarcely be questioned. A similar course based on the physical geography and geology of any locality in this country, and made the core of a course which should draw on all the fields of science for facts and principles that throw light on the relations of the inhabitants to the forces of nature and on the interrelations of these inhabitants with those of other physiographic regions, would undoubtedly be exceedingly valuable, if organized and taught by a person the breadth and thoroughness of whose scientific knowledge were sufficient

[1] Appleton, N. Y., 1879, 377 pp., illus.

411

to meet the demands of the case. But there are few Huxleys, and not many persons who are capable of constructing such courses; and such a course planned for one locality could not be very well adapted to the instruction of children living in a different sort of physiographic region.

This book, therefore, while a very useful one for teachers to read because of its suggestiveness as to how a general introductory course in science might be organized and presented, was never widely used as a textbook, and is not now well known.

Content, organization, and method of Huxley's course. — It seems worth while, therefore, to give here a list of the chapters in order to show what was the scope of content and method of organization.

1. *The Thames.* North and south. The pole star and the compass. Hachures, contour lines, and maps. River basins and water partings. 2. *Springs.* Mineral water. Permeable and impermeable strata. Faults. Artesian wells. 3. *Rain and Dew.* 4. *Snow and Ice.* 5. *Evaporation.* 6. *The Atmosphere.* 7. *The Chemical Composition of Pure Water.* 8. *The Composition of Natural Waters.* 9. *The Work of Rain and Rivers.* 10. *Ice and Its Work.* 11. *The Sea and Its Work.* 12. *Earthquakes and Volcanoes.* 13. *Slow Movements of the Land.* 14. *Living Matter and Its Effects.* Fossils. Coal. 15. *Formation of Land by Animal Agencies.* Coral land. 16. *Foraminiferal Land.* 17. *Geological Structure of the Thames Basin.* Its interpretation. 18. *Distribution of Land and Water.* 19. *Figure of the Earth.* Construction of maps. 20. *The Movements of the Earth.* 21. *The Sun.*

Note that here the Thames basin is the center of the logical organization; that its origin, history, and utility to man constitute the motive and furnish the problems; that the starting point in every case is some feature near at hand, directly connected with the river or its basin or the familiar activities going on within it; and that the figure of the earth, its movements, and the sun, involving the things that are farthest away, least familiar, and most abstract come at the very end of the course after everything else that leads up to them has been made clear. Furthermore, Huxley always begins with a simple description of the facts, illustrated by pictures, maps, or experiments, and leads gradually to explanations, conclusions, and general principles.

Current methods contrasted with Huxley's. — Let the reader examine for himself all the modern textbooks of general science or of any of the special sciences, and see how very, very few of them are built on this plan. On the other hand, nearly all of them do just the opposite. They start with an abstract general principle, citing a piece or two at most of evidence in its favor and none against it, or perhaps " illustrating " it by an experiment, and then proceed to reason from it deductively and describe its applications, or to explain new facts by reference to it. It is this tendency of textbooks and teachers alike that is mainly responsible for the unsatisfactory results in high school science work that are constantly being complained of by superintendents and high school principals.

Nothing could be more instructive to the teacher who is conducting or contemplates conducting a course in general science, or in fact any science, than to compare this book with almost any of the current textbooks in " general science," physics, chemistry, or physical geography. Let him note the inductive method of approach and the simplicity of the description relating to any topic in the former, and compare it with the deductive and abstract method of approach and the meagerness of description relating to the same topic in the current textbook. Then let him try Huxley's method of presentation in his next lesson, and compare the interest and effort of the pupils in the lesson with that shown by them

in lessons in which the approach was deductive. A fair
trial ought to convince an unprejudiced person that Huxley
was right and many of the modern authors are wrong as to
methods of organization and exposition.

Aims of general science courses. — Since Huxley's argument for an introductory science course is still one of the
best that has been made, and since it is not easy of access,
it seems desirable to abstract it from his preface.

> According to Huxley the aims of a general science
> course were to " initiate young people in the elements
> of physical science "; to lead them to form " a clear
> mental picture " of the phenomena of nature, beginning
> with the familiar facts of daily experience and leading
> them, " step by step, to the remoter objects and to the
> less readily comprehensible relations of things." He
> wanted also to give them " some practical experience
> of scientific method . . . with all the precision of state-
> ment which is what distinguishes science from common
> information " and yet without overstepping their com-
> prehension. He believed that the information and
> the insight into method thus afforded not only would
> be valuable in themselves, " but would facilitate the
> subsequent entrance of the learners into the portals of
> the special sciences." He was emphatically opposed
> to " an *omnium-gatherum* of scraps of all sorts of undi-
> gested and unconnected information "; and he wanted
> to show the connection between cause and effect in
> phenomena in such a way that the young learner should
> be led step by step to the conviction that to understand
> the common things about him even in an elementary
> way he must know " something about the universe,"
> and " that the pebble he kicks aside would not be where
> it is and what it is unless a particular chapter of the
> earth's history had been exactly what it was."

The aims expressed or implicitly assumed in Mill's " Realm of Nature," [1] another English contribution to general science literature, are the same as those expressed by Huxley; but although Mill's selection of content is excellent, his method is a most illuminating example of how not to present scientific information to young people. The mode of organization is that of a very condensed treatise, conveniently arranged and very logical, but adapted to the uses of mature minds rather than to the minds of children untrained in science. It is therefore a book which, although very valuable as a reference book and as an aid in final organization, is not very helpful or inspiring to young students as a lesson guidebook, nor very suggestive to teachers as to methods of presenting science lessons to beginners.

Unfortunately, several of the recent books on general science, — in fact, nearly all of them — are built on the plan of adult logical organization and deductive presentation adopted by Mill, rather than on the more psychological inductive plan used by Huxley.

The various aims of the course, as stated or implied by the recent advocates and by the authors of textbooks of general science, seem to the writer to be fairly summarized as follows, although he may, perhaps, have read into the formulation some ideas that these authors did not have in mind.

1. To furnish in the first year of the high school the information and the training in thinking that are fundamental to the special sciences and are necessary to the successful pursuit of these sciences later on in high school or college.

2. To impart information from the scientific standpoint about the useful and interesting things that are all about us, especially for the benefit of those who will not go on to college and may not go farther in high

[1] Scribner, N. Y., 1892.

school, and who therefore would otherwise remain ignorant of scientific facts and of the scientific way of dealing with the materials and forces that are everywhere available for our use.

3. To give the first-year pupils an attractive view of the content of all the sciences, so that they may find out where their tastes and capabilities lie, and thus choose more wisely among the studies that are offered them in later courses, or that they may find the field in which they may prefer to read, work, and study after leaving school. One writer regrets the failure of the schools to produce the crop of amateur scientists which is essential for keeping alive the popular interest in science so necessary to scientific progress in the nation. It would seem to be a worthy aim of a general science course to stimulate and foster such amateur interest in science.

4. The teacher of a general science course, by avowedly divorcing himself from all ambition toward getting college credit for his pupils, and from all attempts to present a " comprehensive and connected view of the facts and principles " of any one science, is free to disregard the logical fences that specialists have for convenience erected between their subjects. He may therefore pick and choose for his lessons those facts which lie nearest the interests of his pupils and are best adapted to their intellectual, economic, and social needs. He is free to organize these materials with reference to these interests and these needs and to make voluntary problem-solving and purposeful information-getting the proximate aim of the pupils. He may thus hope to train the youngsters in methodically gathering information and applying systematic thought to the things in the environment that they desire to comprehend and manage.

5. It is thought by some that a general science course may serve to show something of the relations of the sciences to one another, of the order and unity that exist in nature, and of the essential unity of the scientific method, and thus that it may appeal to imagination, contribute to a state of mental poise or balance, and perhaps develop some power of interpretation that could not so well be gained by separate courses in the special sciences.

It will be noted by the reader that the aims just enumerated are substantially the same as those stated or implied by Huxley in the preface to his "Physiography" forty years ago.

Recent courses. Content and organization. — As to selection of content the books lately issued show a common tendency to include much of the physics and chemistry of the atmosphere and of climate.

One author apparently attempts to make equitable selections from the fields of all the special sciences; and his method of treatment is much like that of the textbooks in these subjects. His book is in effect a series of little textbooks on certain portions of physics, chemistry, botany, physiology, and so on, bound together under the same cover; and it shows no essential differences in method of presentation or subject matter from the traditional treatment that is common in school texts on these subjects. No attempt to organize the material with reference to the special interests or needs of first year pupils is discoverable in it.

Another book shows a similar lack of definite pedagogical motive in organization as a whole, and exhibits the same tendency toward formal and didactic presentation. It, however, makes some provision for student initiative by presenting a large number of specific library references. These are good if the teacher make good use of them; but the emphasis on book references, coupled with the formal and

2 E

didactic presentation of experiments and subject matter, as well as the presentation of theories before fact, produces a tendency toward "book science" that few teachers who may use this text would be likely to resist.

A third author has produced a book which is much like these others in mode of presentation, but which has an evident motive of organization. It begins with heat, combustion, food, cooking, digestion, and so on, and sticks pretty close to the scientific questions that center in the home, and radiate from it out into the community. From the standpoint of usable information and training in scientific habits of thought, however, this book shows the faults of the two just mentioned. It attempts to teach too many things; so that in most cases it does not really get to the bottom of the question in hand nor in any way adequately represent the scientific mode of attack. The danger of such a course is that of giving the pupils a smattering of undigested facts and little or no real first-hand knowledge.

Two other plans have been presented in book form, each of which is less open to the objections that have been mentioned. One of these makes earth-science the core of the course, bringing in some of the most interesting and vital facts of physics, chemistry, biology, physiology, and agriculture in places where they are needed for a more intelligent grasp of causal relations in physical geography or where they come in logically in relation to consequences of physiographic controls. The other book uses the pupil's relation to his immediate environment as the motive of organization. It seems on the whole to be much superior to most of the others, both as to organization and content and as to mode of presentation, for the content is methodically selected with reference to the problems of everyday life; and it goes farther toward getting definitely to the bottom of a few important problems, and eliminating scrappy and detached information than most of its rivals do. Also the method of approach is in most cases consistently inductive, beginning with the common experiences and leading to the abstractions or generalizations through these experiences and others that are provided for in the presentation. That it departs wholly in certain spots from this psychologized procedure, and slips into the deductive and oracular style of treatment with which we are so familiar and to which so many of the shortcomings of present science teaching are attributable, only goes to show how difficult it is for us to break away from adult habits of thought and to put ourselves in the attitude of young learners. If the authors could have brought themselves to exclude from first year science all attempts to teach the atomic and molecular theories they would probably have avoided slipping into these pitfalls.

The project and problem method. — The plans of two other advocates of general science courses should be mentioned. Professor Fred D. Barber of Normal, Ill., has worked out a series of projects and problems involving the physics and chemistry of common things, which in his hands has been very successful in accomplishing such aims as have been mentioned. He has put these into the form of a syllabus for his students in the normal school. The course, at least until lately, was not taught with a textbook. The approach is through observation and experiments, and the organization and formulation of principles are done largely through oral teaching and notebook work. This seems to be the method toward which we must look for real success with such a course.[1] Each teacher of general science should make his own course, adapting it to the needs of his own pupils; and he should avail himself of the freedom from textbook-and-syllabus prescriptions from outside the school that the absence of a textbook gives him. The writer has not yet been

[1] Professor Barber has recently published his course in the form of a textbook, which is admirable in its choice of projects and problems, its organization, and its scientific spirit. See reference list, p. 433.

able to free himself from the opinion that very few teachers who are not competent thus to work out their own courses, and to teach them without a textbook or a syllabus originated by some one else, ought to attempt to give a course in general science at all. This opinion has been strengthened rather than weakened by the observations that he has made of the workings of general science as it is taught in many schools. General science is being taught in many places as a textbook study, by teachers who have been given the task in spite of their admitted inadequacy for it both as to depth and breadth of scientific training, and in spite of the fact that adequate provision has not been made for either the time or the laboratory facilities that are necessary for inductive teaching.

The other plan that should be mentioned is that of Professor John F. Woodhull of Teachers College, Columbia University. Professor Woodhull is a prominent advocate of project teaching, and has done much experimenting in the way of devising and trying out suitable projects for first year science, especially in the physics and chemistry of everyday things. As chairman of the General Science Subcommittee of the National Commission on the Reorganization of Secondary Education he is now at work devising, and collecting from volunteer helpers, suitable projects for a first year general science course. The committee has made several preliminary reports indicating its policy, but as yet few specific projects have been formulated and published by it. It is to be hoped that in the near future a comprehensive report on the subject, including a large number of sample lessons and projects that have been tried out by experienced teachers, may be forthcoming from this committee. In the meantime the reader who is interested in carrying forward this line of work should correspond and coöperate with Professor Woodhull.[1]

[1] For references touching the views and work of Professor Woodhull consult the list of titles following this chapter, pp. 433–435.

The following summary of the views of his committee came to hand in May, 1916.

SOME FUNDAMENTAL PRINCIPLES

Formulated by the Committee on General Science of the N. E. A.

1. The fundamental purpose of all teaching of science in all grades of schools is to foster the development of the true scientific spirit.

2. Since all normal children are endowed by nature with the elements of the scientific spirit, the purpose of science teaching is accomplished most successfully when the science classes merely furnish an environment in which the scientific spirit can grow from the crude and instinctive childish form into the more finished and logical adult form.

3. The scientific spirit is characterized by three equally important elements; namely: (1) A desire to understand more fully the meaning and uses of things, leading to the definition of problems concerning the meanings and uses of things. (2) A firm faith that the solution of these problems is worth while and possible. (3) A method of thinking that leads to the most expedient and useful conclusions. A science teaching that fails to recognize in practice all three of these elements is necessarily defective.

4. The most effective method of science teaching yet devised, in which all three of the elements of the scientific spirit receive due recognition, is called the method of teaching by *projects*.

5. Every project is characterized by three equally important elements, which are coördinate with the three elements of the scientific spirit; namely: (1) A desire on the part of the pupil to understand better the meaning and use of some fact, phenomenon, or experience. This leads the pupil to ask questions. (2) A firm faith that it is worth while and possible to secure a better understanding of the thing in question. This causes the pupil to go to work with enthusiasm. (3) The gathering from experience, books, and experiments of the needed information, and the application of this information to answer the question in hand. This settles the question temporarily at least.

6. Any question that any one asks concerning the phenomena of nature and of life is a legitimate basis for a project.

7. A *project* differs from a *topic* in that (1) a project originates in some pupil's question, and not in an adult's logical sequence of ideas. Its implications need not, therefore, be confined like a topic to any of the arbitrary divisions of science, such as physics, biology, etc., which have been devised for the intellectual convenience of adults. (2) The project involves the active and motivated participation of the pupils in carrying it out. It does not, therefore, like the topic, lend itself to didactic, formal treatment in which the teacher does all the thinking and the pupils passively absorb. (3) The project never ends in a complete, final, or absolutely finished conclusion. It is, therefore, far less likely than is the topic to leave the pupil with the idea that he has heard the last word on the subject. It leaves him open-minded.

8. In the project method the outline and backbone of the course is derived from the spirit of science, whose growth it aims to foster. The organization of the work depends on the skill of the teacher and the enthusiasm of the class. It need not, therefore, be constrained like the topical order to the narrow bounds

of the arbitrary classifications which the adult specialist has found convenient for his own intensive work.

9. The project method of teaching when well done leaves the pupil with a well-organized mass of useful information plus a love of the scientific spirit which will lead him to continue to acquire more. This entire discussion arises from the fact that the logical topical method has failed to do just this.

10. The present need of the schools is for a large collection of sample methods of treating a given project, which could be used in showing teachers in a given community how to devise and utilize projects adapted to different grades of pupils in their own environment. This the committee is now making. It would be foolish and fatal to the success of project teaching to try at present to divide the high school time into conventional sections of one year of biology, one year of physics, etc.

The information motive vs. *the project motive.* — As to the relative merits of the information motive and approach as contrasted with the project method advocated by Woodhull, Barber, Mann, Orr, and others primarily interested in physical science, and well illustrated in the biological field by the texts and manuals of Hunter, Sharpe, Peabody and Hunt, and the Bigelows, the author of this book has already presented arguments in the preceding chapters in favor of the latter. There is no reason to doubt that the presentation to young people, from the purely informational standpoint, of scientific facts and experimental and observational material concerning their immediate environments may be of great value in giving them significant information and arousing their interest in scientific things; but the tendency to cram them rather than to make them think is too strong to be resisted by many teachers, other than those who are very talented, mature, and well trained. In fact, this tendency, according to the writer's observation, is resisted by relatively only a very few of those now teaching these courses.

On the other hand, the method of starting a project or problem and giving the pupils time to think and study on it, and to work it out for themselves with the assistance of the teacher and their classmates, puts them in a position where they have a strong immediate motive for getting all the information they can that bears on the solution of the problem or the accomplishment of the project.

The project method a logical method. — Thus while the pupils are getting the information they are also learning how to use the scientific method of collecting facts, of organizing them about the problem in hand, and of using systematic methods of experimenting, reasoning, and drawing conclusions. With this method each problem or project becomes automatically a center of logical organization for the information gained, just as it does in the case of the problems worked out by the farmer, the mechanic, the municipal engineer, the industrial manager, or the intelligent home keeper, who brings results to pass in the world of adult activity. Time may be and should be taken, at intervals, to organize the information gained in working out the projects, in accordance with the reference book or compendium type of arrangement; and this work of organization may constitute a series of projects in themselves which will arouse much interest, if skillfully handled. Furthermore, if the advantages of remembering such information for use in solving problems in the future are pointed out and illustrated by concrete examples, the teacher can easily get the pupils deeply interested in formal drills for the purpose of fixing this valuable information and these useful types of method in their memories so that they will stick.

Objections answered. — Thus if the problem method is artfully used it will accomplish all that the information motive can accomplish, and impart something of a working knowledge of scientific method in addition. The only things that can be said against it are that it requires greater skill and initiative on the part of the teachers, and that the pupils can acquire much less of scientific information than they can under the traditional method. The first objection may be admitted, and dismissed with the statement that if the teachers can only be made to get the right point of view and

a little more training, most of which they can give themselves
by private study, provided they have been started right in
their undergraduate courses, *they can acquire the necessary
skill by adopting the problem method, and training themselves
by practice in using it.* This they are free to do since " general
science " has the supreme advantage over the other science studies
of the curricula in that it has no recognized and prescribed subject matter, and there is therefore no " ground " which the
teacher is " required " to " cover."

The second objection may be admitted also; but on the
other hand, those favoring the problem method may raise
the question whether the final result of attempting to have
the pupils learn fewer facts and learn them so they will stick
is not likely to be more satisfactory, as to amount and availability of what is actually retained and associated with permanent interests, than the result of attempting to cram the
youngsters with more facts than they can mentally digest.
Since no experimental test of this question has yet been
made, and since the promptness and thoroughness with
which the science learned in one year of the high school is
forgotten before the next are notorious, the argument for
adopting the new method is certainly as cogent as that for
retaining the old.

Some examples of projects. — A very few examples of such
projects and problems as might be used in a general science
course are chosen at random and suggested here, merely to
illustrate how the thing may be done.

1. (*a*) Select the materials for a " homemade "
fireless cooker. (*b*) Make the working drawing for it.
(*c*) Construct the cooker. (*d*) Add up the costs for
the materials and a suitable allowance for the labor,
and find the total cost of the cooker.

2. Find out the fuel cost of cooking a quart of beans,
oatmeal, or meat stew with the fireless cooker, and with

the ordinary method over the stove-burner, and determine the amount saved. Include in the estimate for the cooker the interest on the investment and a suitable allowance for depreciation and repairs. If gas is employed, the amount used may be measured by the meter. If coal is employed the amount used can be estimated by weighing.

3. Compare the cost of keeping a rug clean for a year by means of sweeping with a broom and " beating " at house-cleaning time with that of keeping it clean by means of an electric vacuum cleaner. Take into account the time and cost of labor in each case, the time used in running, oiling, and emptying the cleaner, the interest and depreciation charge on the cleaner, the cost of brooms worn out.

4. Compare (*a*) the totals of time and labor costs and fuel costs between cooking a given weight of meat stew in a steam pressure cooker and an ordinary stew pan; (*b*) the total amounts of gelatine, soluble salts, etc., extracted from equal quantities of soup bone by equal quantities of fuel in the two methods of cooking. (Dry and weigh the bones after cooking and determine the amounts extracted by subtraction.)

5. Get the necessary information, and make up a set of rules for the most efficient manner of operating the home heating plant.

6. Make a lifting pump and a force pump with cylindrical lamp chimneys, corks, and pine wood. Use sheet rubber and pins for valves.

7. Make lists of birds and spring flowers as they appear in the spring, and find out all you can about the food, habits, and utility of the birds and the plants.

8. Make a set of homemade telegraph instruments and set up a line between your home and that of a schoolmate, or party line with four or five on it.

9. Investigate all the types of refrigerators for sale in your town and determine which one is best in construction, using all the information you can obtain in making your judgment. If another pupil selects a different one establish the superiority of your choice in a debate with him.

Vital problems emerge from projects. — These projects all suggest a multitude of subsidiary problems and questions which will arouse curiosity and interest in the scientific aspects and relations to which attention will be called in connection with working them out, and which the pupils may be incited to set up as problems for solution. The teacher may so guide the interest that only significant and useful problems will be chosen. Thus, the first two projects involve the properties of nonconductors and of radiating surfaces, the phenomena of transference of heat by conduction and radiation and absorption, the calorific values of fuels, and how they are determined, of heat units, of how gas meters work, of the structure of flame, of combustion, and so on. One thing leads to another, so that if the projects are carefully chosen, and the problems that arise out of them are skillfully directed and organized by the teacher, the content of the course may be made to include what is most desirable and significant for the pupils to learn. They may be stimulated so as to learn these things because they themselves *want to know them now* instead of because the teacher tells them that these are good for them to study and may be useful to know some time in the future. The advantage to the pupils of the former motive over the latter should be obvious to any one who knows either youngsters or psychology.

Equipment. — The items of scientific subject matter that are included in the course in general science will largely determine the kind and amount of apparatus, supplies, and illustrative materials that are required in teaching it. One should not embark in the enterprise of giving such a course without being able to make provision for amply illustrating it with concrete objective materials, visual aids, experiments, and opportunities for home and field observation. A course of science instruction of any kind using textbooks or talks only, without such materials for first-hand observation, is futile, — a mere travesty of scientific information or training. This is a fact which, in large schools where general science is required of all ninth grade pupils, has not been given adequate consideration by school administrators; and some of them are assigning large classes to teachers whose scientific training has been of a very limited and elementary sort, without making even a sincere attempt to provide them with either demonstration tables or materials for demonstration, or to arrange their schedules so that they may have time for preparing demonstrations or planning their lessons ahead of the day's work.

There are two ways of attacking the equipment problem for general science. One is to plan the course in detail as to subject matter, then go over it carefully to determine what experiments and demonstrations are to be made, and finally to make a list of the apparatus and materials that are necessary. After this has been done the teacher must make his plans for purchasing, making, or otherwise accumulating the materials, for providing storage place for them, and for having them ready to use when needed. In making these plans he will, of course, take into account what he may borrow when it is needed from the equipment of other departments, or get the children to bring in from their homes. The other plan is to start from the other end, making a survey of all the available sources from which illustrative materials may be gathered and then planning such a course as may be adequately illustrated by the available materials. No matter from which standpoint the teacher begins, he should not attempt to teach anything that he cannot adequately illustrate with concrete materials.

General science not a cure-all. — In many quarters, general science is a phrase to conjure with, and in the minds of some it stands for a nebulous something or other that is going to remedy all the defects, and compensate for all the shortcomings that exist or are thought to exist in the teaching of the special sciences as they are now conducted. The reader will readily gather from what has gone before in this chapter that the writer is not so sanguine about it as some of its advocates are. While entirely sympathetic toward the work of those who are carefully studying the general science proposition from various standpoints, and are working out courses from these points of view in a truly open-minded spirit, he deplores the partisan attitude adopted by some of those who are discussing the subject. He frankly questions the wisdom of the widespread introduction of such courses in schools where the conditions are such that they cannot be worked out by adequately trained teachers, with adequate equipment and abundant time for careful planning and assiduous study. His observations in schools where this " subject " has been introduced have led him to the conviction that nothing has been gained and a good deal has been lost by introducing it and teaching it by the same formal textbook methods that were used in the biological or geographical courses for which it has been substituted. Given a teacher thoroughly and broadly trained, who is dissatisfied with the results gained through the teaching of biology or geography, and who, possessing initiative and the experimental attitude toward his teaching problems, desires to try out such a course, it seems probable that he will make a success of it, and may accomplish through it some or all of the aims that have been set up for it. Yet it seems at least probable that a course in civic biology, or physical geography, or for pupils in rural high schools or schools in villages that are social and economic centers of surrounding rural districts a good introductory course in agriculture, would be much more effective for scientific education if taught from the viewpoint and in the spirit that have been outlined in the preceding pages. Nothing need stand in the way of introducing into any of these courses such projects and such facts and ideas and demonstrations from the other sciences as may be needed to supply the greater breadth and clearness that may be desirable or necessary. Even if the aim be to change the course into one that shall give a broader insight into the immediate environment or the universe as a whole than any of these special sciences as now delimited can give, would it not be better to bring about this change by continuing the course in its main outlines as formerly given and letting it develop into a general science course by gradually eliminating the materials that are less significant to the pupils under instruction and substituting for them the more significant materials that it is desired to introduce? By a process of trying out such substitutions, a few at a time, with careful testing of results, the change might be made as an evolution, rather than a revolution, and thus numerous and serious mistakes might be avoided.

Science in the elementary schools. — One highly important phase of the general science question seems to have escaped the attention of all but a very few of the advocates of this kind of instruction. *This is the urgent need of elementary science throughout the grades below the high schools.* Young children are strongly attracted toward the more obvious and elementary facts and processes of nature, and every normal child, in his childish and immature way, is an observer and investigator. From the kindergarten to the high school there should be in the elementary curriculum a series of lessons taken from the fields of all the sciences, and arranged in such a progression as to appeal to the interests and capacities of the children as they advance through the grades.

These lessons should be very informal and very simple in the lower grades; and should never be so difficult as to discourage the children or become degraded into task work. They should be so graded in difficulty as to challenge the powers of the youngsters, but never to defeat them or reduce them to a state of blind and credulous dependence on the authority of teachers or books. Each lesson or each small group of lessons should be a unit in itself and there should be no attempts at logical organization from the adult viewpoint in grades lower than the seventh or eighth, and very little of it in these latter.

This has been attempted in some or all of the grades in a good many school systems; but very few have attempted to work it out in a systematic and thoroughgoing manner, or to educate the elementary teachers in the right ways of presenting it. Much has been done in the right direction, through the widespread *nature study movement*, by leading biologists, but in general thus far the surface only has been scratched. The splendid materials that might be drawn from the fields of physics, chemistry, observational astronomy, and geology have scarcely been touched. The excellent work that has been done by the makers of modern textbooks in geography should not be overlooked; but unfortunately a great majority of the teachers have not been trained to use these books from the observational and heuristic standpoint; and they do not know how to use illustrative materials and experiments from the other sciences in correlation with the physico-geographical material presented by these splendid texts. There are two agencies by means of which a generation of teachers competent to give this important science instruction can be reared. One of them is to be found in the enlightened and progressive state and city normal schools that are rapidly increasing in numbers and efficiency. In these schools are found many enthusiastic and competent teachers who are giving to students preparing to teach in the elementary schools just the kind of instruction in science that is essential in working out science lessons for the elementary grades.

Supervisors of science instruction. — The other agency, unfortunately, is seldom to be found at work; and its absence is a serious indictment against the administrations of most of our city school systems, and a still more serious indictment against the bodies of scientific leaders whose recommendations and utterances should help these administrators to work out their policies with regard to the dissemination of scientific knowledge. The agency referred to as generally absent where it should be at work is the supervisor of science instruction. The function of such a supervisor is perfectly obvious. He, or she, should be charged with the duty of planning a course of science lessons for all the grades below the high school, of teaching the teachers how to give the lessons, of supervising them in the work, and of personally giving lessons for the purposes both of trying these lessons and testing them experimentally, and of showing the teachers how the teaching should be done. The supervisor should also have authority to call the high school teachers into consultation and advise with them in working out a suitable articulation of the science lessons in the elementary grades with the science courses in the high school. Such conferences would be mutually helpful and stimulating and would bring about exchanges in viewpoints and information, as well as assist in stimulating, directing, and crystallizing scientific interest and activities in the community.

The future trend of the movement. — In communities where the *junior high school plan* is being tried out it seems to the writer that the place for introducing general science is in the grades below the ninth in such high schools; and that it should be gone at in a much less formal and bookish manner than is now found to be common. Whatever may be the plan of high school organization, it is his present opinion

that better things would be accomplished for science instruction in the end, if those who are now interested in the general
science proposition would direct a good share of their enthusiasm and effort toward such a general system of science
lessons throughout the elementary grades, as has been here
briefly indicated; and toward securing a less bookish and a
more psychological type of teaching in connection with the
content of the special sciences that are now taught in the
high schools.   That the agitation for projects and problems
as centers for motivation and for organization both of facts
and principles, and of methods of attack, will be productive
of much good, there can in any event be little doubt.

QUESTIONS FOR FURTHER STUDY

1. Can you think of some local feature or activity near your home
which could be used as a problem around which an introductory
course might be organized after the idea of Huxley's Physiography?   If
so make a condensed outline of such a course.

2. Examine the various aims that are stated for a first year high
school science course and arrange them in the order of their relative
values and importance.

3. Select any of these aims, and show by argument and illustration
either that (1) it can be best accomplished by a "general science course,"
or (2) that it can be accomplished as well or better by one of the special
sciences, if properly taught.

4. Examine several of the current general science texts.   Select a
limited body of scientific information or an example of method of attacking a problem that is common to all of them.   Make a critical comparative study of these.   Report, with reasons, which one embodies the
best mode of teaching for accomplishing the aims of general science.

5. Prepare a project for general science.   Work out a lesson plan
for it, explaining in the plan the aim, the method of working it through
with the class, and adding a summary of the scientific items (content
and method) of value that it will contribute to the course.   Submit this
to your colleagues for criticism; and after revising it send it to Professor
Woodhull.

6. Discuss the statement on project teaching by the Woodhull
committee.

7. Argue either for or against the position that project teaching as here described is logical.

8. Are the answers given to the objections urged against project teaching valid and convincing? If not, refute them.

9. What do you think of the idea of introducing a general science course by a process of evolution as suggested, rather than by a process of revolution?

10. Outline your views as to the position taken by the author with reference to elementary science in the school grades below the ninth.

11. Briefly discuss the subject, "Science in the Junior High School." Base your discussion on your own convictions, rather than on an outline of the author's views.

REFERENCES

ARMSTRONG, HENRY E. The Teaching of the Scientific Method. Macmillan, N. Y. 1910. 504 pp. $1.75. Contains much information and many suggestions of value to teachers of general science.

BARBER, F. D., and others. First Course in General Science. Holt, N. Y. 1916. 7 + 588 pp. $1.25.

BARBER, F. D. The Physical Sciences in Our Public Schools. The Normal School Quarterly, Series 12, No. 49. Normal, Ill. October, 1913.

BARBER, F. D. The Present Status and Real Meaning of General Science. School Review, Chicago, Vol. XXIII, No. 1. January, 1915, pp. 9–24.

BARBER, F. D. Tendencies of General Science Courses. Proc. N. E. A. 1914. pp. 758–764.

BRIGGS, THOMAS H. General Science in Secondary Schools. Teachers College Record, Jan., 1916, Vol. XVII, No. 1.

CALDWELL, O. W., and EIKENBURY, W. L. General Science. Ginn, Boston. 1914. 302 pp. 85 ¢.

CLARK, BERTHA M. An Introduction to Science. American Book Co. 1915. 479 pp. $1.20.

COULTER, JOHN M. The Mission of Science in Education. University of Michigan. 1900. Also — same title, School Review, Vol. XXIII, Jan., 1915, pp. 1–8; and School Science and Mathematics, Vol. XV, pp. 93–100.

COULTER, JOHN M. What the University Expects of the Secondary Schools. School Review, Chicago. 1908. Vol. XVII, pp. 81–82.

DOWNING, E. R. The Scientific Trend in Secondary Schools. Science, N. Y., N. S., Vol. XLI, pp. 232–235.

EIKENBURY, W. L. Some Facts About the General Science Situation.

School Review, Chicago, Vol. XXIII, No. 3.   March, 1913, pp. 181–191.

EIKENBURY, W. L.   Further Discussion of General Science.   School and Society, N. Y.   Vol. I, No. 12.   March 20, 1915, pp. 417–420.

FLEXNER, ABRAHAM.   A Modern School.   Publications of The General Education Board.   Occasional Papers, No. 3, N. Y.   1916.

HARTMAN, CARL.   The General Science Situation in Texas.   School Science and Mathematics, Vol. XVII, No. 2, pp. 141–146.   February, 1917.

HUMMEL, W. G. and B. R.   Materials and Methods in High School Agriculture.   Macmillan, N. Y.   1913.   385 pp. $1.25.

HUNTER, G. W.   Civic Biology Presented in Problems.   American Book Co., N. Y.   1914.   418 pp. $1.25.

HUNTER, G. W.   Laboratory Problems in Civic Biology.   American Book Co., N. Y.   1916.   281 pp. (with bibliographies).   80 ¢.

IVINS, LESTER S., and MERRILL, FREDERICK A.   Practical Lessons in Agriculture.   Amer. Book Co., N. Y.   1915.   225 pp.   84 ¢.   Contains much of value for general science courses.   Book lists and lists of material to be obtained free.

MORRISON, ADELBERT H.   Applied Science, and its Relation to the Rest of the Work in an Up-to-date Technical High School.   Proc. N. E. A.   1914, pp. 764–771.   (Discussion by Comr. P. P. Claxton.)

RANDALL, JOHN A.   Project Teaching.   Proc. N. E. A.   1915, pp. 1009–1012.

RICHARDS, ELLEN H.   Sanitation and Daily Life.   Whitcomb and Barrows.   1907.   60 ¢.

SHARP, R. W.   A Laboratory Manual for the Solution of Problems in Biology.   Amer. Book Co., N. Y.   1911.   352 pp.   75 ¢.

SNYDER, WILLIAM H.   The First Year of Science.   Allyn and Bacon, Boston.   1914 and later.   493 pp. $1.10.

TIMBIE, WILLIAM H.   Tendencies of General Science Courses.   Proc. N. E. A.   1914, pp. 752–758.

WOODHULL, JOHN F.   Projects in Science.   Teachers College Record, January, 1916.   Vol. XVII, No. 1.

WOODHULL, JOHN F.   Science Teaching by Projects.   School Science and Mathematics, Vol. XV.   March, 1915, pp. 225–232.

WOODHULL, JOHN F.   The Natural Method.   School and Society.   Vol. III.   No. 54.   January 8, 1916, pp. 64–65.

WOODHULL, JOHN F., Chairman.   Report of Committee on Practical Chemistry to New York Science Teachers Association.   School Science and Mathematics, Vol. XIII.   1913, pp. 294–298.

WOODHULL, JOHN F., Chairman. The Committee on General Science of the National Education Association. Science, N. S. Vol. XL. No. 1034. October 23, 1914, pp. 601–602.

WOODHULL, JOHN F. What Specialization has done for Physics Teaching. Science, N. S., Vol. XXXI, No. 802. May 13, 1910, pp. 729–731.

WOODHULL, JOHN F. How the Public Will Solve Our Problems of Science Teaching. Wisconsin State Teachers Assoociation, November 12, 1908. Issued by C. P. Cary, State Supt., Madison, Wis. 21 pp.

WOODHULL, JOHN F., and VAN ARSDALE, M. B. Physical Nature Study Library: Home-made apparatus; Simple experiments in chemistry; Simple experiments in physics — mechanics, heat and fluids; Simple experiments in physics — sound, light and electricity. Barnes, N. Y. Each 128 pp. 65 ¢.

Books of Information to Accompany Simple Experiments in Physics. American Book Co., N. Y. 2 vols.

For references on junior high schools and high school reorganization see list at end of Chapter XI.

CHAPTER XXIV

EXAMINATION AND TESTS

Teachers' estimates of daily work. — In the preceding chapters we have considered the nature of scientific work, and methods of instruction in science. In the present chapter we shall attempt a critical analysis of the various ways in which it is possible to measure the abilities of the pupils receiving the instruction, in order to determine the progress that they may have made in consequence of it. In a very large and important sense, the pupil is measured or tested by the teacher almost daily in connection with his performance and achievements in the classroom and laboratory. He is required to recite on topics or answer questions, or take part in discussions in the classroom; and the teacher while instructing him along with the others, mentally takes his measure or estimates his ability or success by observing what he says and does, and comparing it with a sort of ideal or mental standard representing a satisfactory sum-total of performance or achievement in the classroom duties that have been assigned to him. The teacher keeps in mind, and usually records in his grade book from time to time, numbers or letters representing grades or steps on a scale. On this scale the highest grade represents the teacher's notion of perfection or the best that the student can be expected to do; the lowest grade represents no progress, or failure, and the other grades represent various degrees of positive achievement approximating more or less nearly to perfection.

In a similar manner the pupils are graded with regard to

their success in performing the laboratory experiments, with regard to the quality of the notes that they make on the laboratory work, and with regard to the excellence and promptness of the reports that they make on special library assignments or other pieces of work that they may be required to do.

These estimates by teachers of pupils' achievements are approximate measures of their daily or weekly progress, and are of considerable value; but they are admitted to involve an inherent weakness in that they are almost wholly subjective. That is, they are based wholly on the individual judgment of a single person, and are not expressions of values as to the exact meaning of which all competent observers would agree.

Variability of teachers' estimates. Central tendency. — If 25 teachers of, say, geography were to listen to a recitation or conference conducted by one of them, and to estimate the performance of each pupil on a scale, say, from 0 to 20, the grades that these teachers assigned to any given single pupil would show an astonishingly wide variation. A few would grade him relatively high, and a few relatively low; while the majority of the grades given would probably cluster more or less closely about a grade that would represent a " central tendency." A numerical value for the central tendency may be found in any one of three different ways:

1. By adding together the numbers representing the 25 grades given to this pupil, and dividing the result by 25, the number of such grades. This number is the *average* of the grades given by the 25 teachers to this one pupil. It is likely to be nearer to the true value of the pupil's performance than the grade assigned him by any one of the 25 observers.

2. By arranging the grades in an ascending or descending series according to their magnitudes and choosing such a number within the series that just as many of the grades lie above it as lie below it. This grade is called the *median* of the series, or distribution, of grades assigned by the 25 teachers to the given pupil.

3. By choosing the grade that is assigned to the pupil by the largest number of the 25 observers. This grade is called the *mode* of the distribution or series. Thus if 10 of the 25 teachers assigned the pupil a grade of 15, while the remaining 15 teachers gave him grades above and below 15, but no other grade was given by as many as 10 teachers, then 15 is the mode. In other words, the mode is the number that has the greatest frequency of occurrence. Sometimes it may happen that there are two or more modes representing as many groups of observers whose members agree very closely among themselves as to the meaning of the grade that they assign, but differ somewhat as to this meaning with members of other groups.

Measures of variability. — Now, if we subtract arithmetically the average from each of the grades that is higher than it, we shall obtain a difference value for each of these grades which represents its *deviation* from the average, and is called a positive (+) deviation. So if we subtract from the average each grade that is lower than it, we shall have for each of these lower grades its deviation from the average; and these are called negative (−) deviations. In like manner we might find the deviations from the median or mode. Finally, we might find the average or the median of the numbers that represent the deviations from the average or from the median or from the mode; and thus we should get measures of the deviations from these expressions of the central tendency. The first would be called the *average deviation* from the central tendency (*i.e.* from the average, median, or mode), and the second would be called the *median deviation* from the central tendency. The median deviation is often also called the *probable error*.

Now, if such an experiment were made, it would show by the large, numerous, and varied deviations from the average or median that teachers in general differ widely from one another as to what a grade means. In other words, 15 on a scale of 20 steps, or 75 on a scale of 100 steps, or C on a scale of 5 steps as A, B, C, D, E, may mean something, perhaps fairly

to represent the standing of the pupil, on a scale of 100, for the whole examination.

Defects of examination marks as measures of ability. — In this procedure it is tacitly assumed that each question or problem is equal in value to every other, and that the ten questions as a whole represent an equitable sampling of the whole body of knowledge and skill that the students are expected to have acquired during the period of effort covered by the examination. So if a pupil receives a grade of 80 on the examination, and that grade is taken as the measure of his achievement to be entered in the school records, it is to be inferred that because he has been able to do 80 per cent of the work set him by the examination questions he is therefore known to have become possessed of 80 per cent of the whole body of knowledge and skill that the teacher expects him to acquire during the period intended to be covered by the examination questions. It is clear, however, that, unless the questions are really equal in difficulty, and unless they constitute, as to difficulty and kind, a thoroughly fair and representative sampling of demands for the kinds and amounts of responses that the pupils are supposed to have learned to make, the examination grade may be very far from a true measure of the actual abilities that the pupil has developed in consequence of the practice given in the instruction. This would be true even though it were supposed that the teacher's marking were absolutely accurate. But it is very hard to find questions and problems that are equal in difficulty even within groups of questions or problems that are essentially alike in kind ; and the more widely different they are in their essential characteristics the harder it is to find samples of the different kinds that are equally difficult. Then, too, *the difficulty to the students of any given question will depend as much on how well they have been trained for answering it as on the inherent difficulties of the question itself.* Its difficulty will also depend largely on how recently the pupil has reviewed and applied the principle involved in it, or answered other questions that are like it, for if sufficient time has elapsed, since his training on the subject of the question, for him to have forgotten it, and no opportunities have been provided for reviewing or relearning it, he will probably have difficulty in recalling it. In such cases the difficulty of recalling a given fact or principle is usually far greater than that involved in learning it in the first place. Again it often happens that a pupil who knows a principle well, and has recently responded by using it successfully in solving a problem in the classroom, will fail to recall and apply it in an examination, and we say that " he did not do himself justice." Not infrequently a good classroom scholar " goes to pieces " in an examination. The reason for this is to be found in the relative unfamiliarity of the situation, the relatively large personal interests at stake, and the consequent emotional strain on a delicately organized nervous system. The mind is likely to become fixed on the disastrous consequences of failure, and is thus inhibited from attending to the details of the questions. To some girls, especially, calm reflection and efficient thinking in an examination are nearly impossible; and the pale mouth, the flushed cheek, the distressed knitting of the brows and pushing back of the hair are unmistakable signs of the perturbed state of mind. This fault of the examination is mainly due to several causes that might easily be removed. The novelty and strain of the situation usually can be removed by accustoming the students to the situation through practice on frequent written recitations, weekly tests, and monthly examinations.

Failure to recall principles not recently used can be provided against by holding reviews before the tests and examinations, so as to cause the forgotten principles to be relearned.

The dread of the final examination due to the feeling that so much is at stake is often overcome by excusing the best pupils from the final examination. This has a tendency to make the pupils work harder through the semester in order to " get out of the exam. "; and it avoids the strain on the good but nervous workers. Yet, on the other hand, it degrades the examination into a punishment from the point of view of those who are required to take it; it does not mitigate, but rather intensifies, the strain on the pupils who are conscientious but weak; and it often makes it possible through a cramming process for an able but lazy student to pass at the end of the semester, although his daily work is all the time below passing grade. A better way to remedy this defect is to make the final examination count for less in making up the final grade. In many schools in past times the examination grade used to be the only basis for estimating the pupils' standings and making promotions. At the present time some schools use the average obtained by adding together the teacher's estimate of daily work for the semester and the grade obtained in the final examination, and dividing the result by two. Others use the number obtained by adding together the teacher's estimate for the semester and half the sum of the grades obtained in the final and a mid-term examination and dividing the result by two. A more equitable grade, in the judgment of the writer, is obtained by adding together the teacher's estimate for the semester, the final examination grade, and the average of all the weekly and monthly tests, and dividing the result by three. Under no circumstances should the final examination be held up before the pupils as a specter to scare them into doing their daily work.

Another common fault of examinations is making the questions too difficult. The teacher is apt to pass over the questions that he feels confident will be correctly answered by all the pupils, and give them those about which he thinks their knowledge is doubtful. This procedure usually serves the purpose of confirming his doubts, but does not accomplish the purpose of measuring the progress and mental growth of the pupils, because the questions do not constitute a fair proportional sampling of the work to be tested. The best remedy for this tendency is for the teacher to keep a card file of questions and problems that are suitable for tests and examinations, placing a question, or two or three questions, of the same sort, on each card. Along with each question comments may be entered as to the kind of knowledge or ability that it is adapted to test, as to its relative difficulty, and so on. The cards should be made up as one goes along with the teaching of the various topics, and from them he can be putting together his examination list piecemeal as the class progresses, instead of making it up hastily at the end of the month or semester, as the case may be. With the former procedure he is likely to use far better judgment than with the latter. The defect of inequality of difficulty in the different questions can be partially remedied in the scoring by assigning them values or " weights " that are proportional to their relative importance and difficulty; or they may be equalized by grouping a number of easy ones together so that the difficulty and importance of the group shall be more nearly equal to the difficulty and importance of other single questions. Thus if a certain problem counts ten points, a group of five short questions judged to be relatively worth two points each may be taken also to count ten in the list.

Coaching for examinations. — Another fault of examinations shows itself prominently in schools where the questions are made up by some outside authority, instead of by the teacher himself, — by the supervisor, for example, or, as is the case in New York, by the state educational authorities; likewise in the " Middle States and Maryland," where the standing of the teachers in many of the schools is affected by the ability of their pupils to pass the questions set by the College Entrance Examination Board. In such cases the magnification of the importance of examinations tends toward getting them to be viewed as ends in education instead of means. The result is that the teachers find it very difficult to resist the temptation to " coach " for these examinations rather than to educate their pupils by means of their subjects. They fall into the way of training the pupils to pass examinations of the particular sorts that are set by the external administrative authorities that dominate the school.

Now, if the life work of the pupils touching the sciences were to be such that passing examinations in physics, chemistry, etc., of the types set by these administrators should constitute their main business, then the methods used by the successful examination coaches would constitute one of the most efficient types of vocational education. But since we have agreed that a scientific education should aim to fit the pupils to react by doing things efficiently and thinking out conclusions clearly and methodically in all sorts of situations where scientific facts and principles are involved, we must conclude that the coaching methods, though undoubtedly useful, should occupy a very subordinate rôle in the teaching scheme. They can not be made to do so, however, unless the rôle of the examination itself is reduced to a proper degree of subordination. Successful cramming for an examination involves only a rather narrowly specialized kind of technical skill, which is useful to those who have civil service or other statutory examinations to pass, or who like a lawyer have to cram up a mass of data to meet a temporary necessity. It is a kind of ability that may be of great advantage to almost any one at times, and is well worth some special training. Nevertheless, the teacher should avoid training toward the examination as an aim; and should try to direct all his teaching, examinations included, toward fitting the pupils to react efficiently in the situations of daily life, — both the present daily lives of the pupils and the daily life in which they will find themselves when they have become adult citizens and workers.

Examination grades are subjective and unreliable. — Another weakness of the examination lies in the fact that the judgments of the teacher in grading the answers are subjective and relatively unreliable. The same sort of wide variations that we have described as characteristic of the individual judgments of a group of teachers on the performance of a pupil in the classroom have been found to exist in the grades assigned to a single examination paper by a large group of teachers. For example, a geometry paper was sent out by Professors Starch and Elliott to 180 high schools accredited by the North Central Association, asking that it be carefully graded by the leading teacher of mathematics. Of these, 128 were graded as directed, and returned. The grades given this one paper by 128 leading mathematics teachers from among the best schools of the Middle West ranged from 25 to 90 on a scale of 100 with a median of 70 and a median deviation from the median of 7.5. The mode was at 75; but the marks were not normally distributed, being mostly grouped in bunches around 60, 65, 80, and 85. The teachers in those schools where the passing mark was 70 seemed especially fond of the grades 50, 65, 70, and 75, while those in schools where the passing grade was 75 were partial to 60, 65, 75, and 79.[1]

This experiment of Starch and Elliott effectually disposes of the widely held opinion that grades on mathematics papers are especially reliable, or that the grade of a single teacher on any kind of paper makes any approach to objectivity with the customary modes of grading, simply because the subject matter consists largely of numerical expressions. With examinations, then, as with teachers' estimates, we must conclude that the only way under the ordinary procedure to get judgments that approximate to objectivity, and that have some degree of reliability, is to get for each paper the central tendency of the marks given by a large group of competent teachers, and that even with this method of treatment, the reliability of the central tendency is far less than that of the

---

[1] Cf. Starch, D., and Elliott, E. C., *Reliability of Grading Work in Mathematics*, School Review, Chicago, April, 1913, Vol. XXI, pp. 254–259.

crudest sort of measurements made on physical materials with
the aid of measuring rods or balances and weights, or time-
pieces, or meters for measuring gas, water, or electricity.
Yet, be that as it may, the averages of teachers' estimates of
daily work with their gradings of examination papers are
the only measures we have had, until recently, of pupils'
achievements, and are much better than none.

It is the task of educational experts to devise standards
and scales of educational measurement and methods of using
them that will yield measures as to the meaning of which
more general agreement can exist.

Estimation of standings by ranking. — From what has just
preceded, it is clear that when we are told that a pupil's grade
in any subject is " 87 per cent," we really know nothing definite about him ; because we do not know what the person
who gave him the grade means by 87 per cent. If, however,
in addition to this grade, we are told that this pupil ranks
number 5 in a class of 50, and that the median pupil in the
class received a grade of 78, while the passing mark is 65, we
have a rating of him as to the meaning of which we should
agree much more closely. The meaning of the grade would
be still clearer to us if we were acquainted with the ideals and
standards, and the quality of the instruction, in the school
from which the student comes. The meaning of the " 87
per cent " would be still more nearly unmistakable if we had
before us a distribution table and a surface of frequency including the grades given to all members of the class. It would
therefore contribute to better mutual understanding, to higher
efficiency, and to a more objective and scientific attitude
toward all questions involving the measurement of pupils'
attainments if every teacher would get into the habit of making a distribution table of the grades received by his pupils,
on every important occasion when they are graded. By
means of such a distribution table each pupil can learn
where he ranks in the class, and how far he stands above or

below the median. For promotions, and for comparison of
the standings of pupils in different subjects in the same school,
this modification of the usual system of grading by per cents
or letters alone is found to result in greater uniformity of
meaning among the various teachers. It tends to counteract
the tendency of some teachers to mark too high and of others
to mark too low; and it yields marks that are more nearly :
comparable with one another. It therefore makes easier the
process of adjusting the credits of pupils who go from one
school to another, and of those who go out from the high
schools to enter the colleges. For example, it was found by
Professor W. F. Dearborn [1] that of 472 students from eight
high schools 64 per cent of those who stood among the first
quarter of their class in the average of all subjects for the four
high school years also stood in the first quarter of their class
in the first year in the University of Wisconsin, and 81 per
cent of them stood in the first half. Of those who in general
average stood in the second, the third, and the lowest quarters of their class in high school the relative numbers that
were found in the corresponding quarters of their class in the
freshman college year were 40 per cent, 31 per cent, and 46
per cent, respectively. The degree of correspondence between
rank in high school and rank in college found by Dearborn's
calculations, and expressed in terms of the " Pearson coefficient of correlation " was $+ \frac{80}{100}$. Since no correspondence
is represented by 0 and perfect correspondence by $+ 1$., a
correlation of $+ .80$ indicates a very strong tendency for
pupils in high school to keep their relative rank in college;
and as studies since made of other high school and college
groups all tend to confirm Dearborn's results we must conclude that we can predict very much better whether a student is able to do college work or not if we know in which quarter of his class he ranked than if we are given figures or letters

[1] Dearborn, W. F., *The Relative Standing of Pupils in the High School and
in the University*, Bull. Univ. of Wis., No. 312, Madison, 1909, p. 22.

that state the grades or averages that he received in his various studies.

Better methods of scoring answers. — We have just seen that we may obtain measures of the abilities of groups of pupils that are more reliable, and more nearly objective, by giving distribution tables of the marks received, stating the average or median mark and the average or median deviation from it. We have also learned that we can understand better what is meant by the grade that has been given to an individual pupil if we are told the average or median mark for the class and the deviation of this pupil's mark from this median, or if we are told how many there are in his class and what his rank is in it.

Another way of making examination marks more nearly objective and scientific is to use methods of scoring the answers that are better than that in which a single judgment is made on the quality of the answer as a whole.

Questions whose answers can be scored by points. — The general principle of point scoring is to frame the questions in such a way that the answers can be split up into parts each of which admits of only one interpretation and only one correct answer.

This is by no means easy to do, and in many cases is impossible, but it should be attempted where it is possible. In so far as this can be accomplished, each part of such question can be judged either wholly right or wholly wrong; and when the difficulty or importance of each part of the required answer is judged approximately equal to that of any other, each part correctly answered can be scored one point. In proportion as this principle can be realized in any given question the scores given any answer to it by a number of different teachers marking the paper would differ far less one from another than would the scores given if the question were not so definitely framed. Furthermore, the scoring can be much more easily and quickly done. It must be admitted that questions that can be scored in this simple objective way are mostly questions of pure fact and information. Questions involving judgment and thinking by the pupils are much harder to split up into parts that are relatively nearly equal in value or difficulty; and even when split up into smaller units, these can not ordinarily be marked either wholly right or wholly wrong. Nevertheless the more determined we are in our attempts to split up questions and evaluate their parts, the more nearly we can approach to converting them into something like objective measures of the pupils' abilities.

Examples of questions that can be scored by points. — We shall now attempt to illustrate by example some of the kinds of questions that can be scored after the manner described:

1. Name three classes of coral reefs. 3 points.

2. State four different ways in which shore lines are made regular. 4 points.

3. Show by diagram the difference between a wave-cut terrace and a wave-built terrace. 2 points.

4. On the outline map of the United States designate two important harbors by printing their names. In what states are they? 4 points.

All these questions in geography and many others like them, which the reader can make for himself from this and other sciences, can be very quickly and definitely scored; and there would be pretty general agreement on the numbers of points to be credited to each answer. The first one is manifestly less valuable than the others, however; because it calls only for names which might be correctly given with little knowledge of the concepts for which they should stand.

With these, contrast the following, which are very difficult to score justly, because so many and such varied elements enter into a judgment as to the worth of any answer that might be given:

1. Discuss the economic importance of harbors.
2. What was the influence of the "fall line" on the growth of cities in New England?
3. What are the characteristics of coastal plains?

These questions call for wider knowledge and more thought power than the former list; but the scores given to the answers on a pupil's paper by a group of teachers would vary widely because the teachers would have widely different opinions both as to the relative correctness of the statements and as to the number of different facts and relations that the pupils might reasonably be expected to tell.

Completion tests. — Such questions as these, however, may be restated according to a method which, though it gives less opportunity for the display of ability to organize the materials for the answer, does test both information and thought power well, and does admit of very easy scoring. The change consists in throwing the question into the form of the completion test first proposed by Ebbinghaus. Thus, the question, " Give a brief description of the physiography of Southern New England " may be thrown into the following form:

> Fill each blank with a single word, so that the completed paragraph will make a good and accurate geographical description.
> Southern New England is an —— mountain —— worn down to a ——, surmounted by a few scattered ——. It has since been ——, and tilted toward the ——. The —— have thus been ——, and erosion has reached the stage of ——. In recent geological time the whole region has been highly ——, with the result that many streams have been turned from their old —— and have found new ones, and many others have been partially dammed, producing numerous —— among the hills.

The words required to fill the blanks are as follows and each may be quickly scored one point: *old, region, peneplain, monadnocks, uplifted, southeast, streams, rejuvenated, maturity, glaciated, channels, lakes.*

Association tests. — Another type of test that has been extensively used by psychologists may be used occasionally by science teachers to supplement the sorts already mentioned. An example of this type of test is given below.

After each word in the following list, write a brief statement of some fact, law, or principle that it makes you think of:
(1) Pressure, (2) expansion, (3) submerged, (4) coefficient, (5) work, (6) density, (7) elasticity, (8) flow, (9) float, (10) buoyancy.

As a means of revealing something of the contents of the pupils' minds, this kind of test is likely to be useful, and is worthy of being more often employed in teaching than it is at present. In scoring this one any correct statement of a fact in physics that may logically be associated with the word after which it is written may be scored one point. Such a test may be made still more free and untrammeled by writing the introductory sentence thus: " After each of the following words write what it makes you think of." The most common method of using such tests in psychological experiments is to read the list of test words one at a time, and have the subject respond orally by giving the first single word that he thinks of. The time between giving each word and getting the response is measured with a stop watch. Delayed responses are indicative of some emotional states in the subject, due to thoughts associated with the word given, and often enable the experimenter to find out something which the subject does not wish to tell. In such detective or diagnostic experiments, the test words are usually mixed with an equal number of " innocent " words which cannot be suspected by the subject of having any significance in connection with what is on his mind.

This type of test may be very useful to teachers in diagnosing the interests of their pupils. Questionnaires given to students asking them what their interests are do not usually give reliable results; because the questions tend to suggest to the pupils the answers that the teacher desires to receive, and because pupils have a habit of giving answers that they think will satisfy teachers, rather than answers that actually reveal the free state of their own minds.

Hence, if it be desired to ascertain what a pupil's chief interests are, it is better to arrange a series of 50 to 100 words, half or three fourths of which are likely to be suggestive of such interests as it is desired to test for, and the remainder of which are " innocent " words that have no connection with such interests. The pupils may be examined singly and their responses be given orally, or the words may be read to the entire class and the responses be written on slips of paper. Analysis of the response words will usually reveal something about what each pupil is interested in. To confirm results in any case, a new list may be made out with half the words such as are associated with the special interests that were indicated by the previous responses of the pupils and the other half such as have no relation to these special interests. If the results of the second or specific test are followed up by informal conversation about the subject of interest, still further and more definite revelations may be expected to occur.

Association tests with visual material. — An interesting and useful variation of this sort of test may be made by showing pictures instead of words. The pictures chosen should be such as are suggestive of various lines of scientific interest, and may be cut from the advertising pages of magazines that present a special appeal to young people. The catalogues from mail order department stores, sporting goods houses, manufacturers of machinery or farm implements, seedsmen and stock breeders — all are prolific sources from which pictures useful in testing for scientific interests may be drawn. The pamphlets and folders issued by railroad and land companies also contain many such pictures. The pictures may be mounted on cards, and shown singly, or copied as lantern slides and shown to a whole class at once ; otherwise the procedure would be the same as that described for the tests with lists of words for stimuli.

Recognition tests. — Another good method of testing for scientific interests is to show a series of pictures of the sorts that have been described, say twenty-five in number; then mix them with an equal number of similar ones not shown before, and show them again.   The teacher makes a column of the natural series of numbers representing the order in which the pictures are to be shown on the second round ; and opposite these in another column, he places the numbers which have been written on the backs of the pictures for the purpose of identifying them.   Each pupil during the second showing has before him a paper with the column of numbers that represents the order in which the pictures are to be shown ; and as each picture is viewed he writes, opposite the ordinal number representing it, a + sign if he thinks it is one of those shown before, or a — sign if he thinks it is not one of those shown before.   He is instructed to guess if he is not sure.   The score sheets, when collected by the teacher and analyzed, will tell for each pupil which pictures were recognized on the second showing and which were not.   The per cent of pictures recognized by a pupil from each field of possible interest will be a measure of his relative interest in that field.   For example, if a boy recognized all of five pictures representing electrical devices and only one or two from each of the other groups such a result would point toward stronger interests in the line of electricity than in the other lines represented.   To be conclusive such a test would have to be followed up with a confirmatory test in which the proportion of pictures representing the particular interest indicated is larger than in the first test.   Pictures or words used in testing for interests should not be those that have been previously used in the course of regular instruction.   In all the sorts of association tests that have been mentioned, pieces of apparatus, maps, biological preparations, or specimens of various sorts might be used instead of pictures, and to very good advantage. So also might short articles with summarizing headlines, such as are found in popular and scientific magazines and in the newspapers.

Technique of marking examination papers. — In starting to mark a set of papers it is best to pick out the papers of two or three of the best pupils, of two or three of the poorest, and of as many of medium ability, and read these papers through rapidly in order to get a general idea of how well the pupils have done on the questions. When the serious business of grading is begun one question should be graded through all the papers before taking up any other question on any paper.

When grading a question, arrange the papers in a row, as they are read, in the order of the excellence of the answers. This changes the procedure from a process of grading exclusively according to a vague and fictitious mental standard of absolute value to a process of grading by relative rank. The latter procedure is much easier and more accurate because it is much easier to decide that John's answer is better than Joe's but not so good as Frank's than it is to decide offhand whether John's answer is worth 6 or 7 or 8 points out of 10. This is particularly true when we are marking an answer that cannot be split up and scored by single points, but has to be judged according to its general excellence when taken as a whole. When the papers, after marking a given question, are arranged in several different piles, each pile containing papers on which the question is given the same or nearly the same mark, it becomes very easy to compare answers that are nearly equal in merit, and slightly readjust the grades as may be necessary. With this method of marking, the teacher acquires facility of judgment on the question in hand as a result of the uninterrupted practice in grading it on the first eight or ten papers. He can then grade it on the remaining papers with greatly increased speed and accuracy.

If any one who has been used to grading each paper entire before passing to the next will try the procedure described here, he will become convinced of its superiority.

QUESTIONS FOR FURTHER STUDY

1. Let the members of the class and the instructor each grade a student's oral recitation; then let the grades be read off, so that each individual has the list of them. Let each student convert this list into a distribution table, and calculate the average, the median, and the mode. How do the values of these expressions of the central tendency compare with one another in magnitude?

2. Using the distribution table (Question 1) let each member of the class find the deviations of the individual measures from the average, from the median, and from the mode. Now let each member of the class make a distribution table of the deviations from the average, and calculate the average deviation from the average and the median deviation from the average.

3. In like manner let each one calculate the average deviation and the median deviation from the median, and the average deviation and the median deviation from the mode.

4. What, now, is your opinion as to the relative reliability of a teacher's (single) mark?

5. In grading why is it better to mark as often as is possible without taking your attention too much from your teaching?

6. What are the principal faults of examinations as measures of school achievement?

REFERENCES

AYRES, L. P.   Child Accounting in the Public Schools.   Cleve. Ed. Survey Reports, Cleveland Foundation, Cleveland, O.   1916. 68 pp.   25 ¢.

AYRES, L. P.   The Measurement of Educational Processes and Products. Russell Sage Foundation, N. Y.   1912.   9 pp.

BRINTON, W. C.   Graphic Methods of Presenting Facts.   Published by The Engineering Magazine, N. Y.   1914.   371 pp.   Illus. $4.00.   An elaborate illustrated discussion of the interpretation of statistics through graphic methods, with criticisms of some prevalent practices.

CATTELL, J. McKEEN.   Examinations, Grades, and Credits.   Popular Science Monthly, Vol. 66, pp. 367–378.

DEARBORN, W. F.   The Relative Standing of Pupils in the High School and in the University. Bull. Univ. of Wisconsin No. 312, Madison. 1909. 44 pp.

DEARBORN, W. F. School and University Grades. Bull. Univ. of Wisconsin No. 368, Madison. 1910. 59 pp.

FULLERTON, G. S., and CATTELL, J. McK. On the Perception of Small Differences. Pub. Univ. of Pa., Phil. Series No. 2. May, 1892. Univ. of Pennsylvania Press, Phila.

JUDD, C. H. Measuring the Work of the Public Schools. Cleve. Ed. Survey Reports, Cleveland Foundation, Cleveland, O. 1916. 50 ¢.

KELLY, F. J. Teachers' Marks. Their Variability and Standardization. Teachers College, Columbia Univ., N. Y. 1914. 137 pp. Important review and study of marks, standards, and tests, with a very complete bibliography.

MEYER, MAX. The Grading of Students. Science, Vol. 28, pp. 243–252.

STARCH, DANIEL. Educational Measurements. Macmillan, N. Y. 1916. vii + 202 pp. $1.25. A brief general treatise on the subject, by a leading authority, with extensive bibliography.

STARCH, D., and ELLIOTT, E. C. Reliability of Grading High School Work in English. School Review, Chicago, Vol. 21, pp. 254–259.

TERMAN, LEWIS M. The Measurement of Intelligence. Houghton, Mifflin & Co., Boston. 1916. 358 pp. $1.50. An explanation of and a complete guide for the use of the Stanford revision and extension of the Binet-Simon intelligence scale.

THORNDIKE, E. L. An Introduction to the Theory of Mental and Social Measurements. 2d Ed. Teachers College, Columbia Univ., N. Y. 1913. 271 pp. $2.50. The best available explanation of statistical methods for students of education.

WHIPPLE, GUY M. Manual of Mental and Physical Tests. Warwick & York, Baltimore, Md. 2 vols. 1914. 678 pp. $2.25 and $2.00. Chapter I gives a brief explanation of statistical methods.

APPENDIX A

A SELECTED LIST OF SCIENCE BOOKS FOR THE HIGH SCHOOL LIBRARY

BIOLOGY

AGASSIZ, LOUIS. Methods of Study in Natural History. Houghton, Mifflin & Co., Boston. 18th Ed. 1887. 319 pp. $1.50. In this famous book Agassiz gave his reasons for not accepting the evolution theory. It should be in every library, that teacher and pupils may learn something on the other side from "the greatest opponent of Darwinism."

BERGEN, J. Y. and F. D. A Primer of Darwinism and Organic Evolution. Lee & Shepard, Boston. New Ed. 1890. $1.25.

CLODD, EDWARD. Primer of Evolution. Longmans, N. Y. 1895. 75 ¢.

CLODD, EDWARD. Story of Creation. Longmans, N. Y. 128 pp. $1.25.

CLODD, EDWARD. Pioneers of Evolution, from Thales to Huxley. Appleton, N. Y. 1897. With portraits. 274 pp. $1.50. Clodd's books are remarkable for their simplicity and the charm of their appeal to young people.

DARWIN, CHARLES. Vegetable Molds and Earthworms. Appleton, N. Y. 1892. 326 pp. $1.50.

FRANKLAND, PERCY FARADAY. Our Secret Friends and Foes. Society for the Promotion of Christian Knowledge, London, Eng. 1897. 238 pp. $1.00. A good book on bacteriology for the general reader.

OGDEN, HENRY N. Rural Hygiene. Macmillan, N. Y. 1913. 425 pp. $1.50.

OSBORN, HENRY FAIRFIELD. From the Greeks to Darwin. Macmillan, N. Y. 1899. 2d Ed. 1902. 259 pp. $2.25.

SEDGWICK, W. T. Principles of Sanitary Science and the Public Health. Macmillan, N. Y. 1902. 338 pp. $3.00.

THOMSON, J. ARTHUR. The Biology of the Seasons. Holt, N. Y. 1915. 379 pp. $2.75.

TOLMAN. Hygiene for the Worker. Am. Book Co., N. Y. and Cincinnati. 1912. 231 pp. 50 ¢.

WARDALL, RUTH A., and WHITE, EDNA N. A Study of Foods. **Ginn,** Boston. 1914. 169 pp. 70 ¢.

WARREN, G. F. Elements of Agriculture. Macmillan, N. Y. 1909. 434 pp. $1.10. A standard textbook.

BOTANY

APGAR, A. C. Trees of the Northern United States. American Book Co., N. Y. 1892. 224 pp. $1.00.

ARTHUR, J. C., and MACDOUGAL, D. T. Living Plants and Their Properties. Baker & Taylor, N. Y. 1898. $1.25.

ATKINSON, G. F. Mushrooms, Edible, Poisonous, Etc. Holt & Co., N. Y. 1903. 275 pp. $2.50.

BAILEY, L. H. Plant Breeding. Macmillan, N. Y. 1915. 474 pp. $2.00.

BAILEY, L. H. Survival of the Unlike. Macmillan, N. Y. 1896. 515 pp. $2.00.

BEAL, W. J. Seed Dispersal. Ginn, Boston. 1898. 87 pp. 60 ¢.

CLUTE, W. N. Laboratory Botany for the High School. Ginn, Boston. 1909. 75 ¢.

CLUTE, W. N. Agronomy. Ginn. 1913. 296 pp. $1.00. A practical course in gardening for high schools — with reference lists.

CLUTE, W. N. Our Ferns in Their Haunts, a Guide to All the Native Species. F. A. Stokes Co., N. Y. 1901. $2.00.

CLUTE, W. N. The Fern Allies of North America, North of Mexico. Stokes, N. Y. 1905. $2.00.

CONN, H. W. Bacteria, Yeasts and Molds in the Home. Ginn, Boston. 1903. 293 pp. $1.20.

DARWIN, CHARLES. The Various Contrivances by Which Orchids Are Fertilized by Insects. $1.75. The Effects of Cross and Self-Fertilization in the Vegetable Kingdom. $2.00. Different Forms of Flowers on Plants of the Same Species. $1.50. The Power of Movement in Plants. $2.00. Insectivorous Plants. $2.00. Movements and Habits of Climbing Plants. $1.25. All published by Appleton, N. Y.

DE CANDOLLE, ALPHONSE. Origin of Cultivated Plants. Appleton, N. Y. 1886. $2.00.

DE VRIES, HUGO. Plant Breeding. Comments on the Experiments of Nielson and Burbank. Open Court Publishing Co., Chicago. 1907. 360 pp. $1.50.

FERNOW, B. E. Economics of Forestry. Crowell, N. Y. 1902. 520 pp. $1.50.

FERNOW, B. E.   The Care of Trees in Lawn, Street and Park.   Holt, N. Y.   392 pp. $2.00.   Ill.

GIBSON, W. H.   Blossom Hosts and Insect Guests.   Newson & Co., N. Y.   1901.   197 pp.   80 ¢.

GIBSON, W. H.   Our Edible Toadstools and Mushrooms, and How to Distinguish Them.   Harpers, N. Y.   1902.   337 pp. $3.50. Illus. and colored plates.

GROUT, A. J.   Mosses with a Hand Lens (2d Ed. including the Hepatics). A. J. Grout, 360 Lennox Rd., Brooklyn, N. Y.   1905.   416 pp. $1.75.

HARWOOD, W. S.   New Creations in Plant Life.   Macmillan, N. Y. 1907.   430 pp. $2.00.   An account of the work of Luther Burbank.

LUBBOCK, SIR JOHN.   Lord Avebury.   Flowers, Fruits and Leaves. Macmillan, N. Y.   1888.   147 pp. $1.75.

MACDOUGAL, D. T.   Nature and Work of Plants.   Macmillan, N. Y. 1900.   211 pp.   80 ¢.   (Out of print, 1917.)

MACDOUGAL, D. T.   Elementary Plant Physiology.   Longmans, N. Y. 1902. $1.20.

NOYES, W.   Wood and Forest. The Manual Arts Press, Peoria, Ill. $3.00. Describes 67 species of woods with maps of the habitat, leaf drawings, life size photographs and microphotographs of sections. Profusely illustrated.

OSTERHOUT, W. J. V.   Experiments with Plants.   Macmillan, N. Y. 1905.   492 pp. $1.25.

PINCHOT, GIFFORD.   A Primer of Forestry.   Supt. of Documents, Government Printing Office, Washington, D. C.   30 ¢.

SARGENT, F. L.   Corn Plants.   Houghton, Mifflin & Co.   1899. 106 pp.   75 ¢.

SPALDING, V. M.   Guide to the Study of Common Plants.   Heath, Boston.   1893.   246 pp.   90 ¢.

UNDERWOOD, L. M.   Our Native Ferns and Their Allies.   Holt, N. Y. 1908.   158 pp. $1.00.

UNDERWOOD, L. M.   Molds, Mildews, and Mushrooms.   Holt, N. Y. 1899.   236 pp. $1.50.

WARD, H. N.   Disease in Plants.   Macmillan, N. Y.   1901.   309 pp. $2.00.

ZOÖLOGY

BALLARD, J. P.   Among the Moths and Butterflies.   Putnam, N. Y. 1891.   34 + 237 pp. $1.50.

BLANCHAN, NELTJE.   Bird Neighbors.   Doubleday, Page & Co., N. Y. 1898.   234 pp. $2.00.

BLANCHAN, NELTJE. Birds that Hunt and are Hunted. Doubleday, Page & Co., N. Y. 1899. 359 pp. $2.00.

CHAPMAN, F. M. Handbook of Birds of Eastern North America. Appleton, N. Y. 1895. 375 pp. $3.00.

CHAPMAN, F. M. Bird Life. Appleton, N. Y. Popular Edition. 1901. $2.00. Contains colored plates and appendix for teachers.

COMSTOCK, J. H. and A. B. Manual for the Study of Insects. Comstock Publishing Co., Ithaca, N. Y. 1909. 701 pp. $3.75. Profusely illustrated.

COMSTOCK, J. H. and A. B. Insect Life. Edition with colored plates. Appleton, N. Y. $1.75.

CRAGIN, B. S. Our Insect Friends and Foes. Putnam, N. Y. 1895. 374 pp. $1.75.

DEAN, B. Fishes, Living and Fossil. Macmillan, N. Y. 1895. 300 pp. $2.50. (Out of print, 1917.)

FRENCH, N. S. Animal Activities. Longmans, N. Y. 1901. 262 pp. $1.20.

HOLLAND, W. J. The Butterfly Book. Doubleday, Page & Co., N. Y. 1898. $3.00.

HOLLAND, W. J. The Moth Book. Doubleday, Page & Co. 1903. $4.00.

HORNADAY, W. J. The American Natural History. Scribner, N. Y. 1904. $3.50.

HOWARD, L. O. The Insect Book. Doubleday, Page & Co., N. Y. 1902. 27 + 429 pp. $3.00.

HYATT, ALPHEUS, and others. Guides for Science Teaching. Commercial and other Sponges, Corals and Echinoderms, Mollusca, Worms and Crustacea. D. C. Heath & Co., Boston. 20–25 ¢ each.

JORDAN, D. S., and EVERMAN, D. W. American Food and Game Fishes. Doubleday, Page & Co., N. Y. 1903. 573 pp. $4.00.

KELLOGG, V. L. Elementary Zoölogy. Holt, N. Y. 1901. 492 pp. $1.20.

MERRIAM, F. A. Birds of Village and Field. Houghton, Mifflin & Co. Boston. 1898. 398 pp. $2.00.

MIALL, L. C. Injurious and Useful Insects, an Introduction to the Study of Economic Entomology. Macmillan, N. Y. 1911. 256 pp. $1.00.

MORGAN, C. L. Animal Behavior. An introduction to animal psychology. Longmans, N. Y. 1908. 344 pp. $3.50.

NEEDHAM, J. G. Lessons in Zoölogy. American Book Co. 1895. 302 pp. 90 ¢.

NEEDHAM, J. G. Outdoor Studies. American Book Co. 1898. 90
pp. 40 ¢.

SHALER, N. S. Domesticated Animals, their Relation to Man and to his
Advancement in Civilization. Scribner's, N. Y. 1895. 267 pp.
$2.50.

SHARP, D. L. Wild Life Near Home. Century Co., N. Y. 357 pp.
$2.00.

.STONE, W., and CRAM, W. E. American Animals. Doubleday, Page
& Co., N. Y. 1902. 318 pp. $3.00.

WRIGHT, M. O. Four-footed Americans. Macmillan, N. Y. 1898.
413 pp. $1.50. Contains key to the animals of North America.

NATURE STUDY

BAILEY, L. H. The Nature Study Idea. Macmillan, N. Y. 4th Ed.
1909. 159 pp. $1.25.

BIRD, R. M. Modern Science Reader. Macmillan, N. Y. 1911.
323 pp. $1.10.

BUCKLEY, A. B. Life and her Children. Glimpses of Animal Life
from Amœba to Insects. Appleton, N. Y. $1.50.

BUCKLEY, A. B. (Mrs. Fisher.) Winners in Life's Race, or The Great
Backboned Family. Appleton, N. Y. $1.50.

BURROUGHS, JOHN. Squirrels and other Fur-bearers. Houghton
Mifflin Co., Boston. 1900. $1.00.

BURROUGHS, JOHN. Wake Robin, A Year in the Fields, Locusts and
Wild Honey, Signs and Seasons, etc. Houghton Mifflin Co.,
Boston. $1.25 per volume.

COULTER, J. M., and J. G. and PATTERSON, ALICE J. Practical Nature
Study and Elementary Agriculture. Appleton, N. Y. 1909.
$1.35.

DAVENPORT, EUGENE. Domesticated Animals and Plants. Ginn,
Boston. 1910. 14 + 316 pp. $1.25.

FERNOW, B. E. The Care of Trees in Lawn, Street and Park. Holt,
N. Y. 1911. 392 pp. $2.00.

GIBSON, W. H. Eye Spy. Harper, N. Y. $2.50.

GIBSON, W. H. Sharp Eyes. Harper, N. Y. $2.50.

GRAY, ASA. How Plants Behave. American Book Co., N. Y. 1875.
54 ¢.

HODGE, D. F. Nature Study and Life. Ginn, Boston. 1902. 514 pp.
$1.50. One of the best books on nature study and how to conduct
it.

2 H

HOLDER, C. F., and JORDAN, D. S. Fish Stories Alleged and Experienced, with a Little History, Natural and Unnatural. Holt, N. Y. 1909. $1.75.

HOLTZ, F. L. Nature Study. Scribner, N. Y. 1908. $1.50. Manual for teachers and students.

INGERSOLL, E. Nature's Calendar. Harper, N. Y. 1900. 270 pp. $1.50.

INGERSOLL, E. Wild Neighbors. Outdoor Studies in the United States. Macmillan, N. Y. 1897. 301 pp. $1.50.

KELLOGG, V. L. Insect Stories. Holt, N. Y. 1908. $1.50.

KELLOGG, V. L. American Insects. Holt, N. Y. 1908. 649 pp. $5.00.

THOREAU, HENRY D. Walden. Houghton Mifflin Co., Boston. 1893. 522 pp. Cambridge Classics. 90 ¢. Riverside Aldine Series. 2 vol. $1.00.

WEED, C. M. Seed Travellers. Ginn, Boston. 1898. 25 ¢.

WEED, C. M. Stories of Insect Life. 1st series, Spring and early Summer. Ginn. 25 ¢. 2d, Summer and Autumn. Muhrfeldt, M. E., and Weed, C. M. Ginn. 30 ¢.

GEOGRAPHY

AVEBURY, LORD. (Sir John Lubbock.) The Scenery of England. Macmillan, N. Y. 1902. 534 pp. (Out of print, 1917.)

BALL, SIR R. S. The Earth's Beginning. Appleton, N. Y. 384 pp. $1.80.

BARTON, GEORGE H. Elementary Lithology. Boston.

BRIGHAM, A. P. Geographic Influences in American History. Ginn. Boston. 1903. 366 pp. $1.25.

BRIGHAM, A. P. Commercial Geography. Ginn. 1911. 469 pp. $1.30. Attractive high school text on very original and suggestive plan. Worth careful study by every thoughtful teacher and pupil.

BRIGHAM, A. P. From Trail to Railway. Through the Appalachians. Ginn, Boston. 188 pp. Maps and illustrations. 50 ¢.

COMSTOCK, GEORGE C. A Textbook of Astronomy. Appleton, N. Y. 1901. 8 + 391 pp. $1.30.

COULTER, J. M. Plant Relations. Appleton, N. Y. 1905. 264 pp. $1.10.

COX, HAROLD. The United Kingdom and Its Trade. Harper, N. Y. $1.25.

CROSBY, W. O. Common Minerals and Rocks. Heath, Boston. 1893. 205 pp. 60 ¢.

DABNEY, CHARLES. The Cotton Plant. Bull. No. 33. U. S. Dept. Agr., Office of Exp. Sta. Washington, D. C. Free.

DANA, EDWARD S. Minerals and How to Study Them. Wiley, N. Y. 380 pp. $1.50.

DANA, J. D. The Geological Story Briefly Told. Amer. Book Co., N. Y. 1903. 263 pp. $1.15.

DARWIN, CHARLES. The Origin of Species. Appleton, N. Y. 1898. 2 vol. $2.00.

DARWIN, G. H. The Tides. Houghton Mifflin Co., Boston. 1898. 378 pp. $2.00.

DAVIS, WILLIAM MORRIS. Physical Geography, and Elementary Physical Geography. Ginn, Boston. $1.25 each. Standard high school texts. A Teacher's Guide is issued to accompany them, with material invaluable to teachers.

DONDLINGER, P. T. The Book of Wheat. Orange Judd & Co., N. Y. 1912. 369 pp. $2.00.

DRYER, C. R. High School Geography. Amer. Book Co., N. Y. 1912. 518 pp. $1.30. A recent standard text treating of physical and commercial geography with emphasis on human relations.

DRYER, C. R. Elementary Economic Geography. Amer. Book Co., N. Y. 1916. 405 pp. $1.28.

DRYER, C. R. (Editor). Studies in Indiana Geography. The Inland Publishing Co., Terre Haute, Ind. 1905. $1.25. Very useful as showing how studies in the geography of the home city and state can be carried out. (Out of print, 1917.)

EDGAR, W. C. The Story of a Grain of Wheat. Appleton, N. Y. 1903. $1.00.

FAIRBANKS, H. W. Practical Physiography. Allyn & Bacon, Boston. 1906. 542 pp. $1.60. Advanced high school textbook. Full of beautiful illustrations. Gives problematic questions.

FISKE, JOHN. Old Virginia and Her Neighbors. Houghton Mifflin Co., Boston. 2 vol. $2.00 each. Shows influences of geography on early history of Virginia.

GEIKIE, A. The Scenery of Scotland. 3d Ed. Macmillan, N. Y. 1901. 481 pp. $3.25.

GEIKIE, A. Elementary Lessons in Physical Geography. Macmillan, N. Y. 1887. 375 pp. $1.40.

GEIKIE, JAMES. The Great Ice Age. 3d Ed. Appleton, N. Y. 1894. 850 pp. $7.50.

GEORGE, H. B. The Relations of Geography and History. Frowde, London. Clarendon Press, Oxford. 1910. 4s. 6d. $1.10.

GIFFORD, J. C. Practical Forestry. Appleton, N. Y. 1912. 284 pp. $1.20.

GILBERT, G. K., and BRIGHAM, A. P. An Introduction to Physical Geography. Appleton, N. Y. 1908. 16 + 380 pp. $1.25. An attractive high school text. Rather easier than most of the other standard books.

GILBERT, G. K. Teacher's Guide to accompany their textbook. With laboratory exercises, suggested field work, and many helpful suggestions about equipment and collateral readings. 8 + 99 pp.

GUYOT, ARNOLD. The Earth and Man. Scribner, N. Y. 1899. 334 pp. $1.75.

HEILPRIN, ANGELO. Geographical and Geological Distribution of Animals. Appleton, N. Y. 1887. 455 pp. $2.00.

HERBERTSON, A. J. Man and His Work. Black, London. 1s. 6d. Macmillan, N. Y. 1899. 136 pp. 60 ¢.

HERBERTSON, A. J. The Oxford Geographies, Junior, 60 ¢, and Senior, 84 ¢. Clarendon Press, London. 1908.

HERBERTSON, A. J. and F. D. Descriptive Geographies from Original Sources. N. Am., 90 ¢, Asia, 30 ¢, Central and South Am., 70 ¢, Africa, 70 ¢, Australia and Oceania, 80 ¢, and Europe, 90 ¢. Macmillan, N. Y.

HERBERTSON, A. J. Commercial Geography of the British Isles. Macmillan, N. Y. 1910. 151 pp. 75 ¢.

HOPKINS, C. G. Soil Fertility. Ginn, Boston. 1910. 653 pp. $2.25.

HUXLEY, T. H. Physiography. Appleton, N. Y. Rev. by R. A. Gregory. 1904. 11 + 328 pp. 301 illus. $1.10.

JOHNSON, E. R. American Railway Transportation. Appleton, N. Y. 1908. 434 pp. $1.50.

JOHNSON, E. R. Elements of Transportation. Appleton. 1909. $1.50.

JOHNSON, E. R. Ocean and Inland Water Transportation. Appleton. 1906. 395 pp. $1.50.

KELTIE, J. S. Applied Geography. Geo. Philip & Son. London. 2s.6d.

KEMP, J. F. Handbook of Rocks. Van Nostrand, N. Y. 1911. 248 pp. $1.50.

LUBBOCK, SIR JOHN. (Lord Avebury.) The Scenery of Switzerland. Macmillan, N. Y. 1896. 371 pp. $1.50. (Out of print, 1917.)

LUBBOCK, SIR JOHN. (Lord Avebury.) Prehistoric Times. Appleton, N. Y. 1900. 616 pp. $5.00.

LYDE, L. W. Man in Many Lands. Black, London. 2s. 6d. Macmillan, N. Y. 1910. 163 pp. 65 ¢.

LYDE, L. W. A Geography of the British Isles. Black, London. 3s. 6d. Macmillan, N. Y. 1900. 60 ¢.

MACKINDER, H. J. Britain and the British Seas. Appleton, N. Y. 1902. 377 pp. $2.00.

MARBUT, C. F. Physiography of Missouri, in Geol. Survey of Missouri. Vol. 10.

MARR, JOHN E. The Scientific Study of Scenery. Methuen & Co., London. 1900. Crown 8vo. 6s.

MARSH, G. P. The Earth as Modified by Human Action. Scribner, N. Y. 1898. 629 pp. $3.50.

MERRILL, GEO. P. Stones for Building and Decoration. Wiley, N. Y. 1903. 506 pp. $5.00.

MERRILL, G. P. Treatise on Rocks, Rock Weathering, and Soils. Macmillan, N. Y. 1906. 411 pp. $4.00.

MILL, H. R. The Realm of Nature. Scribner, N. Y. 1892. $1.50.

MOORE, W. L. Descriptive Meteorology. Appleton, N. Y. 1910. 344 pp. $3.00.

MUIR, JOHN. The Mountains of California. Century Co. 1911. 389 pp. $1.50.

MUIR, JOHN. Our National Parks. Houghton Mifflin Co., Boston. 382 pp. $1.75. New Ed. $3.00.

MYRICK, HERBERT. The American Sugar Industry. Orange Judd & Co., N. Y. 1899. $1.50.

MYRICK, HERBERT. The Book of Corn. Orange Judd & Co., N. Y. 1904. 372 pp. $1.50.

National Parks Portfolio. Address The Secretary of the Interior, Washington, D. C. A portfolio of splendid views of our great national playgrounds, with maps.

PEARY, R. S. The North Pole. Stokes, N. Y. 1910. 373 pp. $4.80.

Physiography of the United States, by various authors. Am. Book Co., N. Y. 1896. 345 pp. $2.50. The National Geographic Monographs, now issued in one volume. Every high school library should have this important and fascinating collection.

POGSEN, G. A. Germany and its Trade. Harpers, N. Y. $1.00.

REDWAY, J. W. Commercial Geography. Scribner, N. Y. 1911. 423 pp. $1.25. High school textbook.

REYNOLDS, J. B. Regional Geographies. Black, London. 2s. each. British Isles, Europe and the Mediterranean Region, Asia, the Americas, Africa and Australia.

ROBINSON, EDWARD VAN DYKE. Commercial Geography. Rand, McNally & Co., N. Y. 1910. 455 pp. $1.25.

ROOSEVELT, THEODORE. Winning of the West. G. P. Putnam, N. Y. 4 vol. $10.00.

RUSSELL, ISRAEL C. Glaciers of North America. Ginn, Boston. 1897. 210 pp. $1.75.

RUSSELL, ISRAEL C. Rivers of North America. Putnams, N. Y. 1898. 327 pp. $2.00.

RUSSELL, ISRAEL C. Volcanoes of North America. Macmillan, N. Y. $4.00.

These three books are written in a charming style, and make a strong appeal on the literary side as well as the scientific. The first two at least should be in every high school library.

SALISBURY, R. D. Physical Geography of New Jersey. Geol. Survey of N. J. Vol. 4. With map.

SALISBURY, R. D., BARROWS, H. H., and TOWER, W. S. Elements of Geography. Holt, N. Y. 1912. 616 pp. $1.50. An attractive high school textbook.

SEMPLE, E. C. American History and its Geographical Conditions. Houghton Mifflin Co., Boston. 1903. 466 pp. $3.00. Student's Ed. $1.60.

SEMPLE, E. C. Influences of Geographic Environment. Holt, N. Y. 1911. 683 pp. $4.00.

SERVISS, G. P. Other Worlds. Appleton, N. Y. 1912. 282 pp. $1.20.

SERVISS, G. P. Pleasures of the Telescope. Appleton, N. Y. $1.35.

SERVISS, G. P. Astronomy with an Opera Glass. Appleton, N. Y. 1910. 158 pp. $1.35.

SHALER, N. S. The Story of Our Continent. Ginn, Boston. 1892. 290 pp. 75 ¢.

SHALER, N. S. Aspects of the Earth. Scribner, N. Y. 1890. 344 pp. $2.50.

SHALER, N. S. Nature and Man in America. Scribner, N. Y. 1915. 290 pp. $1.50.

SHALER, N. S. Sea and Land. Scribner, N. Y. 1894. 252 pp. $2.50.

SMITH, J. R. The Ocean Carrier. Putnam, N. Y. 1908. $1.50.

SMITH, J. R. The Story of Iron and Steel. Appleton, N. Y. 1908. 193 pp. 75 ¢.

STARR, FREDERICK. Some First Steps in Human Progress. Flood & Vincent, Meadville, Pa. 1910. 13 + 305 pp. $1.00.

SURFACE, G. T. The Story of Sugar. Appleton, N. Y. 1910. $1.00.

SWEZEY, G. D. Practical Exercises in Astronomy. Appleton, N. Y. 1904. $1.00.

TARR, R. S. New Physical Geography. Macmillan, N. Y. 1903. 457 pp. $1.20. A standard high school textbook, containing more special suggestions for teachers and students than any other one book on the subject.

TARR, R. S. Elementary Geology. Macmillan, N. Y. 1906. 30 + 499 pp. $1.40.

TARR, R. S. Physical Geography of New York State. Macmillan, N. Y. 1902. 397 pp. $3.50.

THOREAU, HENRY D. Cape Cod. Houghton Mifflin Co., Boston. 1908. 252 pp. $2.00. Tells about sand dunes and spits of the cape.

TODD, DAVID P. New Astronomy. Am. Book Co., N. Y. 1897. 480 pp. $1.30.

TOWER, W. S. The Story of Oil. Appleton, N. Y. 1909. 270 pp. $1.00.

TYNDALL, JOHN. The Forms of Water. Appleton, N. Y. 1892. 196 pp. $2.50.

TYNDALL, JOHN. Hours of Exercise in the Alps. Appleton, N. Y. 1888. 473 pp. $2.00.

TYNDALL, JOHN. Glaciers of the Alps. Longmans, N. Y. $1.50. Dutton, N. Y. 75 ¢.

U. S. Hydrographic Office, Washington. Illustrated Cloud Forms. Colored chart, with text. Address Supt. of Documents, Govt. Printing Office, Washington, D.C.

U. S. Weather Bureau, Washington. Instructions for Voluntary Observers. 1899.

VAN HISE, C. R. The Conservation of the Natural Resources of the United States. Macmillan, N. Y. 1914. 413 pp. $2.00.

WALDO, FRANK. Elementary Meteorology. American Book Co., N. Y. 1896. 373 pp. $1.50.

WALLACE, ALFRED RUSSEL. Island Life. Macmillan, N. Y. 1892. 522 pp. $2.50.

WARD, R. DE C. Practical Exercises in Elementary Meteorology. Ginn, Boston. 1899. 199 pp. $1.12. An indispensable guide for teacher and pupils in weather work.

WHITSON, A. R., and WALSTER, H. L. Soils and Soil Fertility. Webb Pub. Co., Minneapolis, Minn. 1912. 315 pp. $1.25. Describes soils, fertilizers, erosion, underground water, how to lay drains, dry farming, etc. Simple and interesting.

PHYSICS

ADAMS, J. H. Harpers' Electricity Book for Boys. Harpers, N. Y. $1.75.

BAKER, RAY S. Boys' Book of Inventions, and Second Boys' Book of Inventions. Doubleday, Page & Co., N. Y. $2.00 and $1.60.

BENJAMIN, PARK. Age of Electricity. Scribner, N. Y. 1892. 8 + 381 pp. $2.00.

BLASERNA, P. Theory of Sound in Relation to Music. Appleton, N. Y. $1.50.

BONNEY, G. E. Electrical Experiments. Macmillan, N. Y. 80 ¢.

BONNEY, G. E. Electro-Plater's Handbook. Van Nostrand, N. Y. 221 pp. $1.20.

BOYS, C. V. Soap Bubbles and the Forces that Mould Them. S. P. C. K. London, Eng. 1900. 178 pp. 85 ¢.

CARHART, HENRY S. Primary Batteries. Allyn & Bacon, Boston. 1891. 183 pp. $1.50.

COLLINS, A. FREDERICK. Manual of Wireless Telegraphy. Wiley, N. Y. 1906. 216 pp. 2d Ed. 1909. $1.50.

DAVIDSON, J. B. Agricultural Engineering. Webb, St. Paul, Minn. 1913. 546 pp. $1.50.

DUNCAN, R. K. The New Knowledge. Barnes, N. Y. 1905. $2. Popular account of the new theories of matter, in physics and chemistry.

GIBSON, C. R. Electricity To-day — Its Work and Mysteries Described in Non-Technical Language. Lippincott, Philadelphia. $1.50.

GIBSON, C. R. The Romance of Modern Electricity. Lippincott. $1.50.

GIBSON, C. R. Scientific Ideas of To-day. Lippincott. $1.50. A non-technical account of the modern theories of matter.

FLEMING, J. A. Waves and Ripples. S. P. C. K., London. Gorham, N. Y. 1902. 12 + 299 pp. $1.75. A fascinating treatment for young people.

FRANKLIN, BENJAMIN. Autobiography. Houghton Mifflin Co. Boston. School Ed. 1915. 50 ¢.

HOPKINS, G. M. Experimental Science. Munn & Co., N. Y. 2 vol. $5.00. The best single collection of experiments for teacher and pupils.

HOPKINS, G. M. Home Mechanics for Amateurs. Munn & Co., N. Y. 1907. 370 pp. $1.50.

HOUSTON, E. J. The Wonderbook of Light. Stokes, N. Y. $1.50.

ILES, G. Flame, Electricity and the Camera. Doubleday, Page & Co., Garden City, N. Y. $2.00.

ILES, G. Inventors at Work. With Chapters on Discovery. Doubleday, Page & Co., $2.50.

ILES, G. Leading American Inventors. H. Holt, N. Y. 1912. 447 pp. $1.75.

JACKSON, D. C. and J. P. Elementary Electricity and Magnetism, and their Applications. Macmillan, N. Y. 1913. 482 pp. $1.40. One of the best books obtainable on the application of theory in modern practical electricity.

JENKS, TUDOR. Electricity for Young People. Stokes, N. Y. $1.50.

JONES, D. E. Elementary Lessons in Sound, Light and Heat. Macmillan, N. Y. 16mo. 280 pp. 70 ¢.

KENNELLY, A. E. Wireless Telegraphy and Telephony. Moffat, Yard & Co., N. Y. 1910. 279 pp. $1.00.

KING, F. H. A Text-book of the Physics of Agriculture. Mrs. F. H. King, Madison, Wis. 1910. 604 pp. $1.75.

LUCKIESH, M. Color and its Applications. Van Nostrand, N. Y. 360 pp. 129 ill. and 4 color plates. $3.00 net.

LUCKIESH, M. Light and Shade and Their Applications. Van Nostrand, N. Y. 277 pp. 135 ill. and 10 tables. $2.50 net. For both $5.00.

MAXIM, SIR H. Artificial and Natural Flight. Macmillan, N. Y. 1908. $1.75.

MAYER, A. M. Sound. Appleton, N. Y. 1878. 181 pp. $1.00. A fascinating little experimental treatise for boys and girls.

MAYER, A. M., and BARNARD, C. Light. Appleton, N. Y. $1.00. A similar treatment of light phenomena.

MENDENHALL, T. C. A Century of Electricity. Houghton Mifflin Co., Boston. 1887. 229 pp. $1.25. Vol. 1 of the Riverside Science Series. Simple, readable and authoritative.

MILLER, C. M. Kitecraft and Kite Tournaments. The Manual Arts Press, Peoria, Ill. 1916. $1.00. Construction and flying of all kinds of kites. Making and using of kite accessories, air-planes, gliders, propellers, motors, etc. Illus.

RAFFERTY, C. W. An Introduction to the Science of Radioactivity. Longmans, N. Y. $1.25.

RIGHI, AUGUSTO. The Modern Theory of Physical Phenomena — Radio activity, Ions, Electrons. Macmillan, N. Y. 1904. 161 pp. With Bibliog. $1.10.

ROTCH, A. L. Sounding the Ocean of Air. S. P. C. K., London, Eng. Gorham, N. Y. 85 ¢.

STEWART, BALFOUR. The Conservation of Energy. Appleton, N. Y. 1890. 236 pp. $1.50.

PERRY, JOHN. Spinning Tops. Gorham. Romance of Science Series. 1910. 136 pp. 85 ¢. A popular lecture by a great physicist.

SLOANE, T. O'C. Electric Toy Making. Henley, N. Y. $1.00.

SLOANE, T. O'C. Liquid Air and the Liquefaction of Gases. Henley, N. Y. $2.00.

ST. JOHN, T. M. How Two Boys Made their Own Electrical Apparatus. T. M. St. John, N. Y. 1898. 141 pp. $1.00.

ST. JOHN, T. M. Things a Boy Should Know about Electricity. T. M. St. John, N. Y. $1.00.

THOMPSON, S. P. Elementary Lessons in Electricity and Magnetism. Macmillan, N. Y. 1899. 14 + 456 pp. New and Rev. Ed. $1.50.

THOMPSON, S. P. Light, Visible and Invisible. Macmillan. 1910. 283 pp. $2.00. One of the best recent books on light for teacher and ambitious pupils.

THURSTON, R. H. Heat as a Form of Energy. Houghton Mifflin Co., Boston. $1.25.

TIDY, C. M. Story of a Tinder Box. S. P. C. K., London, Eng. Gorham, N. Y. 70 ¢. Methods of getting fire — with experiments.

TYNDALL, JOHN. Lessons in Electricity. Appleton, N. Y. 1895. 10 + 113 pp. $1.00.

TYNDALL, JOHN. Faraday as a Discoverer. Appleton, N. Y. 1894. 171 pp. $1.00.

WILLIAMS, ARCHIBALD. How it Works. T. Nelson & Sons, N. Y. 1911. 483 pp. $1.25. Sully and Kleinteich, N. Y.

WILLIAMS, ARCHIBALD. How it is Done. Nelson, N. Y. 1908. $1.25. Sully and Kleinteich, N. Y. 484 pp. 268 ill. $1.20.

WILLIAMS, ARCHIBALD. How it is Made. Nelson, N. Y. 1908. $1.25. Sully and Kleinteich, N. Y. 474 pp. Ill. $1.20.

WILLIAMS, ARCHIBALD. How to Make Things. Sully and Kleinteich, N. Y. Ill. $1.20.

WILLIAMS, ARCHIBALD. Another popular science series published by Lippincott, N. Y.

WOODHULL, J. F. Manual of Home-made Apparatus. Barnes, N. Y. 1906. 65 ¢.

WORTHINGTON, A. M. Physical Laboratory Practice. Allyn & Bacon, Boston, 1891. 308 pp. Many experiments with simple apparatus.

CHEMISTRY

Alembic Club Reprints. Extracts from papers by great chemists on their researches. Edinburgh and London. The Univ. of Chicago Press, Chicago. Very readable and inspiring for teachers and specially interested pupils. Numbering 18. 44 ¢ to $1.25 per copy.

ALLYN, L. B. Elementary Applied Chemistry. Ginn, Boston. 60 ¢.

BAILEY, E. H. S. A Textbook of Sanitary and Applied Chemistry. Macmillan, N. Y. 1906. 345 pp. $1.40.

DUNCAN, ROBERT KENNEDY. The Chemistry of Commerce. Harper, N. Y. 1907. 262 pp. $2.00.

DUNCAN, ROBERT KENNEDY. The New Knowledge. Barnes, N. Y. 1905. $2.00.

CORNISH, VAUGHAN. Practical Proofs of Chemical Laws. Longmans, N. Y. 1895. 104 pp. 21 experiments. 75 ¢.

DOBBIN, LEONARD, and WALKER, JAMES. Chemical Theory for Beginners. Macmillan, N. Y. 1892. 236 pp. 80 ¢.

FARADAY, M. The Liquefaction of Gases. Univ. of Chicago Press, Chicago, Ill. Alembic Club Reprints. 80 pp. 54 ¢.

FARADAY, M. Chemical History of a Candle. Harper, N. Y. 1862 and later. 223 pp. $1.00.

FURNEAUX, WILLIAM S. Elementary Chemistry. Longmans, N. Y. 1894. 170 pp. 155 experiments. 80 ¢. "A brief outline of the chemistry of common things."

HARDIN, WILLETT LEPLEY. The Rise and Development of the Liquefaction of Gases. Macmillan, N. Y. 1899. 224 pp. $1.50. Excellent for teacher and pupils.

HATCH, KIRK L. Simple Exercises Illustrating Some Applications of Chemistry to Agriculture. U. S. Dept. of Agriculture, Office of Experiment Station. Bull. 195. Washington, D. C. 22 pp. Illus.

JOHNSTON, JAMES F. W. Chemistry of Common Life. Appleton, N. Y. 1879. 592 pp. $2.00.

LASSAR-COHN, DR. Tr. by Muir. Chemistry in Daily Life. H. Grevel & Co., London, Eng. Lippincott, Philadelphia. 1898. 336 pp. $1.75.

MELDOLA, RAPHAEL. The Chemistry of Photography. Macmillan, N. Y. 1889. 382 pp. $2.00.

ORNDORFF, W. R. Laboratory Manual of Organic Chemistry. Heath, Boston. 1893. 40 ¢. For pupils, to accompany Remsen.

RICHARDS, ELLEN H., and ELLIOT, SOPHRONIA M. Chemistry of Cooking and Cleaning. Whitcomb & Barrows, Boston. 1907. $1.00.

SHERMAN, HENRY C. The Chemistry of Food and Nutrition. Macmillan, N. Y. 1911. 355 pp. $1.50.

STADTLER, S. S. The Chemistry of Familiar Things. Lippincott, Philadelphia. 320 pp. $1.75.

STEWART, A. W. Chemistry and Its Borderland. Longmans, N. Y. $1.50.

THORNTON, ARTHUR, and PEARSON, MARCHANT. Notes on Volumetric Analysis. Longmans, N. Y. 1898. 83 pp. 75 ¢. "Brief and accurate. Intended for pupils."

THORP, F. H. Outlines of Industrial Chemistry. Macmillan, N. Y. 1899. 528 pp. $3.75. Good for reference and library assignments.

APPENDIX B

BIBLIOGRAPHIES FOR SCIENCE TEACHERS

Annual Reports of the Proceedings of the National Education Association. Ann Arbor, Mich. Consult the indices.

Annual Reports of the United States Commissioner of Education. Consult the indices.

CHUTE, H. N. A High School Library for Physics. School Science and Math., 1 : 126–30, May, 1901.

DODGE, R. E., Editor, and Committee of the National Federation of Teachers of Mathematics and the Natural Sciences. Bibliography of Science Teaching. U. S. Bureau of Education. Bull. 1911. No. 1.

MILL, R. H. Guide to Geographical Books and Appliances. Geo. Philip & Son, London, Eng. 1910. 5s. "Most complete bibliography of the kind in English."

New England Association of Chemistry Teachers. A list of books in Chemistry. The L. E. Knott Apparatus Co., Boston. 32 pp.

NOYES, F. K. Teaching Material in Government Publications. U. S. Bureau of Education. Bull. 1913. No. 47. Free. Address Commissioner of Education, Washington, D. C.

Price lists of United States Documents. Address Supt. of Documents, Washington, D. C. Free.

11 Food and Diets.

15 Geological Survey Publications.

18 Engineering, Mechanics, Electricity.

20 Lands. Publications of General Land Office, Conservation, Drainage, Forests, Irrigation.

21 Fishes.

24 Indians.

25 Transportation.

31 Education.

32 Non-Contiguous Territory, — Alaska, Canal Zone, etc.

35 Geography and Explorations. Geodetic Survey.

36 Periodicals by Bureaus.

38 Animal Industry.

40 Chemistry Bureau.

41 Insects.

42 Agricultural Experiment Stations.

43 Forestry.

44 Plant Life.

45 Public Roads.

46 Soils.
47 Crop Statistics.
48 Weather Bureau.
51 Health. Hygiene.
53 Maps by Various Bureaus.
55 National Museum Publications.
56 Smithsonian Reports.
58 Mines and Mining.

Report of Committee on United States Documents Usable in Secondary Schools. Proc. N. E. A., 1909, p. 802 ff.

School Science and Mathematics. Smith and Turton, 2059 E 72d Place, Chicago, Ill. Consult the annual indices.

State High School Inspectors, Ohio. A List of Library Books for High Schools. State of Ohio, Department of Public Instruction, Columbus. 1916. Free in Ohio.

University High School, Chicago.
A list of books suited to a high school library. U. S. Bureau of Education. Bull. 1913. No. 35. 104 pp. Free. Address the United States Commissioner of Education, Washington, D.C.

U. S. Bureau of Education.
Bibliography of Education 1909–1910. Bull. 1911. No. 10. Watch the lists of the publications of the Bureau for other bibliographies and titles touching science teaching. Later bulletins. Same title and subject.

U. S. Department of Agriculture.
Free lists of bulletins of interest to schools. Write request to the secretary, Washington, D.C.

APPENDIX C

SCIENTIFIC PERIODICALS

I. GENERAL

The General Science Quarterly. State Normal School, Salem, Mass. $1.25 per yr. A journal especially devoted to the interests of "general science" teachers.

Nature. A weekly illustrated journal of science. English. Macmillan, London and N. Y. 6d. per copy. 1£ 8s. per yr.

Popular Science Monthly. 239 4th Ave., N. Y. 15 ¢ copy. $1.50 per yr. Contains short, illustrated articles on all kinds of scientific subjects, especially electrical, mechanical, and industrial inventions and projects.

School Science and Mathematics. 2059 E. 72d Place, Chicago. 9 numbers per yr. $2.00. Free to members of the Central Asso. of Teachers of Mathematics and the Natural Sciences, whose annual dues are $2.50. Members are entitled also to the annual volume of proceedings, etc.

Science. Garrison-on-Hudson, N. Y., or Substation 84, New York City. Weekly. $5.00 per yr. Free to members of the American Asso. for the Advancement of Science, whose dues are $3.00 per yr. L. O. Howard, Sec'y, Smithsonian Institution, Washington, D. C.

The Mentor. 52 E. 19th St., New York City. Twice a month. Single copies 15 ¢. $3.00 per yr. "Established for the development of popular interest in Art, Literature, Science, Nature, and Travel."

The Scientific American, and The Scientific American Supplement. Munn & Co., N. Y. Both weekly. $4.00 and $5.00 per yr. respectively. Very attractive to boys. The best periodicals on applied science.

The Scientific Monthly (formerly entitled The Popular Science Monthly). Substation 84, New York City. $3.00 per yr. Authoritative scientific articles of interest to the general reader, adult rather than juvenile.

The World's Work. Doubleday, Page & Co., Garden City, N. Y. Monthly. $3.00 per yr.

II. BIOLOGICAL

Bird Lore. Macmillan, N. Y. Bimonthly. $1.00 per yr.

The American Botanist. Willard N. Clute, Joliet, Ill. Quarterly. $1.00 per yr.

The American Naturalist. Ginn, Boston. Monthly. $4.00 per yr.

The Botanical Gazette. University of Chicago Press, Chicago, Ill. Monthly. $7.00 per yr.

The Nature Study Review. Ithaca, N. Y. Monthly. $1.00 per yr.

The Plant World. Tucson, Ariz. Monthly. $1.00 per yr.

Torreya. The Torrey Botanical Club, Columbia University, N. Y. $1.00 per year.

III. GEOGRAPHICAL

The Geographical Review. American Geographical Society, Broadway and 156th St., New York City. Monthly. $5.00 per yr.

The Journal of Geography. Madison, Wis. Monthly. $1.00 per yr. 10 months.

The National Geographic Magazine. The National Geographic Society, Washington, D. C. Monthly. $2.50. Profusely and magnificently illustrated. With occasional valuable and timely maps.

Travel. Robert M. McBride & Co., Union Square, North, New York City. 25 ¢ per copy. $3.00 per yr.

IV. PHYSICAL AND MECHANICAL

Everyday Mechanics. 33 W. 42d St., New York City. $1.00 per yr.

Popular Mechanics. 6 N. Michigan Ave., Chicago. $1.00 per yr.

Science Abstracts. Section A. — Physics. Spon and Chamberlain, New York. Monthly. $4.50 per yr. The best single publication for keeping up with the progress of research and discovery in physics.

The Electrical Experimenter. 233 Fulton St., New York City. 15 ¢ per copy. Illus. Short popular articles.

The Physical Review. The American Physical Society, Ithaca, N. Y. Monthly. $6.00 per yr. Research papers and news items.

The Wireless Age. 42 Broad St., N. Y. Monthly. $2.00 per yr.

V. CHEMICAL

Chemical Abstracts. Ohio State University, Columbus, O. $6.00 per yr.

The Journal of the American Chemical Society. Chemical Publishing Co., Easton, Pa. $6.00 per yr. Reviews of chemical research, and chemical news items.

The Journal of Industrial and Engineering Chemistry. New York City. $6.00 per yr.

These three journals are free to members of the American Chemical Society, whose dues are $10.00 per yr. Dr. Charles L. Parsons, Sec'y, Box 505, Washington, D. C.

Die Zeitschrift für den Physikalischen und Chemischen Unterricht. Julius Springer, publisher, Link-Str. 23–24, Berlin W. 9. Six numbers per yr. 13.50 M per yr.

INDEX

Printed in the United States of America.

THE following pages contain advertisements of
a few of the Macmillan books on kindred subjects

A Cyclopedia of Education

EDITED BY PAUL MONROE, PH.D.

Professor of the History of Education, Teachers College, Columbia University;
Author of "A Text-Book in the History of Education," "Brief
Course in the History of Education," etc.

The need of such work is evidenced: By the great mass of varied educational literature showing an equal range in educational practice and theory; by the growing importance of the school as a social institution, and the fuller recognition of education as a social process; and by the great increase in the number of teachers and the instability of tenure which at the same time marks the profession.

The men who need it are: All teachers, professional men, editors, ministers, legislators, all public men who deal with large questions of public welfare intimately connected with education — every one who appreciates the value of a reference work which will give him the outlines of any educational problem, the suggested solutions, the statistical information, and in general the essential facts necessary to its comprehension.

Among the departmental editors associated with Dr. Monroe are Dr. ELMER E. BROWN, U. S. Commissioner of Education, Prof. E. F. BUCHNER, of Johns Hopkins, Dr. WM. H. BURNHAM, Clark University, M. GABRIEL COMPAYRÉ, Inspector-General of Public Instruction, Paris, France, Prof. WILHELM MÜNCH, of Berlin University, Germany, Prof. JOHN DEWEY, of Columbia University, Dr. ELLWOOD P. CUBBERLY, Stanford University, Cal., Prof. FOSTER WATSON, of the University College of Wales, Dr. DAVID SNEDDEN, Commissioner of Education for the State of Massachusetts, and others.

Complete in five large quarto volumes, $25.

THE MACMILLAN COMPANY

64-66 Fifth Avenue, New York

BOSTON   ATLANTA   DALLAS   CHICAGO   SAN FRANCISCO

Principles of Secondary Education

EDITED BY PAUL MONROE

Cloth, 8vo, $1.90

In the preparation of this work Professor Monroe has been assisted by a force of some thirty contributors of the highest standing in the educational world. Thus, in a single volume of some 800 pages are presented the most advanced and practical views concerning the various phases of secondary education, which are now attracting public attention. The contributions are grouped under the following headings : Secondary Education, Its Meaning and Scope; Historic Development of Secondary Education ; European Systems of Secondary Schools ; The High School System of the United States ; Organization of the High School ; The Private Secondary School ; Psychology and Hygiene of Adolescence ; Moral Education in the High School ; The Vernacular ; The Classical Languages and Literature ; Modern Languages ; The Natural Sciences ; Mathematics ; The Social Sciences ; The Fine Arts ; The Household Arts ; The Vocational High School ; Physical Education and Hygiene ; Athletics in the High School ; Social Aspects of High School Education ; Reorganization of Secondary Education.

A Syllabus of a Course of Study on the History and Principles of Education

By PAUL MONROE

Paper, 12mo, 92 pp., 25 cents; Cloth, 50 cents

Designed to accompany the text prepared and used in the author's own classes.

THE MACMILLAN COMPANY

Publishers   **64-66 Fifth Avenue**   **New York**

The Teaching of Physics

By C. RIBORG MANN

Associate Professor of Physics, The University of Chicago.

$1.25

The distinction between cultural and vocational seems to be wholly beside the mark in any true system of general education. It owes its origin to the mistaken ideas of the doctrine of formal discipline. This book is an effort to show how, in the case of physics, the two points of view may be amalgamated into one.

The book is divided into three parts. The first of these traces the development of the present situation. The second traces the origin of physics, and seeks to establish its leading characteristics and to define its possibilities as a means of general education. In the third part the purpose of physics teaching is stated, and hints are given as to how this purpose may be attained.

In addition to the references given as footnotes to the text, the chapters in Parts Two and Three are supplied with lists of "collateral reading." In order to make these lists brief, they include in general only references to recently published works. Older works are included when they contain material that has not been dealt with more briefly in recent writings.

THE MACMILLAN COMPANY

NEW YORK	**BOSTON**	**ATLANTA**
CHICAGO	**SAN FRANCISCO**	**DALLAS**

PRACTICAL PHYSICS

By N. HENRY BLACK

Science Master in the Roxbury Latin School, Boston

AND

Professor HARVEY N. DAVIS

Of Harvard University

Cloth, 12mo, Illustrated, ix and 487 pages, $1.25

The remarkable record that this text has made in the short period it has been on the market is sufficient testimony as to its adaptability to high school needs. And it is not difficult to sum up the features of the book that give it preëminence in its field.

It is written by experts in the field who are, moreover, thoroughly acquainted with the needs and limitations of the high school course.

It is practical in fact as well as in name. It connects the fundamental principles of physics with the everyday affairs of life, by introducing each subject through some familiar experience, by using the appliances of modern industrial and commercial life as illustrations of the principles studied, and by suggesting research questions at ends of chapters that send pupils afield for information.

The rate of progress is adjusted to the ability of the average class to proceed. The pace is slow in the early part of the book, more rapid later. Topics under any one subject are arranged in what experience has shown to be the most teachable order.

The manner of presentation shows exceptional skill in the actual work of teaching. The method is inductive and pedagogically sound — first, the familiar facts, then the underlying principles, then the application to less familiar facts. New subjects are introduced by illustrations from daily life — *not* by definitions. Principles are introduced by illustrative experiments or by appeal to familiar experience — *not* stated first and illustrated afterwards.

THE MACMILLAN COMPANY

64-66 FIFTH AVENUE

CHICAGO   NEW YORK CITY   DALLAS

SAN FRANCISCO   ATLANTA   BOSTON